Water and the Land
A History of American Irrigation

*"Every successful enterprise starts with a vision.
This book celebrates visionaries in the irrigation industry
— past, present and future."*

Pepper Putnam
Executive Director
The Irrigation Association

Irrigation Association

Cover photograph by Larry Kassell
presents a panoramic view of the
Bonneville Dam on the Columbia River,
43 miles east of Portland, Oregon.

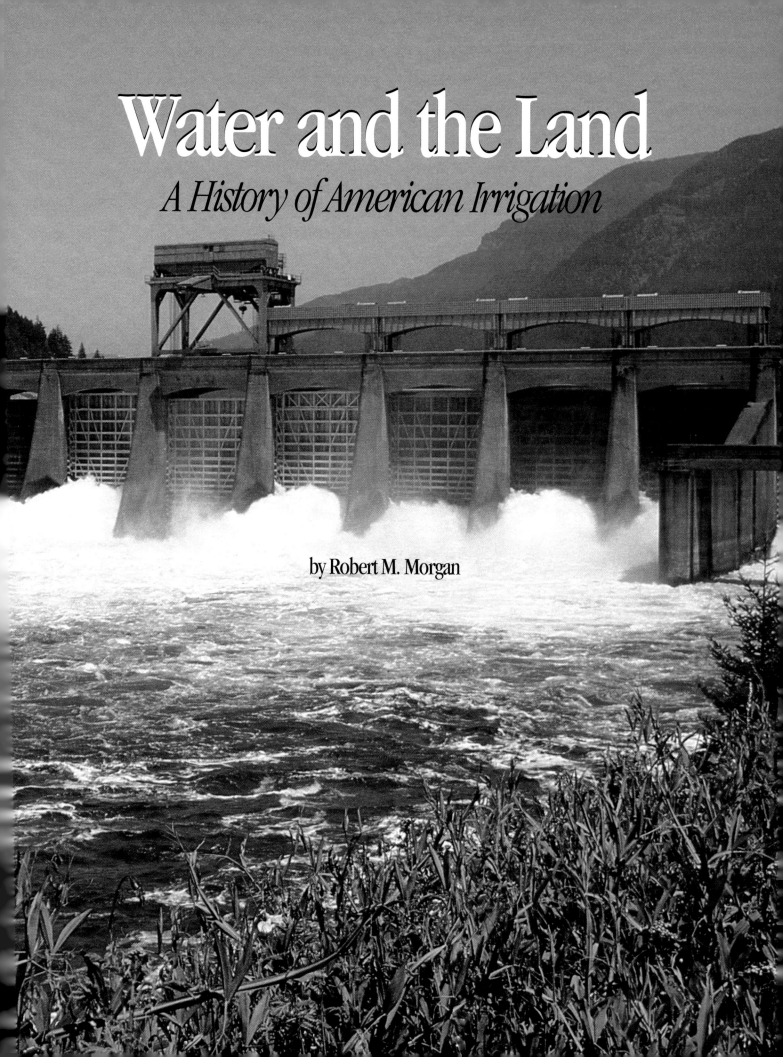

Water and the Land

A History of American Irrigation

by Robert M. Morgan

Water and the Land
A History of American Irrigation
By Robert M. Morgan
Copyright 1993, The Irrigation Association, Fairfax, Virginia

For information, address The Irrigation Association:

The Irrigation Association
8260 Willow Oaks Corporate Drive, Suite 120
Fairfax, Virginia 22031
(703) 573-3551   FAX (703) 573-1913

Board of Directors of the Irrigation Association:

Water and the Land
A History of American Irrigation

Editors:
Bruce F. Shank and Matthew Trulio
Adams Publishing Corp., Cathedral City, CA

Design and Production Art:
Irene Gresick and Karen Vitkus
Premiere Editions, Placentia, CA

Library of Congress Catalog Card Number: 93-079961
International Standard Book Number: 0-935030-02-6

Contents

Courtesy, Valmont Industries

Valley center pivot with corner system, 1976.

Acknowledgments

Below, the author lists several individuals who, in one way or another, provided valuable information and keepsake photographs for this historical document. To a great extent, this book exists because of them. We thank them for their contribution.

Others deserve our appreciation, too. For without their commitment, this book simply would not exist. Presidents Bob Emmerich ('91), Tom Kimmell ('92), and Bill Koonz ('93) inspired everyone to press on in the face of many adversities. These three gentlemen motivated us all, even when no way appeared to finish the book.

Our thanks also go to Bill Pogue for volunteering to head up the successful effort to re-enlist the support of our Partners in Progress, and to convince others that the endeavor was worthy of their commitment.

Four past presidents volunteered to serve as an Editorial Committee and to review the raw manuscript. It was a labor of love, and well done. Our thanks to Jack Liddell ('81), Jim Wearin ('80), Bill Pogue ('88) and Glenn Tribe ('90).

Bob Morgan prepared an excellent manuscript which was, as you can see, polished to a fine gloss by our editorial and book production consultants. Bruce Shank worked with Bob on editing and re-writing the text, and in selecting photographs that best illustrate each chapter. Irene Gresick and Karen Vitkus of Premiere Editions were responsible for the format and appearance of the book. They are a great team who were as committed as any of us to successfully complete this published tribute to the industry.

The problem and real danger in acknowledging by name all of the exceptional people who helped bring this book to fulfillment is the probability of leaving someone out. We thank you all and hope that the high quality of *Water and the Land* will, in some small way, make up for our omission.

Many thanks are extended to these individuals and companies who generously contributed their time, knowledge and materials to our on-going history project and, ultimately, the success of *Water and the Land*:

- Richard Bean, R.C.B. Assoc., Seattle, WA
- Ed Brockett, Pierce Corp., Eugene, OR
- Robert Cloud, Assoc. Irrig. Consultants, Los Angeles, CA
- Philip De Marco, Aqua-Flo, Inc., Hammonton, NJ
- Marc Dutton, Marc Dutton Irrigation, Inc., Drayton Plains, MI
- Joe Goecke, Valmont Irrigation, Valley, NE
- James D. Grimm, Stettler Supply Co., Salem, OR
- Margaret Hawkins, John A. Brooks, Inc., Drayton Plains, MI
- Ernie Hodas, Century Supply, Madison Hts., MI
- Charles B. Houston, Hunter Industries, San Marcos, CA
- Richard Hunter, Hunter Industries, San Marcos, CA
- Francisco J. Jimeno, Equipos Y Accessorios Hidraulicos, Inc., Mexico City, Mexico
- Fred Kruse, Ag Rain/Kifco, Inc., Havana, IL
- John Lake, Rain for Rent, Inc., Bakersfield, CA
- Arthur Ludwig, Rain Bird Sales, Inc. Glendora, CA
- Albert W. Marsh, Retired, University of California, Riverside, CA

- John W. Morgan, Universal Sales, Inc., Eugene, OR
- John J. Oldfield, Oldfield Supply, Cincinnati, OH
- Thomas H. Kimmell, Olson Irrigation Systems, Santee, CA
- Jack Liddell, Delta Irrigation, Memphis, TN
- William R. Pogue, Irrometer Co., Inc., Riverside, CA
- William Sarratt, former editor, Irrigation Journal, New Orleans, LA
- Chet A. Sarsfield, American Soc. Irrig. Consults., Brentwood, CA
- Lon Schultz, Ag. Products, Inc., Sun Valley, CA
- John F. Shrunk, Denver, CO
- Kenneth H. Solomon, Ctr. for Irrig. Tech., Fresno, CA
- Winston C. Strong, Retired, Fresno, CA
- Ben Taliaferro, Century Supply Corp., Madison Heights, MI
- Guy O. Woodward, Retired, Utah State Univ., Salt Lake City, UT
- Andrew L. Wright, Mueller Mist Co., Broadview, IL
- Raymon and Sue York, Ewing Irrig. Products, San Leandro, CA

OVER 900 HEADS
ROOSEVELT PARK
MICHIGAN CENTRAL DEPOT-DETROIT

Foreword

*W*ater is integral to survival, sustenance, commerce and enjoyment.

This beautiful 200-page, grandly illustrated book commemorates the part of our history that irrigators played in developing our water resources and the impact that development had on the growth of our great nation. Over 150 photographs and drawings will lead you from the early days of irrigation development to the very scientific and precise products and methods used today.

The reader will visit with the men and women, and the institutions they worked for, who have been instrumental in advancing product and management science to a model for the rest of the world.

Water and the Land honors the pioneers in irrigation development, including their products, management practices and application science. Many of the pioneers of the young discipline of automated irrigation will be reading this book with you. The very important advancements in gravity irrigation and the creative people responsible for those advancements are also celebrated here.

This splendid coffee-table history book celebrates the remarkable achievements of these creative people who have enriched our industry.

Pepper Putnam
Executive Director
The Irrigation Association

Skinner System, first hydraulic oscillater, 1917.

Introduction

This book is a portrait of irrigation taken by the camera of history. Hold this portrait of irrigation history up to the light and view it from every angle. Discover how precious is this industry to which you belong.

As you read the text, appreciate the pioneer accomplishments of those who came before — and let them inspire you to create newer means of practical water application.

This is the history of an industry that can only grow. Others will add to it, be informed by it, and expand the concept of irrigation beyond our present understanding.

The story behind the history of American irrigation is a study of our greatest natural resource — water —the revelations and the romance, the science and the power, the spawning and the need, the life-giving qualities to man, animal and vegetation. All have a bearing on the progress of mankind.

The bounties of water and the ways it has been applied the last 150 years is the foundation for bringing to light the impact of water on our lives.

Early use of siphons along with spiles (R.R. airbrake hoses) on the Columbia River Irrigation Project. Dee Harris, County Extension Agent, in on the right.

Man, whose body is made up of 75 percent water, can live without food for weeks, but barely days without water. The luscious red tomato, stacked high among other fresh vegetables in our markets, is 94 percent water. Water is integral to survival, sustenance, commerce and enjoyment.

The lakes and rivers of our vast country bore the great majority of our commerce through the era of steam power. Water remains prominent as a means of transportation, despite the preponderance of railroad and highway freight.

Utilization of our rivers for transportation, hydraulic power, agriculture and public water supply is a tribute to the ingenuity and inventiveness of Americans. During the 19th century, water in the form of steam allowed the United States to become industrialized and set a pace that its international competitors could not match. Steam was harnessed for locomotives and self-propelled ships to connect states, nations and continents for commerce.

We ponder with great respect the centuries-old practices of native American Indians as they led water to their maize, melons and grains. As our pioneer forefathers ventured west and settled in the vastness of the fertile valleys beyond the Ohio, Missouri and Mississippi rivers, they too, by primitive means fashioned ways to encourage crops with life-giving water.

Historical records reveal that a progressive nation did not concern itself with planned water use and conservation until the 1880s. Alternatives to simply guiding water from its source to a field did not come to man's conscience until the closing of the 19th century. The remarkable advantages gained by sprinkling water to fall on thirsty plant life did not arise until 1892.

A summary by this author of U.S. patents granted for overhead irrigation from 1892 to 1940, a great period of development, revealed that more than 150 patents were devoted to improving the grower's ability to deliver water more effectively for maximum plant growth.

You will find many references to the magnitude of the government's role in reclamation to bring the miracle of water to our society for man's ever-increasing benefit. Not until 1902, however, did the U.S. Congress pass the Reclamation Act, which was designed to reclaim arid and semiarid lands in the West by supplying irrigation water to make them productive.

The monumental strides in water usage during this century are what this book highlights.

Robert M. Morgan
August, 1993

Surface irrigation of a California orange grove in the late 1800s.

CHAPTER 1

Controlled Surface and Sub-Surface Irrigation

"The West is an arid land, hostile to farming and will never be settled, unless the rivers are dammed, holding spring runoffs in reservoirs."
—Major John Wesley Powell, 1869

*T*he destiny of the human race has been influenced by irrigation water ever since man's first attempts at agriculture in the dawn of civilization. Irrigation played a pivotal role in the settlement of North America. It began in the West with primitive technology and spread eastward across the continent. While not as dramatic as the Gold Rush, irrigation's contributions to the development of agriculture and industry across the United States greatly surpassed gold in value.

Irrigation is the controlled, artificial application of water to the soil of arable lands in adequate, programmed amounts to meet crop requirements not satisfied by natural precipitation. Most communities in the American West owe their existence to it.

The Flowering of the West

American irrigation originated in the West. One million square miles (6.4 trillion acres) of the western United States receives less than 20 inches of rainfall in an average year. Vigorous plant growth depends primarily on irrigation in such areas.

Toward the end of the 18th Century, Spanish Padres traveled north from Mexico to establish missions in what is now Southern Arizona and California. Like the Hohokam Indians of the Salt River Valley in Arizona 2,000 years before,

Water wheel lifting ditch water to a higher level on a Washington fruit farm prior to the advent of electric pumps.

Surface row crop irrigation in 1800s before development of precision rills and ditches. Furrows between strawberry plants were made by horse-drawn implements on this Oregon farm.

fields along the great river. High, fertile land was transformed into pristine fields, a sight unmatched for years in the West.

By 1860, a water census of the U.S. revealed a total of 752 farm operations irrigating more than 400,000 acres. Settlements flourished around irrigated farms. This was especially true in California, where Father Palou's initial work spawned communities in areas we recognize today as Riverside, San Gabriel, and Costa Mesa.

The Dawn of American Irrigation Technology

The modern era of irrigation in the United States began in the mid-19th Century as American pioneers moved West. They settled in areas where Spanish irrigation techniques were practiced and wasted no time in adopting them.

The Mormons, the first settlers of Anglo-Saxon heritage on the Western irrigation scene, converged on the Salt Lake Valley of Utah in 1847. Brigham Young displayed his expertise in irrigation by leading his followers in the creation of the first modern American farming venture in the valley. In less than 10 years, the Mormon colonists had 16,000 acres under irrigation. By the end of the century, more than 250,000 acres were irrigated in the territory. The success of the Mormons in the intermountain West became legend and their settlements became the prototypes for later Federal developments.

the Spanish built small diversion dams, ditches and conduits from springs and rivers to supply their missions with water for raising crops, cooking and cleaning. Water was always a first and timeless consideration as the Franciscan Fathers blazed and traveled "The Trail of the Padres."

Spanish settlers accompanying the Padres introduced native American Indians to advanced irrigation methods and to crops that benefited from irrigation. As mission villages became established, canals lined with stone were constructed to carry water to orchards and vineyards.

In 1771, Father Francisco Palou documented the value of such canals as he wrote about Mission San Gabriel, not far from the present center of Los Angeles. "There is good soil for farming and an abundance of water that runs nearby in ditches that flow from the river," the Padre documented in his records. "There are facilities

for taking out the water in order to irrigate the land."

Nearly a century later, Spanish irrigation technology was applied to construct The Peoples Ditch, a canal built to carry water from the Rio Grande in the San Luis Valley of present-day eastern Colorado to

Surface rill method used in 1902 to irrigate orange grove in Riverside, California.

Federal legislation provided the impetus for expanding irrigation. The Gold Rush of 1849 helped generate interest in the West. Shortly thereafter, the Donation Land Act was passed.

Later in the century, the U.S. Congress endeavored to stimulate private and state participation in irrigation planning through legislation. In 1877, it passed the Desert Land Act.

The California assembly joined the movement with

passage of the Wright Act in 1887, which authorized taxation of district lands. Virtually all principal irrigation states have since adopted laws modeled after the Wright Act.

Precedence for the pioneer advancement in crop production was established first by water and then by irrigation practices. Soon to follow were the agricultural and hydrological phases. These included all land and water problems involved in developing and maintaining profitable crop production in irrigated regions. Technology had to be developed to best meet the needs of Western farmers.

Again the Federal government stepped in with legislation. In 1862, the Morrill Act was passed to generate funds for newly established colleges of agriculture and mechanical arts. Each state was granted 30,000 acres for each seat it had in Congress. The state was instructed to sell the land, place the receipts from the sale into a perpetual account, and draw the interest to fund college programs.

In the case of Colorado, the Morrill Act preceded statehood by 14 years. Nevertheless, the Territorial Legislature was given a share of the acreage by Congress. In 1870, with the money generated by the Morrill Act, the Territorial Legislature established the Agricultural College of Colorado in Fort Collins.

The college's first course in irrigation was taught in 1883 by a young engineer named Elwood Mead. In his class, Mead emphasized pressure and water flow as they related to the construction and operation of canals and reservoirs. After leaving the College in 1888, Mead wrote the first irrigation code. He continued his precedent-setting work for the U.S. Department of Agriculture and as a commissioner of the Bureau of Reclamation. The Bureau later recognized Mead's contributions by naming the lake formed by Hoover Dam after him. Lake Mead is a tribute to the agricultural engineer as well as to the importance of irrigation in the West.

Mead's successor at Fort Collins, Louis G. Carpenter, also had great

Major John Wesley Powell surveyed the Colorado River with flood control and irrigation in mind.

influence in civil and irrigation engineering. In 1883, he founded the American Society of Irrigation Engineers.

In 1869, Major John Wesley Powell explored the West for the Federal government, boating down the uncharted Colorado River. His exploits were covered in newspapers across the nation. He told of mountain streams swollen by melting snow in the spring, raging uncontrolled beyond their banks, wasting forever into the seas. "The West is an arid land," said Powell, "hostile to farming and will never be settled, unless the rivers are dammed, holding spring runoffs in reservoirs." Reclamation has since contained those rivers, transforming Major Powell's prophesy into reality.

With Powell, Mead and Carpenter, Colorado and its great college deserve much credit for nurturing the technology of irrigation in the final years of the 19th Century.

The Right to Water

Legislators in western states formed their own interpretations of the rights of individuals to surface water. They were divided almost equally between riparian and appropriation doctrines. The riparian doctrine, which emphasizes land ownership and proximity to water, was adopted by the states of Texas, California, Oregon, Washington, the Dakotas and Kansas. The appropriation doctrine, which allocates water based on an individual's priority of use, was adopted by Colorado, Nevada, Utah, Montana, Idaho, Wyoming, New Mexico and Arizona. In an irrigation-based agricultural setting, water rights are power. Disputes over them fill pages of western history.

As the first Federal projects expanded the distribution of surface water, private enterprise started to develop sources of underground water for irrigation. It wasn't long before laws had to be created to settle disputes over well water. Most states adopted the theory of reasonable use. Under this doctrine, landowners can withdraw ground water providing their use is reasonable in relation to the water rights of others. While this approach dominates the eastern U.S., Arizona, Kansas and Nebraska are the only western states to apply this theory. California adopted a modified system of reasonable use called correlative rights. This provides for additional restrictions for use of water during droughts.

The system of appropriation is the most common in western states. All ground water is considered public and withdrawals are allowed by permit in the order they are requested. Colorado, Idaho, Montana, Nevada, New Mexico, Oklahoma, Oregon, South Dakota, Utah, Washington and Wyoming subscribe to this system of allocating ground water.

Absolute rights to ground water are given to landowners in Texas and much of the Midwest. The owner of land overlying a ground water resource can withdraw as much water as desired with no consideration of the needs of others.

By the turn of the century, rights to ground water became a major issue with nearly 340,000 acres irrigated with subterranean water.

Turn-of-the-century grader for leveling and ditch forming.

Surface Irrigation Wonders

Surface irrigation is, by all measures, the prime means of irrigating U.S. crops. Despite massive strides in overhead sprinkler irrigation following World War II, there are six surface-irrigated acres today for every four sprinkler-irrigated acres. A 1992 survey estimated surface-irrigated acreage in the U.S. to be 34 million. Ten years before, the survey showed this acreage to be more than 40 million.

Surface irrigation methods vary according to soil types, land contours, water availability, crops grown and labor. These limitations have brought about modifications in what began simply as flooding.

Flood irrigation can be controlled or uncontrolled. Wild flooding, as the name implies, is uncontrolled flooding. No attention is paid to preparation of the soil surface. This is the most primitive form of water application.

Controlled flooding, although crude, is still practical in gently sloping, permanent crop lands adjacent to an abundant supply of water. Alfalfa, clover and perennial grasses can thrive with flood irrigation if the slope of the field does not exceed one foot of fall per 1,000 feet of run. Early references to controlled flooding, before soil-surface preparation was practical, do not reflect the advantages of reshaping land contours. Technology to reshape the land had a great impact on the effectiveness of controlled flooding.

Rill, corrugation or furrow irrigation are still widely practiced, mainly on soils with good water retention characteristics. In districts with plentiful, low-cost water, rill irrigation can be cost-effective, even in sloping orchards where adequate vegetation is maintained.

The corrugation method is a modification of the furrow method. It is generally employed on field crops growing on undulating topography.

Strip border irrigation is widely practiced in the vast Imperial, Sacramento and San Joaquin valleys of California, as well as in large sections of Nebraska, Kansas, Oklahoma and Texas. This system is named for a network of parallel borders, spaced 40 to 60 feet apart. The borders are five- to eight-inches-high with gentle slopes so harvesting machinery can traverse them easily. The slope away from the supply ditch, valve or gated pipe should not be greater than six inches per 100 feet. The experienced irrigator, knowing his soil, crop and strip-fall, can turn a head of water into the strip border to his greatest advantage.

The border method of irrigation is an old, but reliable way of handling a large quantity of low-cost water on sandy soils. Since the early days, experienced irrigators have remained loyal to this system as the most effective means of surface irrigating crops.

The border-contour method of flood irrigation is a significantly different practice employed primarily for rice culture. The nature of rice germination and growth requires total submergence of the field at a uniform depth throughout the growth cycle. The best technology in land preparation is required to create levies that correctly follow the contours of a gently sloping field.

Some of America's great inland valleys, favored with planned flood control structures, offer an ideal environment for sub-irrigation. Properly formed creek and river embankments or dikes allow contained stream flows to run at levels above the protected farm lands. They also provide for percolation of the sub-moisture under some pressure, a condition necessary for adequate crop growth.

Much credit for the efficient use of time-honored surface irrigation methods must be given to the U.S. Department of Agriculture, the Bureau of Reclamation, the electric utilities and the Agricultural Extension Service. By working with the irrigator-farmer, they have greatly advanced an old technology.

Great Advances in Irrigation: From Animals to Machines

Surface irrigation depends immeasurably on redesigned soil surfaces and contours for effective water flow, and hence, proper water infiltration by the soil. Reshaping and recontouring the land, however, was not practical until machinery, capable of meeting the size and scope of agriculture, was developed.

Dramatic changes in the methods of farming and land preparation occurred around the turn of the century. With the ability to reshape the land, California farmers began replacing dryland crops, such as small grains, with more profitable irrigated crops. Grain farming bowed to irrigated crops as water resources legislation brought about workable land management practices.

At first, animal-powered land leveling was practiced. It was slow and laborious and took its toll on man, beast and the implements used.

Horse-drawn earthmoving and leveling equipment was bulky and imprecise. The "skip" or "slip" scraper was popular. Drawn by two horses or mules, the teamster maneuvered the scraper from behind. Considerable brawn was needed to control the scoop with two widely-spaced wooden handles from the teamster's position, walking behind the implement. After scraping short distances, the teamster had to dump the full scoop with a mighty heave.

A revelation in horse-drawn earth moving came in 1883. John Porteus, a Fresno Township blacksmith, invented the Fresno scraper. The device was a metal scoop

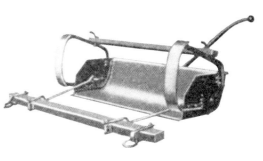

Fresno scraper with cumbersome eight-foot-long handle.

with unique steel runners, pulled by two to four draft animals. Like the skip scraper, the teamster controlled the depth of cut from behind. However, the Fresno scraper was engineered to provide the teamster with greater control. Once loaded, the Fresno could be skidded along for reasonable distances and dumped on a controlled basis. Porteus' invention was an impressive improvement over the skip and the much earlier buckboard scraper.

Various animal-drawn floats and drags were employed for final leveling. The ultimate in early land leveling was accomplished with a

Main irrigation ditch construction by steam shovel near Lindsey, California in early 1900s.

First production crawler tractor being demonstrated by Holt Manufacturing Company in 1908. The tractor would soon become known as the Caterpillar.

four- to six-horse team pulling a wheeled grader with blade. This was a primitive version of present-day diesel powered graders seen working on highway roadsides.

At the dawn of the 20th Century, better ways of levelling land to prepare for surface irrigation were close at hand for the progressive farmer. In 1905, C.W. Hart and C.H. Parr of Charles City, IA, introduced the first gasoline-powered wheel tractor. Designed to pull plows and other implements, the Hart-Parr tractor was a bellwether of early tractors. Many other wheel-tractor designs followed rapidly in the next decade.

Unfortunately, the early, massive, steel-wheeled behemoths were almost useless for preparing sandy, heavy peat or clay soils for surface irrigation. Their power was lost in soft alluvial or bottom-land soils.

A great new era in surface irrigation farming and land preparation was ushered in by the progressive thinking of an inventive wheel-maker, Benjamin Holt of Stockton, CA. In 1908, Holt introduced the first production model of a crawler tractor powered by a gasoline engine. His new tractor moved on continuous tracks, allowing the heavy machine to tread lightly on soft soils or muddy bottom lands.

The Holt crawler tractor came to be known as the Caterpillar, so named by Holt's bookkeeper as he observed it nimbly traversing rough land with its flexible tracks. So great was the success of the Caterpillar that by 1913 huge farming projects throughout the West became practical proving grounds for the machine. Military versions were designed and shipped to Europe during World War I. The crawler concept proved its powers in the muddy horrors of the Western Front, reputedly shortening the hostilities by several months.

The reputation of the Caterpillar in earth moving was soon enhanced when L.G. LaTourneau invented and manufactured the first pull-type, self-loading field scraper. Coupled together, the Caterpillar 75 and the

LaTourneau scraper vastly improved land leveling in heavy construction and agriculture.

Except for small farming, the day of horse-drawn power was waning as the country entered the 1920s. The effectiveness of large earth-moving equipment had been established. Hart, Holt, LaTourneau and Parr paved the way for the advancement of irrigated agriculture in America.

In 1925, Holt merged his company with the Best Company to form the Caterpillar Tractor Company. For the next 30 years, Caterpillar equipment provided the Bureau of Reclamation and the U.S. Corps of Engineers with the power to develop facilities for electric power generation, flood control and irrigation in the American West.

Control Over Surface Irrigation

Prior to the 20th Century, directing irrigation water to arable lands was simply a matter of digging an opening in dikes or berms with a shovel. As irrigated acreage increased, water increased in value and better control devices were needed. Among those utilized were headgates, flashboards and check gates. A different principle of diversion was the canvas draper. Fastened to a rigid wood pole in the supply ditch, the canvas dam caused water to flow gently over the berm. This method can still be observed in certain areas of the Central Valley of California.

By 1900, concrete pipe feeders with vertical riser outlets were fitted with various valves to control flow. One such valve, the Alfalfa Valve, was manually adjusted to discharge water for flooding or supplying strip borders. Modern versions of the Alfalfa Valve are still made by Waterman Industries, Inc. and Fresno Valve and Castings.

As the science of agriculture expanded, breakthrough technologies emerged with increasing frequency. One that irrigation enthusiasts welcomed was a new means of measuring water flows in irrigation ditches. Ralph Leroy Parshall, a graduate and member of the faculty of the Colorado Agricultural College, applied his knowledge of hydraulics to create the venturi measuring flume. The industry rapidly recognized the advantages of Parshall's invention and attached his name to it for posterity. The Parshall measuring flume was one of the first efforts to improve the efficiency of irrigation water flow.

Another leader in irrigation technology in the early 1900s was Milo V. German, a farmer from Cozad, NE. Tired of using wooden lath pipe buried in the sides of ditches to transport water to rows, German explored ways to move water over the ditch bank instead of through it. When a bulky water trough for his animals had to be

New age in power machines brought about precision land leveling for better control over surface irrigation.

Horses and machines worked side by side during irrigation canal construction at the turn of the Century.

emptied, he used a hose and gravity to do the job. By transferring the principle of siphoning to irrigation water distribution, he made the first siphon tubes from heavy, reclaimed boiler tubes. He later experimented with discarded brake hoses from rail cars and then aluminum tubing. By then, World War II made aluminum unavailable for agriculture. Eventually, after a number of setbacks, plastic tubing became the choice material for siphon tubes.

German was a major contributor to the advancement of surface irrigated agriculture. His novel approach to moving water eased the farmer's burden and made irrigation more controllable.

Much credit for the advancement of American irrigation immediately following the war goes to the two largest American aluminum producers, Reynolds Metals Company and The Aluminum Company of America. By 1947, Reynolds had formed an

aluminum tube, six inches in diameter and ten feet long to conform to the contours of an irrigation ditch bank.

William A. Swanson, a Phoenix, AZ businessman, who was looking

for a new venture, obtained a sample of Reynolds' first siphon tube. After extensively testing the tube in the broiling Arizona sun, Swanson perfected a procedure for priming

Lift gates were initial control devices as water increased in value.

TOP RIGHT: Old Hand Pump Primed Six-Inch Aluminum Siphon Tube to irrigate cotton fields in Mississippi River Delta.

CENTER: Siphon Tube Water Transfer from ditch to crop row changed surface irrigation.

BOTTOM: Surge valve and controller direct irrigation water through gated pipe to furrows.

Courtesy, Jack Liddell, Delta Irrigation

Courtesy, Jack Liddell, Delta Irrigation

Courtesy, P&R Surge, Lubbock, Texas

the large siphon tube. Once primed, 300 gallons per minute gushed from the tube into the test field. Simple in design with no moving parts, the siphon tube still has had a major impact on surface irrigation.

The never-ending requirement for irrigation water in Arizona and the arid Southwest has made these regions a proving ground for many other developments in irrigation technology. Products that originated in the Southwest contributed greatly to the efficient transport of ditch water in the 50s and 60s.

Recent innovations in surface irrigation have focused on delivering water to prepared furrows or basins in amounts approximating the infiltration of water into the soil. Such technology utilizes gated pipe, in conjunction with surge valves or cablegation, to control the timing and flow of water onto the surface. Loss of water to deep percolation has been greatly reduced. Furthermore, tailwater can be recovered and recirculated. More uniform soil moisture levels improve crop yields and discourage certain diseases and pests. By gaining control over surface irrigation, farmers have saved both water and energy.

As the 20th Century draws to a close, surface irrigation remains the dominant technology in irrigated agriculture. Water use efficiencies of surface irrigation methods have increased dramatically. While the development of new water sources by the Corps of Engineers and the Bureau of Reclamation helped expand surface irrigation in this century, improvements in water use efficiency will be the key to preserving irrigated agriculture in the 21st Century.

Harvey S. Firestone (right) describes the merits of
The Firestone Irrigation System, forerunner of the
side-wheel roll sprinkler system, to close friend Henry
Ford in 1930. Firestone's portable irrigation system
never made it to production.

CHAPTER 2

Twentieth Century Manmade Rain

The technology for applying water like raindrops to crops allowed more control over water distribution, minimized soil compaction and placed water when and where it was needed.

S prinkler irrigation was developed to overcome limitations of surface irrigation. Sprinklers, with their flexible, efficient distribution of water, permit irrigation of a wide range of soils and contours. These features have enabled man to utilize land previously unsuitable for crop growth.

In most portions of the country, irrigation supplements natural rainfall. Adequate moisture is essential for unhampered development of crops from germination to maturity. Carefully supplying a crop's moisture requirement greatly influences product yield, quality and marketability.

Crop quality is fundamental to consumer acceptance. Food processors in many areas will not issue contracts to farmers unless their fields are sprinkler irrigated. Such stipulations have been in effect since the early 1930s when the connection between superior crop production and sprinkler irrigation was first recognized.

The fact that sprinkler irrigation in America is entering its second century is surprising to many people. The first use of overhead, perforated irrigation pipe was recorded in 1873. Sprinklers, as we know them today, date from 1890 when a Portland, Maine, manufacturer propelled a revolving nozzle with the flow and pressure of the water running through the sprinkler. Many new ideas for sprinkling lawns and gardens emerged in the last decade of the 19th century. By 1898, at least 17 patents had been issued for sprinkler inventions.

One of the first inventors to obtain a sprinkler patent was Charles

Courtesy, Marvin Shearer, Oregon State University

Skinner Overhead Sprinkler System developed in 1894 by Charles Skinner.

Skinner, a farmer from Troy, Ohio. In 1894, he was issued Patent Number 614,507 for a sprinkling system that consisted of manually oscillated, galvanized pipes with orifices spaced at two-foot intervals. As the pipes, suspended six feet above the ground, were oscillated, strips of cropland up to 60 feet wide received the moisture they needed.

Acceptance of Skinner's invention was so great that, by 1911, the Skinner System was as well-known to farmers who irrigated as the John Deere plow was to those who cultivated their fields. The technology developed by both men would change the business of farming forever.

The company recorded one Skinner success after another. Today, pages of farmers' testimony provide rewarding reading for the irrigation nostalgist.

One typical testimonial came from a 1915 Michigan newspaper. It carries the headline, "Kellogg Company Installs One of the Largest Single Irrigation Systems in the Country." The subhead read, "Members of the Firm Consider This One of the Most Revolutionary Steps Made in the History of the Organization."

In similar fashion, word spread across the country about new applications of overhead irrigation, spawned largely by the breakthroughs of Skinner in the 1890s. He should be recognized as the originator of sprinkler irrigation. His technology for applying water like gentle raindrops to crops allowed more control over water distribution, minimized soil compaction and placed water when and where it was needed.

During the first decade of the 20th century, many important events contributed to a surge in irrigation. Developments in land reform for the arid west facilitated land settlement, utilization of natural resources and crop production. By improving the security of western farmers and their families, the government encouraged development of western resources.

Enthusiasm about the West waned briefly during the presidency of William McKinley. However, his vice president, "Rough Rider" Theodore Roosevelt was a famous outdoorsman. When McKinley was assassinated in 1901, Roosevelt's succession rekindled the nation's fascination with the West.

One year later in 1902, Congress passed legislation to establish the Reclamation Service of the U.S. Department of the Interior. The engineering and construction capabilities of the Reclamation Service were a boon to irrigation progress. From 1903 to 1910, the service tamed the waters of several western rivers. Its success led to irrigation opportunities for thousands of settlers who established numerous western communities.

Sprinkler Heads: The Men, the Makes, the Designs

The first three decades of the 20th century were formulative ones for businesses making and selling irrigation sprinklers and accessories.

In 1904, John D. Ross of Pasadena, California, was the first to manufacture sprinklers for lawn and garden use. Twenty years later, botanist Luther Burbank called Ross Sprinkler Company's square-pattern underground sprinkler head the best he had ever used. Ross-Temko Company of Los Angeles had the distinction of having the oldest nameplate in the irrigation business until it went out of business.

The oldest remaining manufacturer of sprinklers today is the Thompson Manufacturing Company. Inventor W. Van E. Thompson, also of Pasadena, introduced his famous "Owl" sprinkler in 1907. The Owl, patented in 1912, was just the first of Thompson's many inventions.

One of Thompson's most innovative inventions was an underground, gear-drive rotary sprinkler called the "Commander" introduced in 1936. An improved version of the Commander is still made by the company, now located in Chino, California. Although the company has changed ownership, it has operated continuously since 1907.

The Skinner Irrigation Company was not actually formed until 1908. Charles Skinner was a farmer first and an inventor and tinkerer second. If it weren't for a chance meeting on an interurban electric train between Toledo and Dayton, OH, Skinner might never have become partners with businessman Walter H. Coles, the manufacturing and marketing expert Skinner needed to spread the word about his irrigation creations.

The success of the company was far more than Skinner imagined or sought. After four busy years, Skinner sold his interest to Coles in 1912. For the next 38 years, Coles guided the company to prominence in the irrigation industry.

Coles' son-in-law Anthony R. J. "Bud" Friedmann joined the Skinner

Walter H. Coles (center) with his two original employees at the Skinner Irrigation factory in Troy, Ohio.

Earliest known side-wheel-roll irrigation lateral with Thompson, arm-type, long range sprinklers. The pipe was reclaimed boiler tubing. Tillamook County, Oregon in 1933.

Irrigation Company and became a driving force in the young irrigation industry. He played a major role in the formation of the Association of Sprinkler Irrigation Equipment Manufacturers in 1949, serving as the group's first president. ASIEM was the forerunner of the Irrigation Association. Friedmann rose to become president of the company, which was sold first to the Ashley F. Ward Company of Cincinnati and then to John S. Greeno. In 1976, the last product with a Skinner label was shipped. Friedmann died at the age of 79 ten years later.

Early sprinkler irrigation history would be incomplete without mentioning L.B. Harris, inventor of one of the first gear-drive heads. The "Harris Precipitator" was patented in 1910. After its inception by Harris, the gear-drive concept would undergo numerous improvements during the 20th century.

The L. R. Nelson Story

In 1906, Lewen Russell Nelson launched what has become the oldest, continuous, single-family sprinkler manufacturing company in the United States. That year, he formed the Nelson and Morrison Manufacturing Company in Boulder, Colorado.

Nelson's first contribution to irrigation was a coupling device for garden hoses, which he patented in 1904. Its success encouraged Nelson to quickly produce numerous other irrigation related products which he manufactured.

Shortly after forming Nelson and Morrison Manufacturing Company, Nelson relocated the company to Peoria, Illinois. In 1911, he achieved the goal of building his own manufactur-

Brass, Self-Fastening Hose Coupling as advertised in 1911 L.R. Nelson Mfg. Co. catalog.

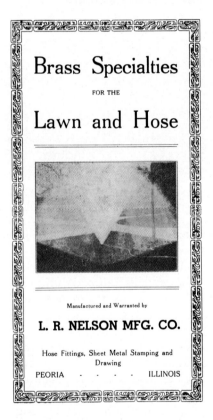

A pocket-sized catalog produced in 1911 featured the L.R. Nelson Manufacturing Company's brass hose couplings, new sprinkler and a hose nozzle.

ing plant and renamed the enterprise Central Brass and Stamping Company.

The new factory started producing Nelson's latest invention, a fixed, square-pattern lawn sprinkler head connected to a hose with his brass coupling. A pocket-sized catalog produced that year featured the company's brass hose couplings, new sprinkler and a hose nozzle. "People want good things and this house will never forget that fact," was printed prominently on the back of the catalog.

The hose-end coupler and sprinkler concept served as a strong foundation for the company, re-named the L.R. Nelson Manufacturing Company in 1921. Nelson had heard about developments in irrigation in the West. In 1925, he decided to become acquainted first-hand, and moved his family to the center of sprinkler irrigation, Pasadena, California. After seeing sprinklers in action in orchards and citrus groves, Nelson was convinced that sprinkler irrigation was a market his company should explore further. With this in mind, he returned to Peoria where he developed a number of new products over the next 15 years. Included among them was an underground turf sprinkler.

Nelson's son, Russell Baldwin Nelson, joined the company at age 23 eventually becoming president in 1952. Under Russell's leadership, the company increased its emphasis on revolving sprinklers for portable irrigation by creating the Rainy Sprinkler Sales division specifically for this technology. The new sales organization concentrated in the 37 eastern states.

Russell also stepped up marketing efforts for the Nelson line of hose-end products by implementing an aggressive mass merchandising campaign. The company became the primary brand-name supplier of oscillating wave sprinklers for Sears, Roebuck and Company.

The third generation of Nelsons joined the business in 1961 when Russell's son, Barton Russell Nelson, worked in manufacturing. From boyhood, Bart was a fond admirer of his grandfather and father, absorbing every figment of their broad experience and tutelage.

He became especially interested in the development of large travelling sprinklers. Determined to increase the mobility of such sprinklers, Bart helped convince the B.F. Goodrich Company to produce a five-inch, draggable hose to supply the travellers. Long since proven highly applicable, such hose is used today for some state-of-the-art, self-propelled linear-move sprinkler irrigation machines.

In 1971, the company created Nelson Irrigation Corporation, a wholely-owned subsidiary, to concentrate its efforts on large sprinklers for agricultural irrigation. The timing was fortunate for Bart Nelson. When the company was sold in 1972 and rechristened L.R. Nelson Corporation, Inc., he was able to purchase the subsidiary.

Having surveyed the potential of agricultural irrigation in the West, Bart created Nelson Irrigation Corporation in Walla Walla, Washington. After building a factory there, Bart began production of the Nelson Big Gun in 1974. The company later began manufacturing a 3/4-inch, impact-drive sprinkler head for farmers.

Bart Nelson's sons, Craig and Reid, are the fourth generation to participate in the family enterprise. With the motto of "Innovation in Irrigation," Nelson Irrigation Corporation continues to develop and introduce new products for the industry.

Post World War I

Interest in lawn and garden irrigation jumped following World War I. A Los Angeles salesman by the name of George Moody envisioned a great market, not just for small sprinklers, but entire sprinkler systems for commercial, residential and municipal applications. In 1922, Moody observed sprinklers watering a newly planted lawn on the corner of Gower and Melrose Streets in Los Angeles. He was so fascinated that he examined one of the small sprin-

Courtesy, Marc Dutton

John A. Brooks installed 2,300 brass, pop-up sprinkler heads in Grant Park in downtown Chicago in the 1920s.

klers and wrote down the name of the company engraved on them, Tuthill. Moody contacted the company and decided then and there that he was going to become involved in irrigation.

He worked out an arrangement to sell for both Tuthill and Thompson. The Thompson head was the only large sprinkler made in the city at the time. Moody intended to use the large Thompson sprinkler in conjunction with the smaller Tuthill heads.

It wasn't long before Moody purchased the rights to a patent from Everett P. Lang. The patent was for an automatic sequencing, hydraulic controller. Linked to hydraulic valves, the controller became the foundation for an automatic sprinkler system.

The first Moody controlled sprinkler irrigation system was installed in 1924 at the McFarlane residence in Holmby Hills in Los Angeles County. Moody retrofitted the existing manual irrigation system

with hydraulic valves and a controller. This remarkable example and others led to his first commercial system for the City of Upland in 1929. The Upland system was complete with sprinklers, pipe, valves, and controller.

The Moody Company weathered the Great Depression, switching to military production during World War II and grew following the war. In 1955, Jack Nees and King Ewing bought the company and changed its name to Moody Sprinkler Company. Three years later, Nees bought Ewing's interest in the venture.

After changing hands twice more, first to Greenbelt Industries of California and then Safe-T-Lawn of Florida, the Moody name became property of the Nelson Corporation in 1979. George Moody, influential in creating automated sprinkler irrigation, died in 1973.

In the early 1900s, long before air conditioning offered comfort on hot, Fresno nights, a railroad trainmaster

by the name of W. A. Buckner sweated after hours to perfect a sprinkler head for large turf areas. Although a comparative newcomer to the verdant irrigated agriculture of California's San Joaquin Valley, he soon recognized the power of sprinklers. Working as a dispatcher for the Santa Fe Railroad during the day, Buckner tinkered in his home workshop at night and weekends attempting to engineer a slow-rotation sprinkler head that could revolutionize turf irrigation, just as sprinklers had changed agriculture.

He obtained a patent for his sprinkler in 1912. Buckner's timing was fortunate. Within weeks of approving the first production model made for him by a company in Cincinnati, he received a call from a group of engineers in San Francisco trying to design a hoseless sprinkler irrigation system for a golf course to overlook the Pacific Ocean near Monterey.

Buckner Turf Sprinkler produced in 1934.

Still employed by the railroad, Buckner made arrangements with a company in San Jose to build the sprinklers if he won the contract. When the Del Monte corporation approved his bid, Buckner suddenly entered the sprinkler irrigation business in a big way, by supplying the sprinklers for the first hoseless golf course irrigation system. The year was 1912. The course was the famous Pebble Beach Golf Club.

Buckner continued to explore irrigation while maintaining his position with the Santa Fe Railroad. To gain more control over production, he contracted with the Lisenby Manufacturing Company in Fresno. In 1925, Harry E. Cleason, a Lisenby employee, became Buckner's partner. With Cleason's expertise, the company started to manufacture its own irrigation products. The following year, Buckner strengthened the company's engineering abilities by hiring John Royer.

Over the next 30 years, the company developed such significant products as the quick-coupling valve, hose swivel, sand resistant bearing and a cam-drive sprinkler. All are still produced. In the mid-1950s, the company's reputation was further enhanced when it produced the components for the first automated golf course sprinkler irrigation system installed at Sea Island, Georgia.

Two other men figured prominently in the company's success. Herbert M. Clark headed the company's engineering department for many years. He provided design assistance for golf course and land-scape architects, conducted clinics on irrigation across the country and kept the company's products in tune with market needs. John H. Muller, long-time sales manager and authority on agricultural sprinkler irrigation, kept the firm responsive to the overhead sprinkler needs of growers.

As Buckner's health started to fail in the 1940s, Cleason assumed a greater role in company operations with the assistance of John Gill and Walter Lauritzen, family relatives. When Buckner died in 1953, his stock was bequeathed to his wife and Cleason became president of the company.

During the 1960s, industrialist James R. Coson purchased the stock from both Cleason and Mrs. Buckner. Operating under the name of General Sprinkler Company while maintaining the Buckner trademark, the firm grew ten-fold between 1961 and 1972. Such growth attracted the attention of industry giant Johns-Manville. The Fortune 500 firm chose to compliment its line of pipe, fittings and sprinklers. It bought General from Coson in 1972 and helped the company make significant strides in micro-processor irrigation

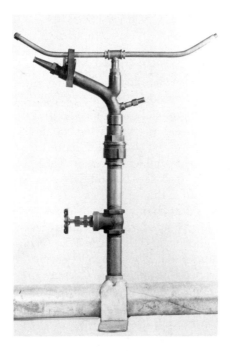

Perfection Sprinkler Company's large sprinkler head used for portable and pivot irrigation.

controls. Three years later, Coson started Royal Coach Sprinkler, Inc.

By 1980, Johns-Manville sought to divest of General Sprinkler. Coson repurchased the assets and merged his old company into Royal Coach, thus restoring the Buckner name in the marketplace. It has been strengthened even further under W. A. Lyles, who purchased Coson's assets in 1985.

While Buckner became motivated through agriculture, others gained inspiration directly from turf irrigation. John A. Brooks, a master plumber in Detroit, recognized the potential for turf irrigation systems among the city's affluent residents. He installed the first systems in the industrial city for the Dodge family of Gross Point and Henry Ford of Dearborn.

Brooks filed patent applications for 27 inventions related to water handling between 1915 and 1950. His first patent, issued in 1916, was for a brass, pop-up turf sprinkler, so durable that some heads can be found functioning today. In 1926, he developed an electric timer that activated a hydraulic controller. Combined with his sprinkler heads, the clock made totally automatic irrigation a reality.

A franchise agreement with Frederick Reinke of Los Angeles in 1924 generated Brooks of California. Reinke later created the Febco line of valves and vacuum breakers for turf applications. Brooks died in 1958, but his legacy is still carried on by Marc Dutton Irrigation, Inc. of Drayton Plains, Michigan.

The importance of sprinkler irrigation was recognized by the United States Department of Agriculture in a 1917 bulletin entitled, "Spray Irrigation." The author was Milo B. Williams, an engineer. It was only the beginning.

The Great Lakes spawned another major player in the sprinkler irrigation industry. While Brooks concentrated on the Detroit area, Daniel and Bernard Wright were introducing irrigation in Chicago, Illinois. As owner of Suburban Landscaping Company, Daniel realized the need for supplemental irrigation in the region. In 1928, after installing his first irrigation system, his interest in irrigation took off with Bernard's encouragement.

The Wrights used copper tubing for the underground laterals of their "spray-mist" systems. The supplier of the tubing was Mueller Brass Company of Port Huron, Michigan. The Wrights reasoned that they would gain credibility in the trade by combining the well-known Mueller name with their spray-mist name. They coined the name Muellermist. The name gained notoriety when the system was installed in "The Homes of the Future" exhibit at the 1934 World's Fair in Chicago.

Muellermist offered a complete automatic underground turf sprinkler irrigation system as early as 1932. Part of the system was the company-designed ball-drive, pop-up head, probably the first in the industry. The company also ventured outside the city with Calco portable sprinkler equipment.

A milestone in irrigation history for Muellermist occurred when the company was awarded the irrigation contract for Arlington National Cemetery. The huge project took two years to complete. The company, now run by Andrew Wright, has also installed irrigation systems for many major stadiums in the Great Lakes region.

Irrigation During the Great Depression

The Great Depression brought dark days to the Nation. Irrigation technology continued to advance despite the poor economic climate. Improved pumps, engines, electric motors, quick couplers and new sprinkler heads arrived on the irrigation scene.

Portable agricultural sprinkler irrigation made significant strides during this period. The earliest applications of portable sprinklers were concentrated in the Willamette Valley and Tillamook County of Oregon, the Sacramento Valley of California and in rural counties of Ohio and Indiana.

Several western counties of Oregon nurtured the development of portable sprinkler technology. Tucked between the majestic Cascade Mountains on the east and the Coast Range on the west lies the rich Willamette Valley. The average annual rainfall in the valley is 25 to 35 inches. To the west of the Coastal Range, Tillamook County receives up to 90 inches of rainfall in an average year. Yet, between June to mid-September, when crops need moisture most, the county receives little rain.

In the early 30s, Oregon Agricultural College in Corvallis, known

Courtesy, Hunter Industries

The first vertical-impact sprinkler made by Fingel C. Orr of Los Angeles in the early 1900s.

today as Oregon State University, became one of the first Land Grant colleges to promote the development of portable sprinkler irrigation. The first demonstration system was installed on a dairy farm in Tillamook County by F. Earl Price and Clarence Hurd of the college's agricultural engineering department and Extension Soil Specialist Arthur S. King. Within the next 12 months, more than 40 Oregon farmers installed sprinkler systems.

In 1932, the farm advisor's office in Los Angeles County conducted a survey of growers regarding sprinkler irrigation in orchards. The majority of the 100 growers polled were satisfied with their overhead

systems. Sprinklers provided farmers with a needed alternative to surface irrigation.

Center Pivot

Often what appears to be a new concept was actually conceived years before. Such is the case with today's widely used center pivot machines. The earliest pivots did not begin to dot the Plains states until the late 1950s, but center pivot irrigation had been recorded long before then.

The concept originated more than 30 years before. A patent for an "Apparatus for Watering by Means of Suspended Pipe" was granted in 1917 to Ernest Eugene Alvarez. Unfortunately, Alvarez failed to describe how movement of the pipe, either laterally or in a circle, could be accomplished. A year before, a patent had been granted to James A. Norton for, "A machine adapted to irrigate relatively large tracts from a hydrant around which it rotates." A third patent granted in 1924 to A. E. Murphy was for an "Irrigator, Self-Propelled Traveling." Of the three, Norton's was best thought out and closest to today's version.

Fingel C. Orr, a Los Angeles manufacturer in the early 1900s, is credited with the design and manufacture of the first vertical impact, slow-rotation sprinkler head. He created both part- and full-circle versions. Buckner was sufficiently impressed with the technology that it bought the license for the ORR and named it "Rocker Jet." The full-circle version is still in Buckner's catalog.

The sprinkler head technology developed by Orr and others not only assisted the introduction of early center pivot systems, but also gave greater impetus to the development of portable quick coupling systems. The first such systems, made of lightweight 16- and 18-gauge galvanized steel pipe with quick-couplers, arrived on the irrigation scene in 1930. The low cost per acre for portable systems changed the direction of the agricultural sprinkler irrigation industry.

John E. Oaks in 1940, his first irrigation year.

Another development during the period was portable, low-pressure perforated pipe. The W. R. Ames Company of San Francisco first marketed the concept, although perforated laterals made of lead pipe had been used in England during the late 19th century. The pipe caught the fancy of irrigators because of its low pressure requirement, generally not more than 20 pounds per square inch. However, its high precipitation rate limited its use to permeable soils with a high intake capacity. Ames Perf-O-Rain was taken seriously in Oregon where it was tested by Everett Davis and Ivan Brantzen at the Oregon Agricultural College and Crawford Reid of R. M. Wade & Company.

The limiting factor of portable pipe was the joint between sections. Ralph H. Pierce, a metal fabricator in Eugene, Oregon came up with the solution, a coupler with a "chevron" design rubber gasket. The combination produced a tight seal at moderate pressure, an ideal solution for connecting portable pipe quickly.

In Pierce's patent application, filed in 1934, he explained, "My invention relates to joining the ends of unthreaded pipe, usually welded steel, too thin to allow threading." The all-important gasket was produced for Pierce by Huntington

Rubber Mills of Portland, Oregon. Pierce's gasket would be appreciated more once aluminum tubing became available after World War II.

Back east, another type of coupler was developed by an Indiana manufacturer of farm machinery. Otto Knoerzer, facing slow sales in the depths of the depression, was keenly interested in new irrigation products. When he stopped at an Ohio friend's irrigated potato field one day, he noticed the dramatic

The O.K. Champion quick-coupling developed by Otto Knoerzer of Hammond, Indiana, in the 1930s with a Skinner sprinkler.

difference between the crop that was irrigated and another depending entirely on rainfall. The sprinklers were attached to heavy, threaded, standard water pipe.

Instead of continuing eastward as planned, he and his wife returned to his Champion Corporation shop where he started to design his quick coupler. In 1934, a line of quick-coupler fittings was introduced with the name OK Champion. Literature for the fittings proclaimed, "Two men can easily lay one-half mile of Champion pipe per hour."

In 1936, Knoerzer's Champion Corp. announced a new method of crop insurance, a "Rain Machine." It was an 80-foot boom suspended 3 feet above the ground by 4 rubber-tired wheels. Between sets, the boom was moved 32 feet by one person operating a windlass. Coincidentally, the water supply line, also on wheels, telescoped as it moved, much like a fishing rod.

More than 2,000 miles west, two dairy farmers in Tillamook County, Oregon, fabricated a side wheel roll system. Fred Kruitz and Wilbur Broughton used Pierce couplers to link sections of reclaimed boiler tubing together. Old hay rake wheels were employed to elevate the pipe and provide mobility.

One of the earliest names in portable sprinkler irrigation was American Rolling Mills Company (Armco). In 1933, the company introduced its Calco Portable Rainmaker. It utilized a "lever-lock" quick coupler with an "O" ring gasket. However, it was impractical for portable sprinkler applications because the seal did not drain for easy moving.

The same year, a Eugene, Oregon, farmer and steel worker used the Pierce coupler to join steel tubing together. R. L. Gheen's company, Gheen Irrigation Works, has lasted three generations to become one of the oldest and most stable manufacturers of portable sprinkler irrigation equipment.

Water pipe fittings have long been the specialty of Northern Indiana Brass Company, established in 1904 in Elkhart. When John Brooks in Detroit developed a pop-up sprinkler head in 1916, Nibco became a Brooks dealer for Illinois and Indiana. By 1938, the company's catalog included a full line of components for manual or automatic turf irrigation systems.

To help generate sales in 1937, the company published a booklet, "How to Install a Lawn Spray System." The author was an engineer and specialist in turf irrigation, M. E. "Max" Snoddy. He would eventually move to Texas and create his own irrigation manufacturing business, Weathermatic.

Nibco gained notoriety when it supplied nearly 2,400 spray heads, pipe and fittings for "One of the world's largest lawn spray systems," along Michigan Avenue in Chicago. Today the company provides a wide range of bronze and PVC fittings and valves.

Rain Bird Takes Flight

No name in irrigation is better recognized than Rain Bird. Named in homage to the American Indian harbinger of rainfall, Rain Bird was the vision of two young Californians during the Depression, Orten Englehardt and Clement LaFetra.

The idea of a horizontal-action, impact-drive sprinkler head originated in a Glendora citrus grove where Englehardt observed closely as his father converted from surface to sprinkler irrigation. Glendora was

First production sprinkler manufactured by Rain Bird in the La Fetra barn in Glendora, California.

just a few miles east of Pasadena where stationary overhead sprinkler systems were first used during the early 1920s because of unusually pervious soils in citrus groves. Working in his citrus grove shop, Englehardt collected sprinklers-of-the-day, explored their inner workings, and created his own designs.

Two types of sprinklers captured his interest most, the Orr-designed vertical-impact drive and gear-drive. In his earliest experiments, Englehardt attempted to construct an elaborate gear-driven sprinkler. Dissatisfied with test results, he

redirected his efforts toward a horizontal-impact drive.

By 1932, Englehardt produced his first prototype. LaFetra urged his neighbor and friend to apply for a patent. The patent was issued in 1934. In a barn surrounded by citrus groves, the two workmen were able to assemble two of the sprinklers per day.

Soon, Englehardt asked LaFetra to assume the details of manufacturing and marketing. By 1935, Englehardt wanted to return to farming. He was content with being paid a royalty for his invention. In October 1935, with a simple handshake, LaFetra and his wife, Mary Elizabeth, took over the manufacturing and sales rights to Englehardt's invention and launched the Rain Bird Sprinkler Company.

One of the company's first customers was Charles Cavanaugh, greenskeeper at the Los Angeles Country Club. The slow, even rotation of the Rain Bird enabled the night irrigation crew to move sprinklers from one position to another without getting wet.

For the next 10 years, Rain Bird sprinklers were manufactured and sold on a special order basis. LaFetra steadfastly adhered to the pact, making royalty payments to Englehardt throughout the 17-year life of the patent.

By the end of World War II, Rain Bird had grown to become an industry leader, a position it shared with pioneers Skinner and Buckner. In 1946, the company moved out of the barn and built a factory in Glendora. As it grew in size and stature, the company hired qualified specialists, such as Jules Coffey, Alfred S. Gray and Crawford Reid. LaFetra, his wife and Reid became instrumental in stabilizing the burgeoning irrigation industry through their early support of trade organizations, including the Irrigation Association.

In 1988, when the Englehardt property was sold to developers, both his shop and collection of sprinklers were saved by the

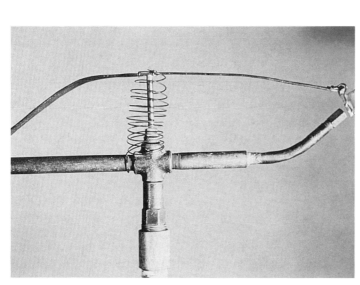

Forerunner of the Rain Bird sprinkler head invented by Orten Englehardt in 1933.

First Wade Rain power unit for Power-Roll, 1953.

Glendora Preservation Foundation. They can be viewed at the new Glendora Heritage Park. A park monument from the American Society of Agricultural Engineers honors Rain Bird.

Three early benefactors of sprinkler-irrigated agriculture in the Los Angeles area were Rainstorm Manufacturing Company, Waterseal Couplings, Ltd. and West Coast Pipe and Steel Company. All made couplings to join sections of portable pipe. Rainstorm introduced the Wallis threadless coupling system in 1934. Its literature enthusiastically claimed 50 percent increases in yield over surface irrigation. Waterseal's streamlined couplings were designed to reduce the labor of moving pipe. "Thirty-foot sections of pipe, four-inches or smaller, can be handled by one man," boasted the company's literature in 1935.

West Coast Pipe and Steel entered the portable pipe and coupling business in 1938 with its Wesco System. The coupling was again the key. "Our system of lightweight, galvanized steel tubing with a positive-locking, ring-socket end, receded to retain a rubber gasket, allows 20 degrees of flexibility per 20-foot joint."

Portable irrigation caught on in Michigan during the Depression, thanks to A.S. Lynden and Charles Bennett, founders of Perfection Sprinkler Company of Ann Arbor. They switched the direction of their business from turf to agricultural irrigation with the introduction of quick-coupling, galvanized steel tubing and fittings. The company has been serving the industry with portable irrigation supplies and sprinklers for three generations.

The Northwest Rains

A farm equipment distributor, R. M. Wade & Company, helped bring manmade rain to the Pacific Northwest. Founder Robert M. Wade first opened the doors of the company in Salem, Oregon, in 1865. That makes the company one of the oldest, continuously operating, family-owned farm equipment distributors in the state.

Wade had relocated his company to the growing metropolis of Portland. By 1930, his grandson, Wade Newbegin, took an interest in sprinkler irrigation, as did the company's pump department manager, Crawford Reid. Both could be found at the early demonstrations and tests conducted by the Agricultural Engineering Department at Oregon State College.

In the spring of 1936, Newbegin and Reid designed and installed the company's first portable sprinkler irrigation system near Salem. By summer, the system drew intense farmer interest. It wasn't long before farmers across the Northwest wanted to install their own "Wade Rain" system.

Agriculture had driven the company since shortly after the Civil War. After World War II, agriculture gave it another boost when the company introduced a lightweight quick-coupler for use with aluminum tubing. As the decade of the 50s began, the Wade Company introduced its Power Roll line, which consisted of a mechanical-move side wheel roll and a tractor-tow lateral.

Two Wade Rain division sales managers served as presidents of the Sprinkler Irrigation Association, Robert M. Morgan in 1957 and Hugh L. Williams in 1968. Wade Newbegin and Morgan have been honored by the Irrigation Association with its Industry Achievement Award.

Today, R.M. Wade & Co. offers both sprinkler and low volume irrigation systems for agriculture.

Fourth generation brothers Edward and Wade Jr. operate the firm.

Just as Wade boosted portable sprinkler irrigation in the Northwest, T. S. Moulton helped spread the new technology in the north central U.S. Created in Minnesota as Modern Irrigation Company in 1936 by T. S. Moulton and A.H. Ames, the company was able to sell irrigation systems in a region with mild weather and significant rainfall. Ames and Moulton convinced farmers that supplemental irrigation was the answer for one-to three-week summer dry spells that affected yields.

Modern Irrigation Company became a Wisconsin concern when Moulton became the sole owner in 1944. After two generations of family ownership, the company was sold in 1989. For more than 50 years, the Moulton name has signified the importance of supplemental irrigation to farmers in the upper Midwest.

An enduring name in portable sprinkler irrigation in North Carolina is that of Crockett. In an effort to bolster poor sales during the Depression, C.G. Crockett, president of Standard Fertilizer Company, won the rights to distribute irrigation products from Champion Corporation and Skinner. As part of a national effort during World War II to increase food production and put German prisoners of war to work, the company installed the first known portable sprinkler irrigation system in the state. It was used to irrigate a 200-acre potato farm near Aurora.

Following the war, Crockett's son, Tom, joined the company before a series of changes. Mathieson Chemical Corporation bought Standard, changing the name first to Olin-Mathieson, then Olin after a merger with that corporation. Throughout the transition, Tom Crockett supervised sales of the company's irrigation division.

In 1970, Crockett purchased the irrigation division from Olin and moved it to Williamston, North Carolina. He named his line of quick couplers and fittings Orbit Master. Vern Parker, his son-in-law, is the

third generation involved in the business.

The Forties

Distracted by World War II, Americans paid little attention to advancements in irrigation during the 1940s. Nevertheless, portable irrigation technology continued to progress, largely with the refinement of quick-coupling systems for pipe.

An example is the work of William Hobart Stout of Eugene, Oregon. By the late 30s, the inventor and promoter had become a force in western sprinkler irrigation development. He received a patent for a quick-coupler for steel tubing in 1941. Unlike other couplers, the rubber sealing gasket was attached to the male end of the tubing.

To produce the novel couplers, Stout and Oren O. Beymer founded Irrigation Equipment Company, Inc. in Eugene in 1943. It wasn't long before Stout sold his interest in the company to Beymer. Edward J. Franzwa joined Beymer and they developed a full line of Ireco quick-coupling irrigation fittings. Stout continued to sell Ireco fittings as a representative of Beall Pipe and Tank Corporation in Portland until 1947.

The following year, Stout purchased the rights to the Wyss quick-coupler and formed Wyss Irrigation, Inc. His versions of tractor-move and side-wheel move sprinkler irrigation systems attracted national attention. Stout, always the promoter, contrived what he thought to be the ultimate trade name for his machines, "StoutBuilt." In 1952, Farmland Irrigation in Texas bought Stout's irrigation interests and strengthened the nationwide distribution of StoutBuilt irrigation systems.

Stout became involved in the development of yet another irrigation company. Along with H.E. Stevenson and Kenneth Roden, Stout formed a partnership called Irrigation Accessories in the mid-50s. The company incorporated in 1961 and is operated today as Irrigation Accessories, Inc., by M. D. Graven. W.

The "irrigator," cranked to provide power for this 1952,
early side-wheel roll overhead sprinkler irrigation system,
on the Louis Bromfield farm in Ohio.

Hobart "Bill" Stout is remembered as a tireless industry innovator.

Marion H. J. Miller was another important innovator of agricultural irrigation based in the Northwest during the 1940s. During the Great Depression, Miller's family farmed well by farming the gravelly soils of Greenacres, Washington.

The porous nature of the soil on the farm precluded surface irrigation methods. Marion and his brother John searched for a system that would be effective in their conditions.

Portable sprinkler irrigation was a mere seven years old when the Miller brothers installed their first system in 1939, one manufactured by R. M.

Wade & Company. Marion was captivated by the scale and potential of agricultural irrigation systems.

In 1946, Marion sold his interest in the farm to John and became manager of the irrigation department of Arnold & Jeffers of Spokane, Washington. Barely one year later, Miller and William Anderson, an irrigation engineer, purchased the irrigation entity from Arnold & Jeffers and formed Anderson-Miller, Inc.

Following the War, an abundant supply of aluminum encouraged innovators to find new uses for the lightweight metal. The new company wasted no time in introducing a permanent-mold, cast aluminum, quick-coupler that embodied the favorable features of lightweight irrigation couplers already on the market. Anderson-Miller's quick-coupling line became a contender among more than 50 competitors as portable sprinkler irrigation boomed in the 1950s. The company was responsible for several firsts which bolstered its position in the marketplace.

Following Anderson's retirement, Miller sold the company to W. R. Ames in 1968 and assumed the role of marketing manager. In 1971, he moved to Colorado Springs, Colorado and formed Marion Miller and Associates, a manufacturer's representative firm for Senninger Inc. of Florida. Miller also manufactured and sold shunt-line venturi flowmeters.

However, Miller's role in marketing fittings and drop pipes for low-pressure center-pivot and linear-move irrigation systems may have been his foremost offering. In 1976, Miller created Irrigation Industries, Inc. to produce the "gooseneck" fittings and drop pipes. They were first constructed of steel, soon followed by durable plastic. He sold the company ten years later but remained the company's agent.

During his long tenure in the trade, Miller stood out as the American irrigation industry's ambassador of good will. He participated in the creation of the Association of Sprinkler Irrigation Equipment Manufacturers, forerunner to the Irrigation Association, and served as its third president. He was honored with the IA Industry Achievement Award in 1978 and is listed as one of the "Eminent Men of the Northwest." With his propensity for leadership in agricultural irrigation, Miller holds true as a pioneer in the field.

Distribution by Design

After the War, California regenerated interest in turf and landscape irrigation. King Ewing, an avid golfer and adept designer of golf course and landscape irrigation systems, helped lead the way.

Ewing, a native of Missouri, possessed an expert knowledge of soil and water management requirements of turf and landscapes. This skill, plus his golf prowess, proved useful when he moved to San

King Ewing, founder of Ewing Turf Irrigation Products, was instrumental in establishing automatic golf course sprinkler system designs.

Francisco in the late 30s. Atlas Lawn Sprinkler Company, the Bay area's most successful irrigation firm with a history dating back to 1922, hired Ewing to help design and sell Buckner irrigation systems.

During the War, Ewing contributed to the war effort as a pipe fitter in the Navy shipyards. When he rejoined Atlas, he had acquired new expertise with brass and copper pipe and fittings. Shortly after returning, he was presented with the opportunity to purchase the design and sales part of Atlas.

Ewing saw turf irrigation as a market of great potential and named his venture Ewing Turf Products. He realized the importance of both design and engineering in marketing irrigation systems. Atlas had represented Buckner since 1926. This background permitted Ewing to fashion an exclusive franchise agreement with Buckner for Northern California, a first in the industry.

By 1963, the business was headquartered in San Leandro. Its influence was spreading beyond the Bay Area. Susan Ewing, his daughter, and son-in-law Raymon York joined the company to help manage its growth.

In 1967, the name of the company was changed to Ewing Irrigation Products, Inc. King Ewing retired in 1974 and lived in Sacramento until his death in 1991. Today, the company has 32 branches in four states throughout the Southwest.

As King Ewing helped shape the turf irrigation market in Northern California after the War, Fred Reinecke and Febco revitalized the market in the Los Angeles area. Reinecke introduced the underground sprinkler technology of John A. Brooks to California in 1924. Having gained knowledge of sprinkler irrigation back East, Reinecke secured an exclusive franchise from the Detroit manufacturer for the "Western States."

Doing business as Brooks of California, Reinecke concentrated on residential irrigation systems for the affluent in Los Angeles. The War had strengthened the airplane industry in Southern California, attracting thousands of engineers and allied suppliers. Bolstered by aerospace and the resurgence of the postwar film industry, Los Angeles entered a boom in turf and landscape irrigation.

Ironically, in 1949, the franchise agreement with Brooks expired. Reinecke formed Febco, Inc. to manufacture automatic controllers, remote controlled piston valves, sprinklers and back-flow prevention devices.

The Febco name was derived from the names of Reinecke's children; Fred, Jr., Edwin, Bill and Charlotte. The "o" stands for "Old Man," referring to himself.

The new company's products experienced strong demand during the decade of the 50s, a time of remarkable growth in turf sprinkler irrigation. By the end of the decade, the Reinecke children were actively involved in the business and Fred was able to move to Portland, Oregon and serve just as a Febco representative.

Having outgrown its Los Angeles facilities, Febco moved to Sun Valley in 1962. Three years later, James Coson, owner of General Sprinkler Company (Buckner), bought Febco and appointed Carroll Wood as division vice president. Together, Wood and Fred Reinecke, Jr., developed a series of vacuum breakers and brass double-check valves to strengthen Febco's line of backflow prevention products.

In 1970, General Sprinkler consolidated all Febco products, except the line of back-flow devices, under the Buckner name. The marketing rights for the back-flow devices were then granted to Charles M. Bailey Company.

Johns-Mansville Corporation purchased General Sprinkler from Coson in 1972. Five years later, Charles M. Bailey Company (now CMB Industries) purchased the

Courtesy, H. Gene Johnson, Telsco

M.E. "Max" Snoddy, Texas Lawn Sprinkler Company founder.

Febco back-flow line and kept it intact. The venerable Febco line remains prominent today.

Sprinkler Irrigation for the Average Homeowner

When the residential lawn irrigation market increased dramatically following the War, Anton and Ralph Pejsa were poised for action. As cofounders of Champion Irrigation Products in El Monte, California, in 1946, the brothers selected as a target market inexpensive, durable fixed spray or pop-up lawn sprinkler heads for the home irrigator.

The easy-to-install, brass sprinklers manufactured at the company's foundry made an underground irrigation system practical for a huge new group of homeowners. With the turn of a simple manual valve, water propelled into the air from a group of carefully spaced heads nourished plants and turf. No longer did the homeowner have to contend with moving hoses and oscillating sprinklers every few minutes.

One Champion product in particular designed by the Pejsas to simplify residential irrigation was the combination manual shut-off valve and anti-syphon vacuum breaker. The component has set a standard in the industry for more than 50 years. Electric valve actuation has since made the device a standard in small, automatic irrigation systems.

Anton's son Tony Pejsa has been chief executive officer of Champion since 1969. For the past several years, the company has produced a complete line of components, except pipe and fittings, for turf irrigation systems.

If a homeowner wasn't capable or interested in installing his own residential irrigation system, another Los Angeles businessman came to the rescue. Eugene E. Jensen, based in Monrovia, California in the San Gabriel Valley, started installing such systems in 1947.

With the guarantee of "consistent high-quality and trouble-free service," E.E. Jensen Sprinklers has

provided a model for irrigation contractors to follow for more than 40 years. Eugene's son, Ernest Jensen now manages the company.

In Texas, M.E. "Max" Snoddy also had his eyes on the lawn sprinkler market. Starting out as Texas Lawn Sprinkler Company of Dallas, Snoddy advertised to extol the merits of sprinkler irrigation. His ad proclaimed, "Rain to order, the Texas Sprinkler System will shower your lawn with life-giving rain at the turn of a valve."

By 1949, Snoddy was producing his new Electro-matic Watermiser turf sprinkler irrigation controller. As the years went by the business grew under the banner of Weathermatic, today recognized coast to coast. In 1959, the company published the successful "Turf Irrigation Manual." A decade later, Snoddy started the Weathermatic College of Irrigation, which consisted of two-week instructional sessions on layout and design of turf sprinkler irrigation.

Max Snoddy, vocal advocate of turf sprinkler irrigation, died at age 75 in 1987. His son, L.O. "Mike" Snoddy now manages the Dallas company.

The Fifties

Raymond Bird, a Kansas farmer, proclaimed before a notary public in 1949 that he was manufacturing a self-propelled sprinkler irrigation machine on wheels that could move across a field at 30 feet per hour. His unusual overhead sprinkler irrigation machine was described in detail in the June 18, 1949, issue of the Kansas Farmer. Even though Bird's invention never received widespread acceptance, it signaled the beginning of a new era in portable agricultural irrigation.

Bird's self-propelled machine was the precursor of linear-move irrigation systems. His brother-in-law, Gerald Cain, added significantly to the system by devising a telescoping supply pipe to deliver water to the moving mechanical lateral. The message was clear, the technology existed to irrigate large farm fields

Proof that Oaks Irrigation Equipment Company's purchase of the first carload of Alcoa extruded aluminum tubing in 1946 was indeed lightweight.

without moving pipe between sets. Eventually, when labor, energy and water costs increased, automated portable irrigation systems would be taken more seriously.

The quick-coupling system market started to mature in the 50s. No longer experimental in nature, manufacturers battled for their share of the quick-coupler market. One of the most persistent and successful companies is Travis Pattern & Foundry, Inc. of Spokane, Washington.

Founded in 1922 by Paul Travis, the company has successfully maneuvered its way from decade to decade. Beginning in the 50s, Travis acquired the rights to a number of quick-coupling systems as their manufacturers lost interest. Beginning with Rainway, Travis added such well-known names as A&M, Moore-Rain and Shur-Rane. By the 1980s, the company had acquired a total of seven aluminum and steel quick-coupling irrigation lines. All are still offered to the industry by Travis.

One of the most recognized names in portable sprinkler irrigation during the 40s was Shur-Rane of Azuza, California. In 1950, soon after

aluminum tubing became readily available, the John Bean Division of Food Machinery Corporation (FMC) acquired Shur-Rane. The acquisition launched FMC into portable sprinkler irrigation. Through the years, the company's powerful sales efforts brought sprinkler irrigation to countless acres of previously unwatered desert lands. Ultimately, the John Bean Division elected to withdraw from the irrigation industry.

Portable sprinkler irrigation came to Texas by way of the Rio Grande Valley during the Depression. By the late 30s, farmers in South Texas, where annual rainfall averages 40 inches or less, were supplementing rainfall with portable irrigation.

John E. Oaks, a Nebraskan who moved to the Rio Grande Valley, saw the trend toward portable sprinkler irrigation. He was quoted in an early issue of the Southern Agriculturist, "Sprinkler irrigation has proved to be the best all-around means of irrigating in the South." Oaks opened his first branch of Rain Service Company in Brownsville in 1940. The

dealership sold and installed O. K. Champion systems that were manufactured in Indiana. Shortly thereafter, Oaks changed the company's name to Oaks Irrigation Company.

In 1946, Oaks had the distinction of receiving the first carload of extruded aluminum tubing manufactured in the United States. With the tubing, he installed the country's first all-aluminum portable sprinkler irrigation system.

John Seitzinger managed the company from 1955 to 1975 after Oaks' untimely death. Seitzinger was among those instrumental in forming the Association of Sprinkler Irrigation Equipment Manufacturers in 1949.

Irrigation in the humid Southeast was all but non-existent in the 40s and early 50s. It took Graham Foster Daniel, the Agricultural Extension Service and an irrigation train to get the ball rolling.

Daniel formed Russell Daniel Irrigation Company in 1950 in honor of his father, an early farm implement dealer in Athens, Georgia. Years before, Russell Daniel had delivered the first farm tractor east of the Mississippi River. In much the same way, Graham wanted to introduce Georgia farmers to portable sprinkler irrigation.

The irrigation company formed by Daniel and partner H. L. Duke was a distributor of Ireco quick-coupling pipe and fittings. In 1952, at considerable expense and after months of planning, the Daniel company and several other dealers joined with the University of Georgia AES and the Southeastern Irrigation Association in a promotional venture they advertised as "The Irrigation Train."

Several railway flatcars were loaded with all the components of a portable sprinkler irrigation system. The train stopped at pre-advertised locations in the country. At each stop, the distributors and extension agents unloaded the components, constructed a sample irrigation system, and gave demonstrations. Many of the farmers were amazed as

they witnessed sprinkler irrigation for the first time.

The company grew substantially during the next two decades, expanding into turf and golf course sprinkler irrigation systems throughout the East.

Senninger Irrigation, Inc. brought citrus grove owners in Florida advanced irrigation technology in the 60s. Joe Senninger, a citrus grower near Orlando, developed the first insect-proof, impact-drive plastic sprinkler head to alleviate problems caused when mud daubers plugged sprinkler nozzles. The insect builds mud nests in nozzle orifices. When the growers turned on conventional sprinklers during the Florida dry season, they were inoperative.

Success from the wide-ranging acceptance of his insect-proof sprinkler launched Senninger into prominence in the U.S. irrigation industry. Other Senninger innova-

tions were the first molded, thermoplastic pressure regulator and the first low trajectory sprinkler for minimum pressure operating center pivot machines. The firm also developed a very adaptable drop sprinkler head for use with low energy precision application (LEPA) systems.

Lewis W. Barton Company helped spread portable sprinkler irrigation in the East. After graduating from Pennsylvania State University with a degree in horticulture in 1929, Barton operated the family farm. His skill as a grower of quality produce was recognized by the managers of the famous Horn and Hardart restaurant chain. Much of his crop was consumed by diners at these restaurants.

One reason for the consistent high quality of his produce was an overhead sprinkler system Barton installed in 1938. It consisted of steel tubing joined by Flex-O-Seal quick-

The Vermeer Towable "Big Boom" was an important midwest irrigator.

Decoto Manufacturing started as a supplier of piston rings for Ford Motor Company.

coupling fittings with Rain Bird #40 sprinklers. A Gorman-Rupp centrifugal pump driven by a tractor PTO pumped water to Barton's vegetables. Such systems were also used for frost protection and low-temperature control.

The Flex-O-Seal quick-coupler, Barton recalled, was originally developed by Walter Miller, a potato grower in Williamston, New York. Chicago Metals Manufacturing Company then took over manufacturing of the coupling.

Realizing the value of irrigation, Barton founded the distributorship carrying his name in 1946. From Cherry Hill, New Jersey, Barton began specializing in portable sprinkler irrigation during the 1950s. With the engineering help of Don Parmalee and Dr. C. W. Thornthwaite, Barton installed a waste water disposal system for Seabrook Farms in Bridgeton, New Jersey.

With its success at Seabrook Farms, the company branched into effluent irrigation systems, many of which were for golf courses. Eventu-

ally the company designed and installed more than 100 automatic underground golf course irrigation systems.

After 26 gratifying years in sprinkler irrigation, Barton sold his interest to his son-in-law, David M. Barclay. In 1982, Barclay sold the company to an Employee Stock Ownership Trust led by principals Gus and Andy Field. The company operates today under the name of Barton Supply, Inc. Both Lewis W. Barton and David M. Barclay have been ardent supporters and directors of the Irrigation Association.

Further north in New England, the Tropeano brothers began selling portable sprinkler irrigation systems in 1950. Joseph and Philip Tropeano built Larchmont Engineering and Irrigation Inc. into a thriving enterprise that has endured more than 40 years.

They have provided layout, design and installation services for farms, golf courses, municipalities and residences throughout New England, a climatological area where western irrigators might wonder just how practical such endeavors might

be. The company also developed and patented a turf-top automatic irrigation sprinkler and valve combination for golf courses, cemeteries and parks.

In the Plains states, where ancient glaciers planed the land virtually flat and rivers flow through almost every county, Gary Vermeer sought a type of portable sprinkler that moved from one set to another with minimal labor. He founded the company in 1948 to produce specialty agricultural farm machinery. One specialty he recognized was irrigation.

Vermeer envisioned a long boom sprinkler pivoting on a truck in the center. A four-inch hose connected to the truck delivered water to a 250-foot-long boom. It was a combination of a traveling sprinkler and a center pivot. Test runs by engineers at the University of Nebraska revealed an average coefficient of uniformity of a remarkably high 85 percent!

Although the Vermeer boom sprinkler enjoyed considerable farmer acceptance, the advent of center pivots and hard-hose travelers, with their self-propelled features, eventually

Linear Trail lines operate near Nampa, Idaho.

made it obsolete. However, as Keith Van Hemert, manager of Vermeer, revealed, "look-alike traveling boom sprinklers are still used to supplement meager rainfall in Argentina, New Zealand and Australia.

Another attempt at developing a mobile boom sprinkler was the "Hydro-Pak" hydraulic wheel-line mover by the Decoto brothers of Yakima, Washington. Raymond, Henry and Roy Decoto first entered manufacturing as a supplier of piston rings for Ford Motor Company in the early 1920s. As the auto giant became less and less dependent upon outside suppliers, the Decotos turned their attention to agricultural sprayers and irrigation.

Cutting their patterns from wood, abundant in Washington,

Henry and Roy developed the components to move a boom, rigged with solid set sprinklers along its length. The system was a step better than drag lines, a way to move portable pipe from one set to the next without taking it apart. They used a farm tractor to power a hydraulic motor that moved the system to the next location.

William Lundgren, Henry's son-in-law, took the business over following the death of his father and uncle, changing the company name to Decoto Manufacturing, Inc. Lately, the corporation has manufactured laterals for use with linear-move machines. These "Linear Trail Lines" were developed by William Reser and Iven Mcchsner of Sprinkler Irrigation Sales in Nampa, Idaho.

The Boss of traveling irrigation had its origin in San Angelo, Texas after World War II. Brothers Robert and George Buescher founded Buescher Irrigation Supply in 1947, along with George's son, George Jr. The company served the Lone Star State distributing Anderson-Miller irrigation systems, aluminum tubing from Reynolds and Alcoa and pumps from CMC Pumps.

In 1960, Robert Buescher joined with John Seitzinger and Charles Kruger of Oaks Irrigation Company, to form Consolidated Pipe & Tube Company. The new company purchased the assets and tubing mill of Habco Manufacturing Company of Columbus, Nebraska. Then they formed a second venture, a partnership call Boss. They hired William

Collett, fondly remembered by his colleagues, to be the sales manager.

Boss focused on big gun traveling irrigation starting in the early 1970s after Buescher purchased the assets of both the Boss and Consolidated Pipe & Tube Company. Under the guidance of Sales Manager Art Schellinger, the Boss name has become known throughout the world. Its traveling sprinklers can be found on pineapple plantations in the Pacific Corridor to gold mines in Alaska.

Today, David Buescher, the third generation of the family, is chief executive officer and president. Many big names in Texas irrigation can be traced to the company. They include Jack Adams, Jack Livingston, Jack Schachle, Frank Huddleston, Mel Ely, John Railey, Chester Alexander, Paul Harless, Sheila Vinyard and William Collett.

Charles P. Lake, a Canadian attracted to California in 1919 by "Black Gold," found his real treasure in irrigation. At first, Lake signed on with the Shell Oil Company. But it wasn't long before he realized that, due to the speculative and short-lived nature of many oil wells, renting the necessary equipment and pipe was a tremendous opportunity. He left Shell in 1934 to start his own oil field supply business in Bakersfield, California. The name of that company was Western Oilfields Supply.

Frequently, oil wells were located near, and in some cases, in the middle of irrigated fields. The similarity between oil field supplies and irrigation supplies struck Lake. As portable irrigation gained steam after World War II, he saw the potential of renting complete portable sprinkler systems. In 1948, this concept blossomed into Rain for Rent, Inc.

With his two sons, Walter (Jerry) and Donald, Lake built an entity that became the largest single purchaser and user of impact sprinkler heads in the annals of U.S. irrigation. At last count, the company has rented 30 million feet of pipe, millions of fittings, and thousands of pumps, engines and truckloads of sprinkler heads.

In 1977, Lake was honored with the Irrigation Association's "Industry Achievement Award." Today, Charles' grandsons, John W., Robert C., and Chris D. Lake, carry on their grandfather's mission.

Some of the nation's brightest inventors contributed to the irrigation industry. Arthur E. Jensen, inventor of the Sunbeam Electric Shaver and a barometric bomb fuse for the U.S. military, launched Thunderbird Irrigation, Inc. of Tustin, California in 1964. One of his contributions to the irrigation industry was a means to drive a side-wheel roll sprinkler lateral. The invention employed a planetary gear transmission, coupled to a drive shaft that closely paralleled the entire length of the lateral. The drive shaft was powered by a portable, light-weight engine. Yet another Jensen invention was the counter-balanced sprinkler base for use with side-wheel roll systems.

Jensen, his wife Jeannette, and his general manager Harold H. Beck demonstrated a true interest in the irrigation industry. He was honored in 1984 with the Irrigation Association's Industry Achievement Award.

The Soil Conservation Service supplied many of the technical advisors for early agricultural irrigators. Two such advisors in Idaho in the mid-30s were Raymond T. Michener, a registered engineer, and Ronald B. Wilson, an expert in soil and water management. They had been called upon often to solve problems with badly designed irrigation installations. In 1948, they decided to form their own irrigation business and offer design and installation services.

Idaho's Columbia Basin, with portable irrigation systems covering 20,000 acres, proved a magnet to the two businessmen by the mid-60s. Michener, Wilson and Rex Greer moved to the Basin and sold many self-propelled, solid-set sprinkler systems known by the trade name Tri-matic. Operating under the name of Michener Associates, Inc., the three were pivotal in converting Idaho from dryland farming to irrigated agriculture.

Michener recalls others vital to irrigation in the Columbia Basin and southern Idaho; Thomas Wolfe, a prominent irrigation dealer in Pasco; Bud Newcomb, credited with promot-

Courtesy, Bob Gray, Rain Bird Manufacturing Company

Big Gun Traveling Sprinkler, cable drawn.

ing irrigation system installation in the expansive Magic Valley; and Claude H. Pair, who served the SCS throughout the evolution of portable irrigation in Idaho. Michener also recognizes Ed Tucker, a visionary proponent of "high lift" sprinkler irrigation in the Horse Heaven Hills of Washington and the Umatilla Basin of Oregon.

Moore-Rane Manufacturing Co. of Corvallis, Oregon capitalized on proximity to Oregon State University and its agricultural engineering department. Starting in 1950 as Moore's Farm Supply, a partnership among Kenneth J. Bush, Henry J. Bush and his wife Martha, the company carved a place in portable sprinkler irrigation. Inspired by OSU's work in irrigation, the Bushes invented a number of products, including the first

four-wheel drive side-roll lateral mover. For 21 years, the Moore-Rane name was found on irrigation systems throughout the rich Willamette Valley.

Portable sprinkler systems and gated pipe for surface irrigation were the specialty of Heinzman Sons of Phillips, Nebraska. Formed by Scott Farle Heinzman in 1941, sons Wayne, Warren and Dale joined the company in the early 50s. The family company became prominent as a manufacturer of high-pressure and gated irrigation pipe, PTO pumps and hose-reel traveling sprinkler machines.

After 39 successful years in the business, the Heinzman plant and enterprise was destroyed by a tornado. The destruction imposed great financial stress and resulted in bankruptcy. Using revenue from a separate

farm equipment dealership, the sons paid off the creditors by 1986.

Not all sprinkler irrigation development took place in the West. It is important to recall that sprinkler irrigation in Massachusetts dates back to the turn of the century. In those early days, Skinner systems brought supplemental irrigation to the state's important vegetable crops. In 1947, a Cape Cod vegetable grower by the name of William Richards developed steel, rubber gasketed pipe with connecting links for use with sprinkler heads on his farm.

Overhead sprinkler irrigation was also important to cranberry growers in Massachusetts. Not only was it used to supplement rainfall, growers applied irrigation water to

Courtesy, Jack Liddell, Delta Irrigation Company

The ASIEM (now IA) was only five years old in 1953 when this "hard way" irrigation was used to water sweet potatoes in Tennessee.

Ed Hunter at 1960 Irrigation Trade Show. In 1952, he started Moist-O-Matic, Inc.

cool their bogs in the summer, to occasionally control frost and to distribute chemicals and fertilizers. On numerous occasions, such as May 30, 1961, bog sprinkling saved the state's cranberry crop from devastation. On the opposite coast, overhead sprinklers had been used for frost protection on cranberry bogs in western Washington and Oregon as early as 1939.

Northeast cranberry culture was enhanced by the work of Professor John S. Norton at the Cranberry Experiment Station in East Wareham, Massachusetts. He recognized that, among many other things, bog sprinkling was important in water savings compared with flooding.

The 1950s began an era of expansion in irrigated agriculture

along the Mississippi Delta, largely due to Delta Irrigation, Inc. of Memphis, Tennessee. W.J. "Jack" Liddell founded Delta in 1954 to distribute portable agricultural sprinkler irrigation equipment.

Liddell's roots extend deep into irrigation. After serving as an airplane pilot in the Army Air Corps during World War II, Liddell returned to work as an agricultural engineer at the University of Georgia. In 1949, Sunset Engineering in Riverdale, New Jersey, hired Liddell to design and sell agricultural systems. He quickly rose to the position of sales manager.

In 1951 H.W. Umstadter, President of Sunset acquired Irrigation Equipment Co. of Eugene, Oregon and formed American Portable

Irrigation Co. Liddell was transferred to Memphis in 1952 to establish a company owned branch operation which distributed their products.

In 1954, Liddell established Delta Irrigation Co. to distribute irrigation equipment to Mid-South growers. During the ensuing years product lines were added as they became available, including gated pipe, traveling sprinklers and in 1966 Valley center pivot systems.

Jack Liddell is a symbolic figure in the development of portable irrigation in the eastern and southern states. He was elected president of the Irrigation Association in 1981. Today, he continues as chairman of Delta Irrigation, Inc. alongside his sons, President Robert Liddell and Treasurer Daniel Liddell. The company now distributes both agricultural and turf sprinkler equipment.

McDowell Manufacturing Company began leading the portable irrigation industry in Pennsylvania in the early 50s. Based in Dubois, the company introduced a quick-coupler it claimed was the first pressure-lock design. The coupler joined sections of pipe without hooks or latches. The firm also led the transition to PVC pipe from steel and aluminum by developing an epoxy-coated steel fitting to join sections of plastic pipe.

Birger Engstrom, president of McDowell Mfg., was a respected proponent of portable sprinklers. He served as the fourth president of the ASIEM (later IA) in 1954 and 1955. John J. Oldfield, one of McDowell's distributors and long time ally, became the 13th president of the association.

After a distinguished period in the irrigation industry, McDowell, then owned by Alico Industries, Inc., suspended all manufacturing on November 1, 1990. Forty years of leadership in agricultural irrigation drew to a close.

One early Michigan manufacturer of aluminum quick couplers and fittings for portable sprinkler irrigation was Rain Control, Inc. of Hudson. Founder Claire Johnson took over a product line created by Hardie Manufacturing Company to gain immediate national distribution.

Without a foundry, Rain Control had its castings made in Santa Clara, California by Felton Aluminum Company. Felton owner William Huntalis was well known in the irrigation industry and was a long-time supporter of the Irrigation Association.

Upon Johnson's death in 1960, his wife assumed ownership but delegated operations to others. Russell J. Timko bought the company from Mrs. Johnson in 1975. The company is now owned and operated as a retail dealership in Adrian, Michigan by Timko's son, Bruce.

A force in Nebraska agricultural irrigation in the 1950s was Midwest Irrigation Company of Henderson. The manufacturer of aluminum irrigation pipe and fittings was founded by three men, Gustav Theiszen, Paul Friesen and D.E. Ratzlaff. The company often pooled its production knowledge with other well known industry names, such as Gheen of Eugene, Oregon, and Rain Chief of Grand Island, Nebraska.

The company went through a series of changes in ownership beginning with Theisen buying out his original two partners in 1956. A year later, Abraham R. and Clarence E. Peters began to buy Theisen's interest in the firm. The Peters became sole owners of Midwest and expanded its production capabilities to provide a complete line of irrigation equipment for Nebraska farmers. The company is operated today by Clarence Peters' daughter and son-in-law, Rosella and Wallis D. Goertzen.

Two men, Jack W. Brockhouse and Victor B. Trac, played a significant role in developing portable, quick-coupling irrigation pipe for growers in temperate Southern California beginning in 1950. The pair first started Water-Ways Irrigation Engineers in Bakersfield. Brockhouse then moved to Santa Maria, California and established Cal-Coast Irrigation, Inc. Both men continued to promote innovative methods of joining sections of portable irrigation pipe. Brockhouse devised a way to roll an integrated coupler into the expanded end of gated aluminum irrigation pipe. Cal-Coast produced a steady stream of new procedures for drilling, routing and punching holes for gated irrigation pipe.

Just as irrigation opened up vast acres of land to agriculture in Idaho, California, and Texas, it also transformed Mexico. Francisco "Paco" J. Jimeno PE, founder of Equipos y Accessorios Hidraulicos, S.A. of Mexico City, was introduced to irrigation as a graduate student at the University of Michigan in Ann Arbor under a Kellogg Foundation grant.

Before entering the irrigation business, he was an engineer for ICA, Mexico's most prominent contracting company. He took part in the construction of some of Mexico's major projects, including the new campus of the University Mexico and the Mexico City Medical Center.

In 1952, Jimeno founded Equipos y Accessorios Hidraulicos to expand his country's interests in agriculture through portable sprinkler irrigation. Under exclusive license agreement, he brought equipment from Alumaex, Wade Rain, Skinner sprinklers and CMC pumps into his country.

Jimeno regards a meeting in 1954 with Crawford Reid, then vice president of Rain Bird Sprinkler Manufacturing Company, as a milestone in acquainting him with constructive elements to enable his company to prosper in the development of sprinkler irrigation in Mexico.

Following Reid's death, the Irrigation Association honored him by establishing the Crawford Reid Memorial Library and a memorial award to recognize irrigation accomplishments by selected individuals outside of the United States.

Jimeno was instrumental in organizing the IA's 1973 annual convention in Mexico City. Ten years later, he was part of a small group founding the Mexico Irrigation Association and served as it first president.

Turf Irrigation Comes of Age

The post World War II focus on suburban family life and outdoor recreation was a boom for turf irrigation of all types. While early companies such as Brooks, Rain Bird and Buckner found turf irrigation demand centered around large estates and golf, other companies like Champion and Nelson thrived on the small residential market. Turf irrigation would come of age during the next 30 years. Much of the growth in turf irrigation came from independent inventors and skilled craftsman who became inspired during World War II and the Korean War to build their own businesses.

One such individual was Lee Caviar, who started Imperial Underground Sprinkler Company in the basement of his home in Lenexa, Kansas. An accomplished plumber, electrician and irrigation specialist,

Caviar was called upon to tackle design and installation of many state-of-the-art irrigation systems in the Kansas City area, including the system for the Harry S. Truman Library in Independence, Missouri. He was especially intrigued by automating such systems with electronic valves and controllers.

In his basement shop, he constructed brass, electrically-actuated, hydraulic, remote-control valves. The valves were recognized for their reliability in tough Midwestern conditions. Today, Imperial Underground Sprinkler Company is owned and operated by Lee's son, Robert.

The full impact on the irrigation industry of Edwin Hunter, the son of another Kansan by the name of L. J. Hunter, remains to be seen. L. J. Hunter moved to Riverside, California, and started Riverside Foundry in 1921. His two sons, Edwin and Joseph, gained valuable experience in metal handling and machinery in the foundry.

During the Depression, Joseph started Riverside Pattern and Machine Shop specializing in machine tool design. He built a reputation in the detail-oriented business and capitalized on this by renaming the company Hunter Engineering Company. Edwin joined the firm in 1936. Hunter Engineering became a nationally-known metal fabricator, notably for inventing tooling machinery that would correctly roll-form metal strips for Venetian blinds. In the late 40s, the company took its first step into the irrigation industry when it introduced a unique cold-extrusion process for forming a heavy-end aluminum tubing that was ideally suited for use with quick-coupling portable sprinkler systems.

Edwin felt challenged by irrigation and the idea of using soil moisture sensing to control automatic turf sprinkler irrigation. He began to explore the concept with Dr. D. L. Richards, a Riverside physicist. In 1952, he started Moist-O-Matic, Inc. for the express purpose of building moisture sensors.

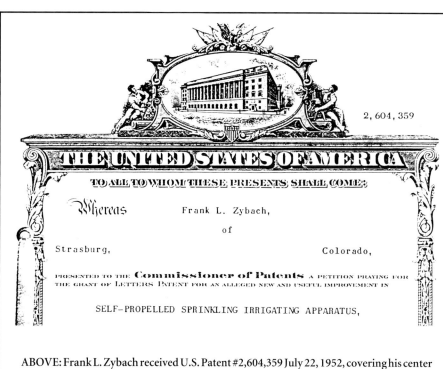

ABOVE: Frank L. Zybach received U.S. Patent #2,604,359 July 22, 1952, covering his center pivot overhead sprinkler irrigation machine.

BELOW: Each tower was equipped with this ingenius water drive that changed the face of American agriculture.

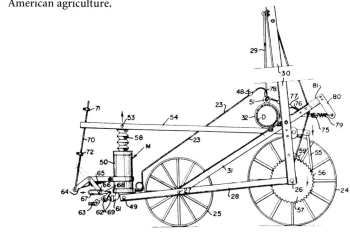

Hunter's genius brought him more than 60 irrigation-related patents. Richards contributed to six of them. If you add his inventions outside of irrigation, Hunter's total patent count exceeds 100.

A number of these patents involve Hunter's next major contribution to the irrigation industry, a gear-driven sprinkler head made of wear-resistant plastic. The slow-revolving, pop-up sprinkler head was smaller in diameter than impact sprinklers, yet still exhibited great reliability and uniformity of application.

After ten years of Moist-O-Matic advances in turf and commercial irrigation, Hunter sold the company to The Toro Company, a 50-year-old mower and turf maintenance equipment manufacturer in Minneapolis, Minnesota. The irrigation line strengthened Toro's position in selling to the growing golf course market. Hunter continued to work

Frank L. Zybach, center pivot inventor, sold his first machine to Ernest E. Englbrecht of Strasburg, Colorado in 1952. The 5-tower machine was operated for 20 years.

for Toro as a consultant, plying his inventive skills.

In 1980, Hunter reentered the irrigation manufacturing business by forming Hunter Industries with his wife Frances, sons Richard and Paul, and daughter Ann. With innovative production facilities in San Marcos, California, the family-run company has continued to set new standards for golf and turf irrigation, largely with the gear-drive sprinkler. Its most recent introduction was a computerized irrigation controller delivered to the customer with historical rainfall data for his or her area built into the controller's memory. Simple to operate yet extremely complex in construction, Hunter products continue to challenge the industry.

With its acquisition of Moist-O-Matic in 1962, Toro entered the field of irrigation. Toro was formed in 1913 as a manufacturer of small tractors and engines in Minneapolis, Minnesota. Through the ensuing years, Toro gained national recognition due largely to its lawn mowers.

Beginning in the 30s, Toro, well-established in the turf and landscape markets, devoted a growing portion of it efforts toward the needs of golf course superintendents. Irrigation was an integral part of both golf and landscaping. Moist-O-Matic was a natural fit. Today, Toro remains the only major manufacturer of golf course maintenance equipment with an irrigation division.

Toro dropped the Moist-O-Matic brand name and emphasized development of large-radius, gear-driven, valve-in-head pop-up sprinklers, as well as advanced electronic controllers. In 1976, the company explored applications for its large, gear-driven sprinklers in agricultural irrigation. The Irrigation Division is still based in Riverside.

Safe-T-Lawn, Inc. was Florida's entry in the expanding turf sprinkler irrigation business. Incorporated in 1962 by William G. Muschett, Safe-T-Lawn manufactured plastic-case, ball-drive pop-up sprinkler heads. All of the company's proprietary products were designed by engineer George Lockwood.

However, the company experienced turbulent times beginning in the 1970s. First, Allstate Financial, a division of Sears-Roebuck, took the company over. After reverting back to Muschett, the company performed as an exclusive manufacturer for L.R. Nelson. In 1976, Moody Sprinkler Manufacturing Company contracted with Safe-T-Lawn to market Moody's line of valves and impact-drive sprinklers in the Southeast. Finally, in 1983, James Hardie Irrigation purchased the assets of Safe-T-Lawn. Hardie dissolved the product line a few short years later.

Weather Tec Corporation of Fresno, California, was organized in 1970 as a manufacturer of agricultural, impact-drive sprinkler heads. However, the company markets to both turf and agricultural irrigation markets today.

Financed by a group of Fresno investors, Weather Tec was managed by former employees of Rain Bird and Buckner. Larry Duckworth, Jack Martina and George Hicks came from Buckner. Richard Malcolm was a former Rain Bird engineer. Their first production item, the Weather Tec Model 10-20, became a prominent market contender with the first delivery of irrigation water to the west side of the San Joaquin Valley in 1971.

Kern County businessman George Pierce was principal owner of the company until 1976 when William H. Rogers acquired full ownership. He also purchased the remaining interests of two of the oldest names in overhead irrigation, Skinner in 1978 and Moody in 1982, to expand the Weather Tec line. An investor group made Rogers president in 1985.

In 1972, David P. Ransberg purchased the manufacturing rights to L. R. Nelson Manufacturing Company's light commercial and residential turf irrigation products. This was the first time the legendary L. R. Manufacturing Company experienced a change of ownership. Ransberg changed the name of the company to L.R. Nelson Corporation.

Ownership of the agricultural segment of the company was transferred to Barton Russell Nelson. He moved that portion of the original L. R. Nelson Manufacturing Company to Walla Walla, Washington and renamed it Nelson Irrigation Corporation.

Mechanized Overhead Irrigation

Granting patent protection to an inventor by no means assures that a unique invention will actually be produced and sold. While patents for mechanized overhead irrigation date back to 1874, the first commercially successful machines weren't introduced until the middle of the 20th century.

The first noted patent for such a device was granted to Henry McKenzie in 1874 for "Improvements in an Automatic Sprinkler for Leaching." McKenzie's invention consisted of two booms with sprinklers that rotated on a fixed axis. Of course, the only power options for pressurizing the water or moving the booms at the time were horses or steam. In 1913, G. S. Williamson was granted a patent for a carriage-mounted sprinkler that traversed along an elevated pipe. As the

carriage moved, it triggered valves located at intervals on the pipe to open and close.

The first inventor to gain a patent for an irrigation system using mechanized transport towers to carry elevated pipe with sprinklers was J. A. Morton of Oderbolt, Iowa in 1909. Ten years later, Ernest Alvarez was awarded a patent for his "Apparatus for Watering by Means of Suspended Pipes." Such was the inventive progression of self-propelled overhead sprinkler irrigation for the first half of this century. Yet, during the same period, a multitude of fixed and portable overhead sprinkler systems became established.

USDA research conservationist Claude H. Pair, who coauthored the Irrigation Association textbook, "Sprinkler Irrigation," defined center pivot irrigation as "a system that consists of a single sprinkler lateral pipeline with one end anchored to a

Courtesy, Valmont

Robert Daugherty, President Valley Manufacturing, purchased market rights to Zybach's self-propelled center pivot system in 1954.

fixed pivot structure and the other end moving in a circle about the pivot."

Pair further described center pivots in the book. "The lateral is supported by towers, cables and trusses, which move on wheeled, track or skid support units located 80 to 250 feet apart along the length. Total lateral lengths vary from 20 to 2,000 feet. The lateral is kept in a straight line as it moves around the

pivot point by an alignment mechanism that increase or reduces the speed of the support units. A mechanism for propelling the lateral is mounted on each support structure."

The center pivot irrigation system, without a doubt the greatest advancement in agriculture since the McCormack reaper, was spawned in Nebraska. That state's pioneers had first put surface irrigation to use to supplement rainfall for their crops. By 1950, portable sprinkler irrigation was heavily utilized there. However, since the land was relatively flat and labor to move portable pipe between sets was not abundant, the stage was set for the development of self-propelled portable sprinkler irrigation systems, such as the center pivot.

In the 30 years following World War II, at least 60 manufacturers embarked on building center pivot machines. Today, the entire production of center pivot irrigation systems in the United States rests with fewer than one dozen manufacturers. Many of the builders who withdrew from production are still active in the industry, manufacturing travelers or side-roll laterals or fabricating portable pipe and fittings.

Valmont Industries

A Colorado dryland wheat farmer named Frank Zybach was the first person to design a commercially successful, self-propelled center pivot overhead sprinkler irrigation machine. Zybach, who lived in Strasburg, Colorado, built his first machine in 1948. It had two towers from which the lateral sprinkler pipe was suspended two feet above the ground.

Zybach used piston actuated mechanisms, driven by water diverted from the sprinkler pipe, to move the towers. Aware that the speed of the tower nearest to the pivot point had to be less than those further out the lateral, he designed a novel tower speed control mechanism. Once the speed of the outermost tower had been set, all the interior towers reacted according to the flexing of the lateral pipeline. A

Reinke Electrogator was the first worm gear drive produced in 1969.

valve on each tower opened by the flexing of the lateral sent water to the driving arm. As the flexing ceased, the valve closed and stopped the propulsion.

After further development, Zybach applied for a patent in 1949 for a "Self-Propelled Sprinkler Irrigation Apparatus. Patent Number 2,604,359 was granted to him in July 1952. By that spring, he had built a five-tower center-pivot machine to irrigate 40 acres near Strasburg, Colorado owned by Ernest Englebrecht. The farmer used the system for 20 years to irrigate alfalfa.

Like most inventors, Zybach needed help to bring his idea to market. He joined with A. E. Trowbridge of Columbus, Nebraska, and manufactured ten center-pivot machines during the following two years. In September, 1954, Zybach and Trowbridge sold the exclusive marketing rights to Robert B. Daugherty, president of Valley Manufacturing of Valley, Nebraska. The two men were paid a five percent royalty on every machine Valley produced for the life of the patent.

Over the next ten years, Valley changed Zybach's concept radically. It was the company's first effort in irrigation. Previously, it had manufactured farm elevators, hay rakes, wagon hoists and tractor front-end loaders. By the mid-60s, nearly every detail of the system had been revised.

Those experimental years finally brought forth a well-built center pivot sprinkler irrigation system. More than 12 million acres in the United States are irrigated with center pivots and more than half of these pivots carry the Valley or Valmont nameplate.

Zybach received the first Pioneer Award ever presented by the Irrigation Association in 1973 for his ingenious device. He died in 1982.

Zimmatic

A Nebraskan named Paul Zimmerer started the company that is today the second largest builder of center pivot irrigation systems, Lindsay Manufacturing Company of Lindsay, Nebraska. Progressing from hand-move, portable irrigation systems in 1955 to tractor-tow wheeled lateral sprinkler systems in 1958, Zimmerer recognized the scope of mechanized portable irrigation.

Until 1961, he assembled irrigation systems from other manufacturers' components. That year he erected a plant to build his own portable irrigation system. Within five years of rapidly expanding demand, Zimmerer built his own tubing mill and recruited his sons, Art and Bernard, to help run the business.

Lindsay's first center pivot machine was produced in 1968. It had an undertruss design and towers driven by electric-powered rubber-tired wheels. Proud of their accomplishment, the Zimmerer's named their center pivot the Zimmatic.

Agricultural giant DeKalb AgResearch, Inc. was impressed with the potential for the Lindsay machine and bought the company in 1974. Reinforced by DeKalb's considerable resources and research bent, Lindsay developed and introduced a planetary

Paul Zimmerer

gearbox drive for its Zimmatic and coined the name Powertrac for the transmission.

T-L Irrigation

T-L Irrigation Company of Hastings, Nebraska, began business in 1955 as an irrigation equipment distributor for Farm Improvement Company of Denver. LeRoy Thom and J.G. Love were the principals of the firm and use the initials of their last names for their company.

In 1959, the company began manufacturing tractor-tow sprinkler lateral lines. Thom and Love's first manufacturing venture drew considerable attention in the "pivot state." In the early 60s, T-L expanded rapidly and started making its own irrigation tubing

The company selected oil-hydraulic motors controlled by a guidance system to move the towers

The original Tumac center pivot overhead sprinkler system.

RainCat, the first and perhaps only center pivot sprinkler irrigation machine equipped to move on endless tracks.

of its first center pivot introduced in 1968. The aerospace industry had proven the reliability of hydraulic systems for operating vital components of large aircraft. Within 12 years, T-L had manufactured and sold more than 2,200 center pivots. Today the company is the fourth largest center pivot manufacturer in the world.

Reinke Manufacturing

The Reinke name continues to be one of the majors in center pivot irrigation. Richard Reinke founded Reinke Manufacturing Company in Deshler, Nebraska, in 1954.

The company's first center pivot was built on contract in 1966 and was designed by Ted and Caroll Olsen of Atkinson, Nebraska. The hydraulic-drive machine generated 50 more orders within the next 12 months.

In 1966, Reinke designed a reversible, electric-powered wheel drive version of the center pivot, which he named the Electrogator. The reversibility of the electric-drive motors became a much desired feature of center pivot buyers. Reinke is also credited with being the first to construct center pivots with light-weight aluminum. The company is the nation's third largest center pivot manufacturer today.

Lockwood Corporation

Lockwood Corporation, a well-known Nebraska manufacturer of potato harvesters and other farm equipment, decided to enter the irrigation industry in the late 60s. After studying several irrigation firms to buy, Lockwood chose the Hydrocycle

Division of the Hydro Corporation of Texas. Center pivot production was moved to Gering, Nebraska soon thereafter.

The Lockwood Hydrocycle center pivot was an electric-drive, cable-suspension machine with 90-foot spans. The development of a cornering option with an end-gun named Flexspan enabled farmers to irrigate 156 acres of a quarter section with one machine.

RainCat

Since California companies had made great contributions to other specialties of the irrigation industry, many expected equally great things from the Layne and Bowler Pump Company of Los Angeles when it produced its first RainCat center pivot machine in 1959. The RainCat had all the makings of a spectacular center pivot machine: 14 towers, electric motors providing power for chain-driven steel crawler tracks at the base of each tower, and 90-foot under-truss spans. Unfortunately, frequent changes in ownership over 20 years broke the momentum of the RainCat.

In 1968, Layne and Bowler sold RainCat to A.O. Smith Company, which sold it to Gordon Johnson of Irrigation Pump and Engineering of Greeley, Colorado. Hope was temporarily restored when the Irrigation Division of The Toro Company bought RainCat from Johnson with the goal of strengthening its position in the agricultural irrigation market. Toro kept production in Greeley.

Richard E. Hunter, son of Hunter Industries Founder Edwin Hunter, bought RainCat in 1979. He was able to maintain production for only one more year. When the Irrigation Pump and Equipment Company sold the Greeley plant in which the RainCats were made, the remaining parts and service operations were moved to Grand Junction, Colorado, where they remain today.

An interesting note about RainCat is that one of its original salesmen with Layne and Bowler, Robert C. Mueller, went on to become the third executive director of the Sprinkler Irrigation Association. He was, by any measure, one of the most enthusiastic proponents of American irrigation.

Sargent Manufacturing

Layne and Bowler Pump Company introduced one of its dealers, Sargent Pump Company of Othello, Washington, to RainCat in the early 60s. Serving the vast Columbia Basin, Sargent was a natural for selling center pivots.

As interest in center pivots grew, Harry Sargent and his brother John moved quickly to manufacture their own systems. For nearly two decades the Sargent Manufacturing Company, Inc. produced and sold its own center pivot to farmers in the Columbia Basin. Today the company still operates as an irrigation equipment supplier.

The White Motor Company, venerable auto-truck manufacturer, almost got into the "Linear" overhead sprinkler irrigation business with this experimental prototype, operated near Mendow, Michigan in August 1967.

The Linears

Linear-move is the most recent innovation in mechanized overhead sprinkler irrigation. Because linears move the full length of a rectangular field, they irrigate 100 percent of the land. There are no corners to contend with as with center pivots. Instead, linears require a water supply that moves with the machine.

There was a measure of interest in Morton's patented Irrigation Apparatus in the early part of the century. However, it was not until veteran sprinkler irrigation equipment maker Wade Manufacturing Company introduced its Square-Matic in 1970 that linear systems gained farmers' respect.

By the late 1970s, some center pivot manufacturers began building their own linear movement machines. The wheels of the towers were driven by electric motors powered by an integral pump engine and alternator. The pump drew water from a midfield ditch straddled by the linear machine.

An example of a center pivot manufacturer adding linear movement machines is Tumac Industry of Colorado Springs, Colorado. The company was founded in 1975 by James McConnell to make conventional center pivot systems. His first systems irrigated roughly 130 acres. McConnell sought ways to provide his customers with greater coverage. By special structuring and using larger lateral pipe, Tumac built some center pivots that could irrigate more than 700 acres.

In 1980, Tumac used some of its heavy-duty techniques learned from producing larger center pivots to construct its first linear-move irrigation machine. It was designed to pick up water from either a ditch or from mainline hydrants.

The company, located in Grand Junction, Colorado, since 1983 is the only center pivot builder that continues to make all three types of drive:

- electric
- oil-hydraulic
- water

Travelers and Other Overhead Irrigators

The main engineering problem with linear-move machines was providing a mobile source of water. This was also the challenge for manufacturers of traveling giant sprinklers. Valmont Industries and Wade Manufacturing were just two of many makers of mechanized overhead irrigation to branch into hose reel travelers.

Fred Kruse, founder of Ag Rain, Inc., of Havana, Illinois, decided to use specially fabricated hoses to supply the large sprinkler on his Water Winch travelers. The hose was 660 feet long and the sprinkler irrigated parallel lanes up to 360 feet wide.

Another Midwest manufacturer of hose reel traveling sprinklers was General Irrigation Company of Carthage, Missouri. General's EZ Rain pulled itself across the field by means of a self-contained cable. Vermeer Manufacturing of Pella, Iowa was another Midwestern supplier with an entry in the hose reel market.

The South was well represented in this technology. Consolidated Pipe & Tube made its Big Boss in Lubbock, Texas. Richard Friedlander started the Cloud Burst Manufacturing Company in Moultrie, Georgia, in 1960. He called them Cloud Burst because he designed them with a giant sprinkler head. Rainbow Manufacturing Company moved to Georgia from Tennessee in 1962 to make self-propelled "volume guns." These large gun sprinklers applied 300 to 2,200 gallons per minute.

Tri-Matic, Inc. of Brownfield, Texas, put a different twist on travelling sprinklers. Its Tri-Matic looked more like a lateral on wheels, except it trailed 320-foot-long aluminum laterals spaced 40 feet apart. The machine applied two inches of water to a ten acre area in 12 hours. Then it had to be moved for the next set.

In 1958, Irrigation Motor and Pump Company of Longmont, Colorado, introduced a self-propelled, giant sprinkler irrigator named Big Squirt. The sprinkler could apply huge volumes of water because it was designed to straddle a supply water ditch as it traveled. It could irrigate a swath of land 440 feet wide using 1,300 gallons of water per minute.

W. R. Ames Company is one of the oldest names in portable overhead irrigation. Samuel Gunnison ran the company for most of its history, beginning at the company's original office in San Francisco. In the early 70s, the company produced the Ames Turbo-Rain, a four-wheeled, self-contained, cable-actuated hose reel traveler. The Turbo-Rain had a very tall sprinkler riser so that it could be used in orchards and groves. The company is headquartered in Woodland, California.

The Big Boom Traveler large area of coverage overhead sprinker irrigation machine.

LEPA

Low energy precision application (LEPA) is a distinctly novel concept in the age-old practice of irrigation. Barely ten years old, LEPA is the newest mechanized method of placing moisture in the soil.

The earliest trials of LEPA were conducted by Dr. William M. Lyle, USDA extension research scientist located at the Texas Agricultural Experiment Station in Lubbock. With the assistance of J. P. Bordovsky, professor of agricultural engineering at Texas Tech, Lyle introduced the concept in 1981 in a treatise, "LEPA Irrigation Systems Evaluation." The work was presented at the winter meeting of the American Society of Agricultural Engineers in December 1982. Once again, the value of government-supported agricultural research was proven.

LEPA was intended to improve upon the application efficiency of linear-move and center pivot machines. Using these time-tested means of mechanized overhead sprinkler irrigation, Lyle and Bordovsky removed the lateral-installed conventional sprinklers. In their place they installed gooseneck fittings that were connected to drops. Special sprinklers were connected to the bottom of the drops, roughly 8 to 18 inches above the soil surface.

Among the many benefits of LEPA are irrigation application efficiencies of 95 to 98 percent. Less pressure is required to deliver the water and less of the foliage is wet by the sprinklers. In water-short areas, LEPA has made it possible to bring a crop to maturity with 30 to 40 percent less water. Using LEPA in conjunction with furrow dikes, small catchment basins created by specialized equipment, improves efficiency even further.

Leon New of Texas A&M University's experiment station in Lubbock, reported that LEPA produced evaporation losses of just 2 to 3 percent, compared to 20 to 25 percent with overhead sprinklers. Such efficiency has opened many doors in agricultural irrigation to LEPA and has spawned a number of companies providing equipment specifically for the technology.

Courtesy, Dick Moulton Irrigation & Tube Company, Somerset, Wisconsin

Vegetable field irrigated with drip tape attached to a lay-flat lateral and mulched by plastic.

CHAPTER 3

Low-Volume Irrigation: Drip and Micro-Spray

"In an area which once required five men to irrigate, two men are now able to irrigate, check the lines and have half their time left over to weed."

— The words of a California strawberry grower
after installing low-volume irrigation.

*L*ow-volume irrigation is a comparatively new method of delivering water to crops and ornamental plants. While the concept of applying small volumes of water to the root zone of plants dates back to World War I, it has only been utilized to any significant degree during the past three decades.

By applying a low volume of water over an extended period of time, soil retains moisture in an amount near field capacity. Maintaining this optimum moisture level reduces the exposure of plant roots to either saturated or drought conditions. Consequently, plant yield and quality improve dramatically.

Precise placement of water by low-volume irrigation has a number of other benefits. It is very efficient because little energy is required to pressurize the system and hardly any moisture is lost to evaporation or runoff. Because evaporation is insignificant, lower-quality saline water can be used for irrigation without harmful accumulation of salt in the root zone. Slow delivery of moisture reduces soil compaction and improves soil aeration.

With low-volume irrigation, water can also be used to deliver fertilizers because placement is directed to the plant's root zone, whether in flat fields or on hillsides. Basically, water is applied only

Courtesy, Roberts Irrigation Products

Orchards were the first major application for drip irrigation on the West Coast.

Dick Chapin (left) with Bernarr Hall discussing drip tape system for tomato field in Southern California.

Orchards Suited Hose and Emitter Systems

The great experiment in Israel was observed first hand by a San Diego County, California, farm advisor by the name of C. Don Gustafson and Bruce Brown, a San Diego sprinkler manufacturer. They returned to the United States and were soon followed by Dr. Baruch Gornat, a researcher at Hebrew University in Jerusalem. In 1969, Gustafson installed test plots at the Trendal Brothers' avocado orchard in northern San Diego County. He utilized emitters and fittings supplied by Brown's newly-established company, Drip-Eze, and components imported from Israel. The purpose of the trial was to compare low-volume drip irrigation with the Trendal's conventional overhead sprinkler system.

The experimental system consisted of polyethylene tubing with small plastic emitters punched into the tubing. Instead of releasing gallons of water per minute, the small orifices of the emitters delivered about one gallon of water per hour. The space between crop rows remained dry and weed-free.

In 1970, Gustafson organized a drip irrigation seminar in Escondido, a city in northern San Diego County with many orchards, to discuss the impressive results at the Trendal orchard and a growing number of other avocado groves. More than 600 growers and other interested people traveled to Escondido for the seminar! Eighteen manufacturers demonstrated drip products, including emitters, filters, tubing, soil moisture sensors, pumps and controllers. It was an amazing demonstration of interest in low-volume irrigation technology.

When the first International Drip Irrigation Congress was held in Tel Aviv, Israel in 1973, a sizeable delegation of Americans attended. So many Americans made the trip that it was decided to hold the Second Drip Congress in San Diego the following year.

In 1973, when Gustafson organized a second seminar in Fallbrook, just north of Escondido, the atten-

where the grower wants it. Therefore, water and fertilizers are not wasted on nourishing weeds between rows or plants. The space between rows remains dry for efficient passage of equipment and labor. In fact, placing the right amount of water exactly in the root zone of desirable plants is the foremost concept of this irrigation philosophy.

Records indicate that the concept of low-volume irrigation was discussed at an irrigation symposium in Riverside, California in 1917. Dr. Lester Kellar of Yorba Linda described the performance of a drip system he designed for avocados. "Pipe uprights extend above the ground 2-1/2 feet from the trunk of the tree. On top of each pipe, I have installed a gas cock instead of a faucet. The first year I basined the trees and turned on the gas cocks with a slow stream every 10 days. The second year, the basins were leveled. The drip system watered the trees every two weeks for 48 hours,

so slowly that it did not run off. The water amounted to two to four barrels per tree. A half-inch pipe, extending down from the gas cock to either side of a tree, distributes the water as required."

Kellar stood almost alone in his advocacy of low-volume irrigation and faced considerable skepticism. Today, an estimated 60 to 70 percent of the U.S. avocado crop is irrigated, much as Kellar had recommended 76 years ago.

In fact, very little attention was paid to low-volume irrigation until after World War II, an Israeli engineer performing research in Great Britain, Dr. Symcha Blass used low-volume irrigation to water and fertilize plants in a greenhouse (glasshouse). He took this technology with him to Israel where he developed new types of emitters during the late 50s. The emitters proved useful in irrigating crops in the Negev Desert, a region characterized by its saline water. Word of Blass' work spread to the U.S., Australia and South Africa.

dance swelled to nearly 1,500 people from across the country. However, greater things were still to come. All attendance records were broken in San Diego during the Second International Drip Irrigation Congress in 1974. Two thousand people from the United States and 29 foreign countries attended that meeting. The list of exhibitors grew to 70, four times the number of suppliers just four years before.

Gustafson was not the only proponent of low-volume irrigation in the University of California system. Bernarr J. Hall, who worked with Gustafson, wrote much of the literature describing proper drip irrigation practices. Hall assisted both growers and manufacturers during the developmental period of the 70s and 80s. Dr. Falih Aljibury with the University of California at Parlier did extensive research and field testing. He worked closely with growers in the Fresno-Bakersfield area and wrote many papers on the subject.

Continuing field research projects in California stimulated an ever-increasing interest in low-volume irrigation. The developmental efforts drew researchers, manufacturers and growers from around the world to view the strengths and weaknesses of low-volume drip irrigation.

Commercialization of drip irrigation occurred swiftly in the early 70s and not all the activity was in California. The first drip system in Florida was installed in a Dade City citrus grove in 1970. The next year, Texas and Michigan growers got into the act with small trials. All of these projects primarily involved orchards and utilized plastic hose and emitters, technology developed in Israel.

Emitters, which controlled the flow of water from tubing laterals into the soil, varied considerably. A myriad of techniques for slowly applying water to the soil were invented. Within the first ten years, dozens of water emission configurations were offered to agricultural and landscape growers and managers. All of them effectively decreased pressure from the inside to the outside of the lateral tubing, allowing the water to emerge as drops or minute trickles. This was accomplished by a wide range of technology, including simple holes in tubing, complicated pathways, vortex chambers, discs, steel balls and miniature manual valves.

Flow rates from the emitters ranged from 1/2 to 2 gallons per hour. Some emitters could be adjusted manually. All were vulnerable to dirty water. Some manufacturers created what they termed self-flushing or automatic flushing emitters. Screen and media filters became an integral part of successful low-volume drip irrigation systems.

Al Wilson, owner of The Engine Cooler Company of Corona, California, took an early interest in the filtration needs of growers with low-volume systems. His coolers had long helped farmers keep their pump engines from overheating. When growers started experimenting with drip in the late 60s, they asked Wilson to develop something different than a screen filter to prevent emitter plugging. He got to know Gustafson and Hall and attended many of the early seminars, including the Second Drip Irrigation Congress in San Diego.

The early filters were crude by today's standards, but substantially improved the performance of orchard drip systems. A consulting engineer named Lee Parker helped Wilson develop a commercially viable sand-media filter. The new filter did a better job of removing algae from the irrigation stream than screen filters and was easily cleaned by backflushing.

Wilson sold The Engine Cooler Company to Yardney Electric Corporation in 1973. For a brief period during the 80s, the company was called Whittaker Water Management Systems. Whittaker sold the division to senior management in 1990 who renamed the company Yardney Water Management Systems. Today the company produces both media and screen filters for agricultural and landscape irrigation applications.

BELOW: Early horizontal sand media filter designed by Al Wilson and Lee Parker of The Engine Cooler Company.

Courtesy, Yardney Water Management Systems

Norman Smith evaluates Long Island melon crop irrigated by Dew Hose in 1965.

Vegetables Inspire Creation of Drip Tape

As the most crucial part of a drip irrigation system, emitters attracted much attention. Many of the early emitters devised were too sensitive to variations in pressure. Changes in elevation, friction loss in tubing, and accidental restriction of flow in a lateral resulted in non-uniform application of water.

It became clear that some form of pressure compensation was needed to achieve the required uniformity. Professor Harry J. Braud of Louisiana State University, Baton Rouge, concentrated his research on this problem. He performed tests for flow and pressure dissipation based on the elasticity of polyethylene tubing used in combination with different types of emitters. His goal was to seek constant low discharge rates at low pressure (5 to 20 psi).

Meanwhile, a Long Island, New York, extension agent was focusing his attention on the needs of vegetable growers. Due to considerably tighter spacing of vegetable plants and the frequent rotation of various crops, hose and emitter systems were impractical. In 1964, Norman Smith sought a less expensive and less permanent system for applying small volumes of water to row crops.

Smith discovered a product that seemed to meet the need. Today, it is known as drip tape. The product consisted of plastic film folded and sewn to form a tube. Water seeped out slowly at the stitches making it less susceptible to plugging. Drip tape could be laid on the surface or buried a few inches deep. This particular drip tape was called Dew Hose and it was manufactured not in Israel or California, but in Upstate New York.

In 1954, in a greenhouse 30 miles from the Canadian border, Richard D. Chapin had automated the laborious task of watering hundreds of pots on greenhouse benches. With intricate networks of tiny polyethylene tubing, one tube per pot, he created a way to improve his production and save labor. From his greenhouse operation in Watertown, New York, Chapin launched a new company called Watermatics in 1962 to manufacture his invention.

Chapin 's labor-saving system started with a central control valve which sent water down selected 3/4-inch main tubes. At each bench, Chapin installed a tee. This was connected to a header that split the water stream into 20 different 1/16-inch tubes. Not only was the labor-intensive process of watering hundreds of pots by hand eliminated, but Chapin used the system to fertilize each pot as well.

His second product was the Dew Hose, a twin-wall tape used by Smith in Long Island. Word of Smith's work with vegetable irrigation reached the West Coast. Bernarr Hall, farm advisor with San Diego County, convinced tomato grower

Tosh Hasegawa to try a new twin-wall drip tape from Chapin on five acres. Robert Grove of Grove Chemical Company helped set up the fertilizer injection system for the test. Tomato production jumped by 25 percent and fruit size increased by almost 15 percent. Between Hall's work with vegetables and Gustafson's work with avocados, California growers could no longer ignore the benefits of low-volume irrigation.

Chapin licensed the twin-wall patent to Reed Irrigation (now Hardie Irrigation) which markets the hose under the trade name Bi-Wall. Still based in Watertown, Chapin has expanded its line of drip products and is managed by Richard's son, William. Drip industry veteran Mel Canterbury is the company's marketing manager.

Sugar and pineapple growers in Hawaii needed certain product refinements similar to vegetable growers in the East, but on a much larger scale. The first experimental low-volume irrigation systems were installed in Hawaii in 1969, reports Michael D. Farrell, president of Irrigation Technology Corp. of Haleiwa, Hawaii.

Olokele Sugar Company was the first to convert one of its plantations in Hawaii to drip irrigation in 1970. The company utilized a twin-wall product from Anjac Manufacturing of El Monte, California. Donald Mock of Anjac Manufacturing and David Wisdom of Wisdom Industries cooperated on the development of the low-volume tape. Mock sold Anjac to Reed Irrigation. Reed thus owned the rights to three of the primary types of drip tape technology, Anjac, Drip-Eze and Dew Hose. Now these products are marketed by Hardie.

By 1988, the vast majority of both sugar and pineapple plantations in Hawaii were drip irrigated (nearly 90,000 acres in cane and 19,000 acres in pineapple).

Hawaii was also one of the first states to embrace drip irrigation for landscape purposes. In the early 70s, Kuluwai Corporation started promoting low-volume irrigation for trees, plant beds and even turf in the many narrow and confined sites such as median strips, mountainside landscapes and resorts. The company explored subsurface applications for turf and ground cover and using low-volume micro-sprays for areas that were seeded and mulched hydraulically. As the resort and hotel market began to compete with agriculture for land and water, low-volume irrigation was a compromise acceptable to both industries.

Another version of tape technology was advanced by Davies Allport and his company, T-Systems International, Inc., of San Diego in the late 70s. The company was founded by Allport, a former low-volume expert with Anjac and Reed.

T-Tape was produced at high speeds and with improved quality to assure growers a reliable product at a reasonable price. In the mid-80s, the company introduced a turbulent-flow design for the tape that was less affected by sediment or soil when buried. Allport eventually offered a larger size tape in order to provide longer runs of irrigation with fewer submains and laterals.

As the use of drip tape increased, finding an efficient method to install the tape in large fields gained importance. The farmers themselves came up with many innovations in tube laying by adapting existing equipment. Most growers use discs or blades mounted to the tool bar of tractors. By carrying rolls of tubing or tape on the tractor, a farmer can install multiple rows beneath the surface. Further advances in water use efficiency of low-volume irrigation have been provided by covering crop rows irrigated by drip lines with plastic mulch. Water loss by both evaporation and weeds is virtually eliminated.

The Micro-Sprinkler Alternative

During the 70s and 80s, low-volume irrigation applications branched out from avocados to cash crops, such as cotton, tomatoes, cantaloupes and citrus. Growers of these crops had depended upon portable sprinkler irrigation for many years. While the advantages of drip irrigation were

BELOW: Greenhouse irrigation of potted plants was one of the earliest uses of low-volume irrigation. Shown is Roberts' Spot Spitter.

Courtesy, Roberts Irrigation Products

Drip irrigation pioneers of the 60s and 70s (left to right): David Wilson of Olson Irrigation Systems after Drip-Eze Company; Mark Christy of Global Irrigation, Subterrain and Wade; H. Ernst Deutsh from Mexico; Donald Olson of Olson Irrigation Systems, Drip-Eze and Reed Irrigation Systems; and Bud Bonnett, an early installer of drip irrigation in Riverside, California.

convincing, sprinkler technology was by no means forgotten.

Low-volume, rotational and fixed-spray sprinkler heads were developed beginning in the late 50s as alternatives to drip emitters. Referred to as micro-, mini- and midget-sprays and sprinklers, they performed well at discharge rates between 1/2 to 1-1/2 gallons per minute. They were often preferred by growers who managed tree crops in light, sandy soils. Such soils had little ability to spread soil moisture delivered by drip emitters through capillary action.

James C. Roberts, a San Marcos, California, citrus grower, developed one of the earliest plastic rotary sprinkler heads in 1961. Roberts demonstrated his "Spot Spitter" at the Second International Drip Irrigation Congress in San Diego and the seminars at Escondido and Fallbrook. He was confident in his product because he has used the mini-sprayer on his own grove since 1964. The farmer Roberts became the manufacturer of Roberts Irrigation Products.

The company expanded into the drip tape business in 1986 using a

new manufacturing process. Roberts added a turbulent flow feature with vortex action.

Another early California drip irrigation manufacturer was Controlled Water Emissions Systems, which was the outgrowth of The Drip-Eze Company. Drip-Eze was founded in 1969 by Bruce Brown to pursue the new drip irrigation technology. The company utilized technology designed by Donald O. Olson, a mechanical engineer with experience in low-volume sprinkler design and plastics manufacturing. Reed Irrigation Systems of Sydney, Australia purchased Controlled Water Emissions Systems in 1973 and appointed Olson president. Another Australian firm, Hardie Irrigation, bought the company in 1978.

After leaving Reed Irrigation, Olson created his own company, Olson Irrigation Systems in Santee, California, in 1976. The company has been a leader in low-volume micro-spray technology for both landscape and agriculture. Olson's products were selected by the Soviet government in 1987 when the USSR made

the decision to produce low-volume irrigation equipment. The cooperative international effort was financed partly by Valmont, manufacture of large mechanized sprinkler systems.

A different approach to drip emitters was taken by Salco Products, Inc. of California in 1967. Previous low-volume technology utilized polyethylene tubing so that emitters could be punched into it. This ruled out the use of standard PVC fittings. By adding plasticizers and carbon black to PVC resin, Salco created tubing compatible with standard fittings.

To add to the attraction of its emitters, Salco made them adjustable so that the flow rate could be changed after installation. However, the concept of adjustable emitters proved to be quite labor intensive. If one emitter was changed, it affected the flow rate of all the other emitters on the line. To correct this situation, Salco devised and patented a pressure-compensated emitter using a silicone membrane.

In 1972, a third-generation Florida citrus grower named Tom Thayer attended an agricultural conference in South Africa. During a field tour of a macadamia nut orchard he discovered the use of an "under the tree" low-volume spray jet. The tiny sprinkler wet an area smaller than a conventional sprinkler and larger than a drip emitter. Thayer brought samples back to the States to try in his groves.

He ran tests in cooperation with Dr. Koo of the University of Florida Experimental Station in Lake Alfred, Florida. The advantages of the micro-sprayer over impact sprinklers were that they were less expensive to install, required less pressure to operate and used less water. They also could be used to apply fertilizers and nematicides.

Thayer started supplying the spray jets to peach and pecan growers across the South. Western growers found them effective for grapes, avocados and apples. During the winter of 1977, Thayer discovered almost by accident that the spray jets provided frost/freeze protection of citrus by raising the dew point.

In 1982, Thayer started manufacturing his own spray jet and called it the Maxijet. The company, now managed by Susan Thayer, recently introduced a pop-up adapter for converting high-volume sprinklers to micro-sprayers. This product simplifies conservation efforts in landscape irrigation.

Mark Christy of Orange County, California, was another pioneer in sprinkler irrigation and low-volume irrigation. Christy's company, Subterrain Irrigation, developed pressure-compensating emitters beginning in the early 70s. After a name change to Global Irrigation, the company merged into Wade Irrigation.

The latest concept in low-volume sprinkler technology was introduced in 1992 by Wade Irrigation of Portland, Oregon. Instead of using pressurized water directly from tubing to propel water from the micro-sprinkler, Wade incorporated a small rubber bladder and a pressure sensitive valve into each sprinkler. As pressure in the bladder reaches a certain level, the valve opens to send water further than conventional low-volume sprinklers. Called the Pulsator, the mini-sprinkler offers both a larger wetted area and pressure compensation.

Low-Volume Traveling Irrigation

The advantages of low-volume irrigation motivated USDA-ARS researcher Dr. Claude C. Phene to explore its use on linear-move systems. Based at the Water Management Research Laboratory in Fresno, California, Phene adapted a linear system with drops fitted with drip emitters. He called the huge, crawling mechanism the Traveling Trickle Irrigation System (TTIS) in 1981.

The system was randomly described as resembling a series of traveling bubblers.

The linear mainframe used drop pipes with trailing drag tubes to which emitters were attached. In this way, water was delivered with minimal evaporation, no wind distortion and application uniformity of 95 percent. Although TTIS was never a production item, this combination of linear-move and drip irrigation technology offered great potential for use on high-value row crops.

Both the early versions of low-volume irrigation had their drawbacks. Dissolved salts in the irrigation water built up in the emitters and tubing, as well as in the soil. Water had to be much cleaner than that used for surface or sprinkler irrigation. The plastic tubing and emitters were more easily damaged during handling or by pests. The distribution of moisture from low-volume systems depended greatly on the soil type and profile. Fortunately, two decades of field experience have brought about ways to correct these problems.

Low-volume irrigation's benefits have gone far beyond water conservation and improved soil moisture conditions. It is also a very precise method of applying nutrients to the root zone of crops, whether on flat fields or steep grades. Very dilute solutions of water and fertilizer can be delivered to plants as they are needed, with virtually no loss to runoff, leaching, or vaporization.

Low-volume irrigation has brought marginal soils into production and significantly increased the ability of all countries to produce food for their growing populations. Environmentally, low-volume irrigation has lowered energy demands, while extending the availability of limited water supplies. The need for applied chemicals and fertilizers has been reduced, which in turn has helped reduce the concern over irrigation water runoff.

Low-volume irrigation has been accepted throughout the world. As of 1992, more than 1.7 million acres in the United States were drip irrigated, a gain of 15 percent from the previous year. The future for low-volume irrigation is one of the brightest in the irrigation industry.

BELOW: Machine designed to install two lines of drip tape in a raised vegetable bed.

Courtesy, Yardney Water Management Systems

Glen Canyon Dam forms Lake Powell. Named for
pioneer Colorado River Surveyor John Wesley Powell,
the dam stores 27 million acre feet of water.

CHAPTER 4

Great American Reclamation Projects

"What do we want with this vast worthless area? This region of savages and wild beasts, of deserts of shifting sands and whirlwinds of dust, of cactus and prairie dogs; to what use could we ever hope to put these great deserts and endless mountains ranges, impenetrable and covered to their bases with eternal snow?"

— Senator Daniel Webster, from an 1840 speech

Senator Daniel Webster was a powerful speaker and a formidable politician. He was not, however, an agricultural visionary. Yet hard on his eloquent words were pioneers with vision and passion for advancement, which attracted them to the promise of vigorous and satisfying lives in a fresh new land.

Of all the early westward expeditions in the United States, the most famous was that of Lewis and Clark. Authorized by President Thomas Jefferson, the expedition left Wood River, Illinois on May 14, 1804 and returned from its 8,000-mile trek on September 23, 1806.

"The object of your mission," Jefferson publicly stated, "is to explore the Missouri River and such principal streams of it, as, by its course and communication with the water of the Pacific Ocean, may offer the most direct and practical water route across the continent for the purpose of commerce."

The first organized irrigation venture of practical consequence was formed by the Mormon pioneers, directed by Brigham Young in 1847. Their first views of the Great Salt Lake Valley, with its slopes gently inclining toward the Everlasting Mountains, and valley soils awaiting combination with abundant, snow-borne waters must have inspired them in their work. The success of those early Mormon settlers in leading irrigation water to the land was such that, for many years after,

Roosevelt dam, Salt River irrigation project, Arizona. Built in a narrow gorge, each end of the dam is supported by natural rock abutments.

Sternwheel steamboat "E.N. Cooke" at Oregon City locks in 1878.

they were copied by western farmers, as well as federal agencies.

Crucial milestones in American irrigation were established on the frontier scene from the mid-1840s into the 1850s and 1860s. The beginnings of private and public American irrigation projects, both large and small, included a number of historically prominent individuals. Despite their exploits, often unrelated to irrigation, they sometimes figured dramatically in the opening of arid regions of the West.

One such individual was Captain John C. Fremont. In 1844, he was commissioned by the United States government to survey the vast Pacific Coast and intermediate areas as he proceeded west. In his log he documented particularly impressive observations of the Great Salt Lake Valley, later to become part of the state of Utah.

Fremont, who later became a California senator, was a difficult representative of the U.S. government. Despite his recalcitrant nature, however, in the field of exploration Fremont merits a significant place in the annals of the West. His graphic reports, detailing the West's oppor-

tunities, caught the full attention of the Mormons centered in Nauvoo, Illinois, long before their historic journeys to the Salt Lake Valley, which began in 1847. Realizing that growing-season rainfall in that area was limited, they studied irrigation techniques prior to their mass exodus to their chosen land beyond the Wasatch Mountains.

Early Cooperative Ventures

The Mormons planned the Big Cottonwood Creek Canal in 1848. The complexity and magnitude of the project were such that it was impossible for a small group to undertake. A corporate formation or cooperative venture, involving many, was the only practical approach for success. Brigham Young implemented such a venture, thereby introducing the philosophy of joint public enterprise in irrigation works.

Others followed the Mormon example of cooperative endeavor. They included a group of eastern investors led by Nathan Meeker and Horace Greeley of publishing fame, who encouraged land development when they colonized land at the

juncture of the Cache la Poudre and Platte rivers in Colorado.

Corporate irrigation plans were risky because the emphasis was primarily on land sales, promoting the fact that water would cause values to rise. Land values would not increase, however, if careful farming practices were not followed.

Near the end of the 19th Century, despite the enthusiasm of irrigation proponents such as William E. Smythe, federal interest waned. But federal apathy was not enough to quell private interest. Joseph L. Bristow, promoting the merits of irrigation, organized the Interstate Irrigation Association in Salina, Kansas, in 1893. The next year he began publishing the "Irrigation Farmer" to draw further attention to irrigation.

Despite the atmosphere of lackluster federal support for irrigation, private promoters sprang forth in ever-increasing numbers. Finally, in 1897 the United States government acquiesced. That year, the Office of Irrigation Inquiry, within the Department of Agriculture, was formed to study the presence of artesian water sources.

The era of government-sponsored reclamation, bringing irrigation to public lands, was close at hand.

Irrigation Acreage Growth Factors

Gold was discovered in California at Sutter's Fort in 1848. The excitement generated by that discovery brought hordes of fortune seekers and visionaries, over land and sea. Not only did the "Gold Rush" cause great drama, but it also boosted settlement in the central and southern regions of the West.

Numerous other factors contributed to the influx of settlers in the West and Northwest in 1848. The

U.S. Congress determined that the vast lands of the Northwest would be organized as the Oregon Territory. All the region south of the 49th parallel was ceded to the United States when the Mexican-American War ended by treaty in 1848.

Population and irrigation growth in the West and Northwest was explosive. In 1845, 3,000 hardy souls crossed the plains and mountains to settle the rich lands of the Northwest. By 1849, 25,000 more had joined them. Further incentive came in the U.S. Donation Land Claim Act of 1850, which stimulated settlement by offering to cede 640 acres of land of choice, in the Territory, to any man and his wife who agreed to occupy and develop it.

Five thousand acres of land were being irrigated in the Salt Lake Valley in the fall of 1848. By 1865, 1.5 million acres of arable land were being irrigated, from the northern front range of present-day Utah to what is now St. George.

The West continued to grow in both population and area. Ratified in 1854, the Gadsden Purchase added the territories of New Mexico, Arizona, and California to the United States. Those territories, great stretches of unknown lands, particularly those of the Colorado River, needed exploring.

In 1857 the War Department dispatched Lieutenant J.C. Ives to explore and map the Colorado River by sternwheel steamboat. He was to start from its mouth, at the Gulf of California, and travel upstream as far as possible.

Ives started his trip in 1858. He succeeded in traveling up 400 miles of the turbulent river, only to bring his steamboat, Explorer, to total destruction on a submerged rock in Black Canyon. Undaunted, Ives proceeded by small boat through the canyon. He eventually reached the point where Hoover Dam stands today, five miles below what was then known as the Las Vegas Wash.

Irrigation continued to expand steadily in the Northwest. The reaches of Wyoming's high prairies averaged less than 15 inches of precipitation annually. As early as 1853 Mormon pioneers were using irrigation in that state, near Fort Bridger. After the Civil War, railroad construction boosted Wyoming's economy. That increased the demand for beef cattle production and the resultant need for pasture gave farm irrigation a boost.

Missionaries irrigated the Yakima Valley, of what is now Washington State, as early as 1864. Private canal companies developed lands rapidly. By 1902, 120,000 acres were being irrigated from the Yakima River and its tributaries.

In 1869, Major John Wesley Powell, later known as the "Father of Reclamation," was commissioned to survey and map the upper reaches of the Colorado River. His party boated down the Green River from its source in Wyoming and down the Colorado to the mouth of the Virgin River. Major Powell's expedition charted 1,000 miles of unknown rapids, through treacherous canyons, and was the first group of white men to traverse the Grand Canyon by boat and live to tell of their experiences.

Upon completing his incomparable survey mission, Powell exclaimed, "The West is an arid land, hostile to farming, and will never be settled, opening its resources to

Elephant Butte Dam near Truth or Consequences, New Mexico had a torturously long and troubled construction history. Now a National Historic Civil Engineering Landmark, it was started in 1893, yet did not impound the waters of the Rio Grande River until 1930.

America, unless the Federal Government dams the rivers to store winter and spring run-off in reservoirs."

Federal reclamation after 1902 created artificial lakes to regulate the western river flows, thus bringing Powell's prophecy to reality.

Federal Government Involvement

The federal government's role in reclamation increased slowly throughout the latter part of the 19th Century, despite politically turbulent times. By 1889, the federal government was able to move ahead with a plan to enhance investigations of arid lands for probable irrigation. Two years later, the General Revision Act suggested ways of encouraging private enterprise to invest in irrigation projects.

Renowned irrigation engineer Elwood Mead described the condition of western public lands to a Congressional Committee on Irrigation in 1896. Mead faulted the federal government for failing to deal with Western projects prior to 1896. In another report, he commented on the lack of progress in national water conservation.

"Under present conditions, the national government does nothing to conserve the available water supply," said Mead. "It neither aids nor supervises construction of canals."

Such was the institutional environment in which irrigation progress was mired in the 1800s.

Private speculators, however, promoted irrigation in a convincingly attractive way. They suggested that large profits awaited would-be investors intrigued with the prospects of arid land reformation.

Mesille Valley investors proposed Elephant Butte Dam on the Rio Grande River in the Territory of New Mexico. The project was directed by Dr. Nathan Ellington Boyd, who was already famous for his design and construction of the first Aswan Dam on the Nile River in Egypt. According to the plan, Elephant Butte Dam would be located 100 miles upstream from the City of El Paso.

In 1893, the Rio Grande Dam and Irrigation Company was formed. The company raised $5 million to begin construction on Elephant Butte Dam near what is now the town of Truth Or Consequences, New Mexico. News of this development caused farm real estate values downstream, around El Paso, to soar.

Sadly, the federal government tossed a curve at the project. Although the Rio Grande Dam and Irrigation Company's application for construction of Elephant Butte Dam had been approved previously by the United States Department of the Interior, the federal government reversed the authorization and began legal proceedings to further enjoin progress.

Cause for the stoppage arose from the interpretation of a War Department supremacy ruling concerning U.S. waterways. The bureaucratic analysis was that by impounding the floodwaters of the Rio Grande, 1,200 miles upstream from its mouth, navigation could be disturbed.

This was a disastrous turn of events for proponents of the dam. No amount of rationalization on their part could sway the determined federal forces, and the Rio Grande Dam and Irrigation Company eventually was forced into involuntary bankruptcy.

The company was finished; however, the project gained new life a few years later. Following establishment of the Reclamation Act in 1902, federal plans were activated and construction of Elephant Butte Dam began in 1908. Once the Reclamation Service became the sole factor in the dam's construction, the effects of stored water on the Rio Grande's navigational potential somehow became of minimal importance.

The defunct Rio Grande Dam and Irrigation Company project, the largest private undertaking at the time, was re-named the Rio Grande Project when the Reclamation Service took control of the building of Elephant Butte Dam and reservoir. On completion in 1930, it provided water to irrigate 178,000 acres.

In the last years of the 19th Century and the early years of the 20th Century, the reclamation push came from a number of public and private sources. In 1894, the Carey

Photo, James Scott Boyd, Scottsdale, Arizona

Dr. Nathan Ellington Boyd, internationally famous dam builder, formed the Rio Grande Dam and Irrigation Company in 1893 to design and construct Elephant Butte Dam.

Act, introduced by Senator Joseph M. Carey of Wyoming, granted 1 million acres of federal land to a group of 10 arid states. The Carey Act provided that any of the states could offer, as an inducement to settlers, up to 160 acres of land if the recipients would settle and irrigate their tract within 10 years. In the ensuing years, more than 1 million acres were claimed under the program.

William E. Smythe, a journalist for the Omaha Bee, generated great public attention for land reform and development in 1891 with his published views on family settlement of small farms — made productive with irrigation. His beliefs were so powerful and persuasive that he was made chairman of a committee to organize the first National Irrigation Congress, which was eventually held in Salt Lake City, Utah, in September 1891. That same year the voluble Smythe advocated the 160-acre Homestead principle in his "Irrigation Age," which became a platform for land reform studies throughout 1896.

The National Irrigation Congress failed to develop as an institution to promote public and congressional support for western irrigation. Still, it continued to function for several years.

Smythe wasn't alone in his passion for irrigation. George W. Maxwell, a California lawyer with broad experience in western water development, emerged in 1897 as the foremost champion of irrigation initiatives. That year, in Wichita, Kansas, he organized the National Irrigation Association. Despite formidable political odds, he received financial help from the Atchison-Topeka and Santa Fe Railroad and friendly congressional representation from U.S. Representative Francis G. Newlands. Buttressed with such backing, Maxwell fought to marshal public support for reclamation and the resultant benefits of irrigation.

Irrigation proponents Maxwell, Congressman Newland, and Frederick H. Newell, USGS, became a powerful trio. By 1900, they had trumpeted irrigation to the point that it had become a national issue. Their slogan was, "Save the Forests - Store the Floods - Make Homes on the Lands."

Reclamation received an unexpected boost from a tragic chapter in U.S. history — the assassination of President William McKinley in 1901. New President Theodore Roosevelt, who had a ready understanding of the need for reclamation, gave the movement his full endorsement.

Congressman Newland had previously introduced a Reclamation Bill, which quickly passed both houses of Congress. President Roosevelt signed the National Reclamation Act into law, June 17, 1902. The beginning of the 20th Century thereby became a launching

Rio Grande irrigation project, New Mexico.

pad for America's agricultural community to enter the irrigation age.

By 1902, the United States Geological Service had completed general studies of streams, watersheds, suitable lands for irrigation, and potential reservoir sites in much of the West. The Salt River Project in Arizona, which included construction of Theodore Roosevelt Dam, became the first of a long list of federal water control accomplishments resulting from the Reclamation Act. The Theodore Roosevelt was the nation's first "high" dam. Completed in 1911, it ultimately furnished water to irrigate 264,697 acres of Arizona desert.

The second high dam, the Buffalo Bill Dam, named for Colonel William Cody, was part of the Shoshone Project in northwestern Wyoming. It was started in 1904 and by 1920 was storing water to irrigate 108,000 acres near the historic town of Cody. The 328-foot arched, concrete monolith, later commemorated as a National Historical Structure, is distinguished today as a National Historic Civil Engineering Landmark. It functions as it has since it first started storing water and generating electricity.

Harnessing The Rio Grande

The Rio Grande, or the Rio Bravo del Norte as it is known in Mexico, is one of the world's greatest rivers. It begins from a multitude of minute trickles and hidden springs, 13,000 feet up the San Juan Mountains at Stony Pass, high above the town of Creed, Colorado. It flows 1,885 miles to empty into the Gulf of Mexico at Brownsville, Texas.

After leaving Colorado, the Rio Grande surges through the high plains of New Mexico, carving a deep, narrow gorge from black basalt rock. Its waters, already in part depleted by upstream irrigation farming, flow ever southward. Beyond Taos, New Mexico, its bed again runs through broad desert plains.

South through Albuquerque, now drained of much of its volume, the Rio Grande traverses vast, mostly barren deserts, hesitating to create a 40-mile reservoir behind Elephant Butte Dam at Truth-or-Consequences, New Mexico.

Apportionment of Rio Grande waters has long been controversial between those on its southern and northern banks. However, in 1906 a U.S.-Mexico treaty was signed that annually allotted 60,000 acre feet of Rio Grande water to Mexico at Juarez. Much of the remaining water went to the El Paso Valley. A dependable supply of water transformed the El Paso and Juarez valleys into highly productive agricultural regions. The Rio Grande Rectification Treaty and Rio Grande canalization of the 1930s and 1940s later straightened the river from below Elephant Butte Dam to its intersection with the Texas/Mexico border, shortening the river by 65 miles.

About 200 miles south of El Paso, the river is replenished with water from its tributary, the Mexican Rio Concho above Big Bend National park, and then again at the town of Langtry and the Amistad Reservoir.

Downstream from Laredo, productive southern Texas farmland lies next to the Rio Grande course, and the river's remaining precious waters are used to irrigate the fertile fields of the McAllen and Harlingen areas. By the time the Rio Grande reaches Brownsville and fans out into a broad delta, it brings only tiny

Construction of Oregon's Owyhee Dam began in 1928.
Water was delivered to fields from the vast project in 1935.

The Ogalala Formation

Through the centuries, percolated rainfall accumulated beneath the Texas High Plains. A vast underground lake, some 200 to 300 feet deep, was created. Geologists came to know this lake as the Ogallala formation.

In 1954 U.S. Army geologist Jules Marcos led a topographical expedition and noted, "Underground water may be found at depths of 10 to 125 feet, everywhere below Llano Estacado."

This revelation ushered in new hopes for Texas High Plains Irrigation. These hopes were minimal, however, until the turn of the century when large volume pumps came into being to supersede windmill and engine-driven "sucker-rod" well pumps used in production up to that time.

By 1900, improved centrifugal pumps set in well pits and flat-belt-driven from the ground surface, by steam or internal combustion engines, discharged large water volumes. At the same time, vertical-shaft centrifugal installations, often in 30-foot-deep pits, came into use.

In 1901 Byron Jackson Company of San Francisco built the first deep well pump, a forerunner of what

soon would be known as the vertical deep well, line-shaft turbine pump. The development of that concept caught on quickly. By 1910, the Great Plains, the Texas High Plains, and all western agricultural areas in the U.S. were experiencing aggressive drilling of deep water wells, in which vertical turbine pumps were installed. Also that year, The Northern Colorado Power Company was soliciting farmers to electrify their pumps.

First factory production of a stationary four-cycle combustion engine for irrigation, the "Hot Bulb" oil engine, was built by Hornsby-Ackroyd. This type of engine was soon made by many other builders including Primm, Charter, Bessemer, Fairbanks-Morese, and Heer.

Electricity did not broadly come to America until the mid-1930s. For 40 years prior to that, irrigators were obliged to use stationary engines. So reliable did those engines become that even today models, such as the Minneapolis-Moline, natural gas-burning units, out of production for many decades, still perform economically.

Plains pioneer pump man George E. Green of Plainview, Texas, built the

first right-angle-drive gear head in 1915. This development made it possible to drive a vertical turbine pump with a stationary engine. By 1975, 42,255 deep well irrigation turbine pumps were delivering water to high plains crops.

Underground water was irrigating 1,061,949 acres in the area by 1970. Official accounts showed that indiscriminate pumping was taking its toll on the Ogallala ground water reserve. A well in Deaf Smith County, Texas, drilled in 1936 went dry that year, the water level having dropped 79 feet in 34 years.

As late as 1970, Texas had no ground water control legislation. By then the issue had become a matter of high priority.

The hard truth was that the contemporary High Plains region, although still exceedingly productive, could no longer rest on the supposition of an inexhaustible supply of underground water. One of the nation's most prolific agricultural areas to this day faces further decline as the Ogallala formation no longer can meet modern irrigation demands.

rivulets of fresh water to the Gulf of Mexico.

The Idaho Model

Idaho's vivid settlement and irrigation history stands out among the western states in terms of adventure, crop production, and developed acreage.

As with other western states, the rush west to Idaho began with fortune hunters. In 1862, gold was discovered in the Boise Basin and in the northern part of the state. Gold seekers came in droves, driven by potential riches. In

their avaricious pursuit, most overlooked the promise of another kind of riches — an ever-present agricultural homeland just waiting to be established. As the fickle promises of gold wealth waned, the more discerning, forward-looking settlers viewed the richness of Idaho's river valleys.

Idaho statehood came in 1890 and Boise City, renamed simply as Boise, became the state capital. By 1900, 148,000 acres of rich valley soil were irrigated in Idaho.

Two great Idaho reclamation developments were authorized in

1905. First came the Minidoka Project. It was designed to use the waters of the mighty Snake River for irrigation from Henry's Fork Basin in eastern Idaho to Bliss in the state's south-central region.

Because of the multi-purpose design of the project, Minidoka farms received electrical power long before most other areas in the United States. A 1914 newspaper account, announcing that a three-story building in Rupert, Idaho, had just become the first in the nation to be heated and lighted entirely by electricity, drew national attention.

Hand digging an irrigation canal in Nebraska during the late 1800s.

Second of the initial Idaho irrigation plans by the Reclamation Service, the Boise Project, garnered national attention with Arrowrock Dam, completed in 1915. With its arched design, the dam towered 343 feet high — then the tallest concrete monolith in the world. It stored enough water to irrigate 390,000 acres.

The immense Snake River watershed, made up of fine valley soils, drew pioneer farmers as early as the 1870s. Those first settlers built their own flood irrigation systems primarily using teams of oxen and hard manual labor, hauling hand-hewn timbers great distances from mountain forests.

As early as 1871, Nels A. Just, a cattleman, hand-dug an irrigation canal in Bingham County, Idaho. The canal diverted water from the Blackfoot River, not far from where it joins the Snake River. Private Idaho irrigation projects tapping the Snake

River near the turn of the Century included Poverty Flats Irrigation Company, North Rigby Irrigation and Canal Company, Rexburg Irrigation Company, and Teton Irrigation Canal.

Oregon and Washington

The first federal reclamation venture in the state of Oregon was the Klamath Project. Completed in 1909, the project embodies 234,000 acres including Klamath Basin and Tule Lake Basin. The project enabled some of the finest potato and malt barley growing land to be brought into production.

In the same year, the Umatilla Project, bordering the Columbia River and using its water, was designed to irrigate 30,000 acres. The project's boundaries run close to the famous "Old Oregon Trail." Marks of early pioneer wagon wheels, from

when they crossed the arid desert, are still discernable.

The area west of the Cascade Mountains in Oregon has annual rainfalls of 40 inches or more. Most of the state, however, which lies east of the Cascades, is a high desert with annual rainfalls of only 5 to 10 inches.

The Owyhee Project, serving eastern Oregon and west-central Idaho, was authorized in 1926 and the first water was delivered from it in 1935. The project was of great engineering significance because, upon completion in 1932, the 417-foot Owyhee thick-arch concrete dam was the world's tallest dam.

Washington, the "Evergreen State" in the northwest corner of the U.S., has a unique and diverse climate. Its northwest boundaries along the Pacific Ocean have miles of sandy beaches. Native rain forests near the western slopes of the towering

Olympic Mountains receive up to 200 inches of annual precipitation.

Some 80 miles inland are the Cascade Mountains, including 14,408-foot Mt. Ranier. Beyond the Cascades are vast expanses of the great Columbia Basin. Some central regions here receive less than 5 inches of rainfall annually.

Engineering, hydrology, and land development have been practiced with astounding results in Washington. The first federal reclamation undertaking in the state was the Okanogan Project, which began in 1905. Tapping the Okanogan River, the project provided water to irrigate 5,083 acres.

In 1903, Washington's Yakima Valley residents petitioned the U.S. Secretary of the Interior for assistance improving the primitive irrigation facilities there. They had been constructed by missionaries as early as 1864. The Reclamation Service undertook feasibility studies and began construction on the Yakima Project in 1906. Today, the project provides water to 510,000 acres where some of the nation's finest Golden and Red Delicious apples are grown.

Courtesy, U.S. Bureau of Reclamation

Hoover Dam, started in 1933, was dedicated September 30, 1935.

"Big Sky" Reclamation

Called "Big Sky Country" for its mountainous topography, Montana has fresh waters that travel greater distances and touch more land than any other in the Northern Hemisphere. In three distinctive systems, the state's waters flow west of the Continental Divide into the Columbia River, to the east into the Missouri River Basin, and to the north through the Belly and St. Mary's rivers toward Hudson Bay in Canada.

Early Montana settlers found they could not depend on the state's sparse 13 to 18 inches of annual rainfall. The first federally funded reclamation project in Montana was the Lower Yellowstone Project, started in 1905. By 1909, the project delivered irrigation water to 52,000 acres.

Some of the earliest irrigation in Montana, preceding even that of the Mormons in Utah, was practiced by white settlers in about 1841 at St. Mary's Mission. Fruit and vegetables grown there were in great demand by miners, loggers, and railroad workers as late as 1883.

Privately financed developers constructed Como Dam and Reservoir on the Bitter Root River. By 1910, irrigation water was supplied to the Bitter Root Valley's east side. The Bureau of Reclamation took over the project in 1930. Today's Bitter Root Irrigation District delivers water to 15,516 acres. Como Dam remains one of the earliest irrigation projects.,

Engineering Marvel

No account of American irrigation history would be complete without including the engineering feat accomplished in the construction of the Los Angeles Aqueduct. Conceived in 1902 as a metropolitan public works enterprise and supervised by William Mullholland, Los Angeles city engineer, the project was completed in 1913.

With a driving spirit and geological curiosity, Mullholland became engrossed with the idea of bringing Sierra Nevada mountain

The Caterpillar tractor was 20 years old when these hefty diesel
Model 75s, 12 cubic yard earth movers, started construction of
Grand Coulee Dam.

water from the Owens Valley of northern California, 233 miles south, to the Los Angeles basin. From its outset, the project was fraught with political bickering, Owens Valley land takeover litigation, and Owens Valley landowner resentment of what was termed "big city intrusion." The Los Angeles Aqueduct suffered many setbacks, from its inception to final water delivery.

After more than 75 years of operation, the Los Angeles Aqueduct still functions well. When it first began delivering water in 1913,

it was hailed as an engineering marvel, ranking in complexity with the Panama Canal. Unlike modern aqueducts of its magnitude, the entire system functions by gravity. Almost 52 miles of tunnels pierce mountain obstacles in the aqueduct's southern course along the eastern slopes of the Sierra Nevada Mountains.

The Los Angeles Aqueduct was planned to serve a population of 2 million. To say the least, the project's massive water flow was far beyond the requirements of Los Angeles in 1913, which had a population of

250,000. San Fernando Valley agriculture used the surplus water for irrigation for 20 years.

Recorded history sometimes casts unwanted shadows on the achievements of important men. Mullholland, known as a stalwart public servant and state dignitary in the years following his achievements in directing the Los Angeles Aqueduct, eventually became the victim of resentment and scorn. The final blow to Mullholland and his career came on the night of March 13, 1928, when the St. Francis Dam, under

Mullholland's jurisdiction, failed. The ensuing flood swept over portions of the San Fernando and Santa Clarita Valleys, taking hundreds of lives and causing millions of dollars of property damage.

Mullholland's great public prominence ended, his reputation irretrievably shattered. He was obliged to resign his position and retire.

Taming the Colorado River

Flowing from the eternal snows of the northern Colorado Rocky Mountains, the Colorado River meanders south for 1,400 miles. Drained of its turbulent flows, it eventually enters the Gulf of Mexico as a salt-ridden trickle.

Early desert settlers, desperate for drinking and irrigation water, turned increasingly to the Colorado River. Primitive attempts to control what was termed at the turn of the century "the most dangerous river in the West" usually brought destruction and despair. The only clear solution, from views of reclamation engineers, was to harness the river with flood control dams.

In 1924, the Bureau of Reclamation's chief engineer, F.E. Weymouth, did an exhaustive two-year feasibility study. Weymouth suggested constructing a huge dam near Boulder Canyon on the Colorado River. The Boulder Canyon Act became law on December 21, 1928. Two years later, the Secretary of the Interior announced that a dam would be built at Boulder Canyon. In honor of then President Herbert Hoover, it would be named Hoover Dam.

The undertaking was so massive that only a consortium of six western contractors could bid on the proposed dam and appurtenances. A federal contract was awarded in 1931 to the group, known simply enough as Six Companies, Inc. Their bid, $48,890,995.50 was the largest contract ever let by the U.S. government.

The massive structure of the Grand Coulee Dam is so vast the river at spring flood stage creates a thunderous flow that causes the giant concrete mass to shudder relentlessly.

The first bucket of concrete was placed in the footings of Hoover Dam on June 6, 1933. It was followed by another 3,250,335 cubic yards of concrete to form the highest dam in the world, which rises 726.4 feet above bedrock. The federal contract gave Six Companies, Inc., seven years to finish the project. So efficient was every aspect of engineering and construction that the job was finished two years ahead of schedule.

Lake Mead, behind Hoover Dam, was named for Dr. Elwood Mead, Bureau of Reclamation commissioner from 1924 to 1936. The body of water is America's largest man-made lake, containing 28,531,000 acre-feet of water. The surface stands 1,221.4 feet above sea level. At this elevation , it extends upstream 110 miles and has an average depth of 500 feet.

On September 30, 1935, President Franklin Roosevelt dedicated the dam, calling it "another great achievement of American resourcefulness. This is why I congratulate you who have created Boulder Dam," he added.

Originally labeled Hoover Dam from dedication, the monolith was called Boulder Dam for many years after. In 1947, the 80th Congress decreed it would for all time be known as Hoover Dam.

After the construction of Hoover Dam, other great projects followed on the Colorado River. Glen Canyon Dam at Page, Arizona, rising 710 feet above bedrock, stores 27 million acre feet of water. Lake Powell formed behind it was named for John Wesley Powell, famed explorer and national hero of the 1880s.

A division of the overall Boulder Canyon Project, Davis Dam, is 67 miles downstream from Hoover Dam. It was named in honor of Arthur Powell Davis, Reclamation Service director from 1914 to 1923. His courage and vision helped spark the beginning of Colorado River development.

Parker Dam, 155 miles downstream from Hoover Dam, feeds the Colorado River Aqueduct. The aqueduct carries much of the water for the Los Angeles Basin Metropolitan Water District.

Harnessing the Columbia

Called "The Great River of the West," the Columbia River was discovered May 11, 1792, by Captain Robert Gray. It was named for his ship, Columbia Rediviva. Although Gray had observed what appeared to be a huge inland bay on a previous journey up the

1939 was the year that the Missouri River Basin program took shape piloted by Lewis A. Pick, U.S. Corps of Engineers and William G. Sloan.

The Parson's Plan

Although it never came close to being implemented, the Parson's Plan was conceived in 1964 by the prestigious Ralph M. Parsons company, a private engineering firm then based in Los Angeles, California.

The most ambitious water proposal ever, the Parson's Plan included a comprehensive North American Water and Power Alliance (NAWAPA) embracing Canada, Mexico, and the United States. The plan proposed that the three nations would join efforts to satisfy future water requirements for each of their western regions. It was submitted to the U.S. Senate's special subcommittee on Western Water Development.

Envisioned to carry Tanana and Yukon river waters south into what came to be referred to as the Rocky Mountain Trench—a series of elevated valleys that runs southeasterly along the mid-reaches of the western slopes of the northern Rocky Mountains and extends nearly to the headwaters of the Colorado River—a 500-mile-long reservoir would be created. The reservoir would feed a veritable river, flowing to Nevada, southern California, Arizona, and Mexico.

Exceeding any Bureau of Reclamation or U.S. Corps of Engineers program for water storage and delivery, the Parson's Plan would have moved Tanana-Yukon waters across the Peace and Frazer River Basins of British Columbia.

The Parson's Plan included various interchanges of water supplies where the flow intersected main streams. The massive storage project was envisioned to simplify handling the transfer of water to improve the dependability of supplies.

The NAWAPA even stirred the interest of irrigation profession members as far distant as the Texas High Plains (Llano Estacado, as it was known for centuries by the Mexicans), which by 1965 needed other sources of irrigation water. Their own water source, the Ogallala Aquifer, was fast being depleted through indiscriminate use.

Texas High Plainsmen, excited by the plan's prospects of possible surplus water, invited K.D. McFarland of the Parsons Company to address the West Texas Chamber of Commerce in 1966 to explains the intricacies of the enormous idea.

Irrigation Age, then a prominent magazine in the irrigation industry, came out strongly for NAWAPA. The magazine suggested that if the plan became a reality, West Texas would one day be watering their fields with melted accumulations from distant snow fields and glaciers.

Thus, yet another plan to allay the ever-thirsty West passed by without further notice.

Pacific Coast, his discovery was somewhat unplanned, as his main purpose for entering what proved to be the mouth of a large river was to replenish the ship's fresh water casks.

The river served a number of purposes after its discovery, not the least of which were transportation and a bountiful source of chinook salmon. It was not until the summer of 1918, however, that the Columbia's ultimate service was first discussed in the quiet river town of Wenatchee, Washington.

Three men, Rufus Woods, publisher of the *"Wenatchee World"* newspaper, Billy Clapp, and Gayle Mathews, convened and, in the process, changed the course of Columbia Basin history. In *The Wenatchee World*, they disclosed a Clapp-authored proposal that a serious effort should be mounted to stir interest in the feasibility of building a huge dam across the Columbia River. Although it wasn't without opposition, the idea generated great public interest.

One of the primary forces in the early push for a dam on the Columbia was James O'Sullivan, a lawyer and construction contractor, formerly from Michigan. After arriving in the town of Moses Lake, Washington, he became electrified by the town talk of possibly damming the river and bringing irrigation to the vast Columbia Basin desert. He quickly became the chief figure spearheading the fight to build Grand Coulee Dam.

Shortly after Franklin Roosevelt's election as President in 1932, he unveiled his plan for development of the nation's resources. The plan was primarily a means of relieving unemployment, then plaguing the country in the grips of the Great Depression. Roosevelt included construction of Grand Coulee Dam in the new Public Works Administration Program. On September 9, 1933, a group of dam proponents, led by Frank A. Banks, a Bureau of Reclamation engineer, drove location stakes for the axis of Grand Coulee Dam.

Although irrigation water from Lake Roosevelt, behind Grand Coulee Dam, would not bring new life to some 500,000 acres in the Columbia Basin for another 10 years, first electric power came from the initial dam powerhouse March 22, 1941. The immense flow of power came at just the right time to produce atomic and aluminum products that effectively shortened World War II.

As the time came for Grand Coulee water to irrigate the Columbia Basin, an area larger than the state of Delaware, federal land allotments, yet to be surveyed into 320-acre farm parcels, needed to be populated. Any man and wife, each of "good health and character," with a knowledge of farming and a combined net worth of $3,700 were eligible to apply for a farm. Owners would be selected in a drawing, in which 1,157 units would be available. Married war veterans had first choice.

Columbia River water began flowing into the Columbia Basin on August 10, 1951. Combined with the hard work of those early farmers and their descendants, it turned the forbidding lands into an area whose agricultural production is now surpassed only by that of the great San Joaquin Valley of California.

Along the Mighty Missouri

The Missouri River, the source of which is in the Big Belt Mountains of Montana, meanders north to Great Falls, then follows an easterly course past historic Fort Peck into North Dakota at Williston. From that point, it flows east to Garrison, turning south through South Dakota, then southeast to Sioux City, Iowa. The mighty river borders Nebraska past Omaha to Kansas City and finally flows east through Missouri to its confluence with the Mississippi River, 17 miles upstream from St. Louis.

Comprising a land area equal to one-sixth of the 48 contiguous states, the Missouri River Basin is bounded by the Rocky Mountains to the west and Canada to the north. It extends south to the Arkansas River drainage basin in central Colorado and Kansas, then eastward to the Mississippi. In a vast area with annual precipitation ranging varying from 8 to 42 inches, the Missouri River Basin has a weather pattern that includes cyclical droughts, sometimes lasting several years, as well as floods.

In 1939, the U.S. Congress turned to the Bureau of Reclamation, requesting a plan of relief for the drought-plagued lands of the basin's "Dust Bowl." Four years later, devastating floods in the Missouri River Basin motivated the House Committee on Flood Control to ask the U.S. Corps of Engineers to produce a flood control plan for the area.

Both the Bureau of Reclamation and the U.S. Corps of Engineers prepared all-inclusive, multi-purpose concepts for basin-wide irrigation and flood control. Colonel Lewis A. Pick of the U.S. Corps of Engineers detailed the "Pick Plan." William G. Sloan, assistant regional director of the Bureau of Reclamation's upper Missouri Region, was credited with the "Sloan Plan." Although there had been decades of rivalry between the two federal agencies, Congress called for a common understanding. By authorization of the Flood Control Act of 1944, Congress passed legislation in 1970 recognizing the respective conservation visions of Pick and Sloan. Thus, the Pick-Sloan Missouri Basin Plan was brought into being.

Large dams were initially built under the Pick-Sloan Plan, one in Montana, one in North Dakota, and four in South Dakota. Reservoirs created by those dams inundated 550,000 productive acres in North Dakota alone.

The Garrison Division, largest of all Pick-Sloan Basin units, included Lake Sakakawia behind Garrison Dam on the Missouri River. Lake Sakakawia waters were to irrigate one million acres. However, the first stage flow of water did not fully irrigate 250,000 acres. The Garrison Project never became fully functional. Problems experienced with development of the Garrison unit suggested that it was an exercise in federal government futility in attempting to build a publicly funded irrigation project.

Navigation and hydroelectric power benefits from Garrison were realized in North Dakota. However, the University of North Dakota performed studies that showed the

state suffered agricultural production losses because of the failure at Garrision to complete the 250,000-acre first phase. In addition, it was calculated that the annual production losses from the Lake Sakakawia inundation of 550,000 acres of farm land amounted to $131,000,000 annually in gross volume.

The natural resources of the five-state area encompassed by the Pick-Sloan Missouri Basin Project remain. So too does endless litigation by public-interest forces and a somewhat less tolerable climate than that enjoyed in the Columbia River Basin. Yet great hopes still stand for the ultimate effective use of Missouri River waters.

Building on Success

One the most inspiring irrigation studies is that of successful agricultural developments resulting from the California Water Project. First envisioned by Colonel Robert B. Marshall in 1916, the plan was broadly publicized by the California Irrigation Association. The impressive successes of the Los Angeles Aqueduct had stimulated statewide public interest by that time.

In 1921 comprehensive evaluations of California water resources were ordered by the State Legislature. Innumerable public restraints, mostly over the state's system of riparian water rights and electric power interest objections, blocked progress toward a workable, state-sponsored irrigation plan into the depression years.

The California Legislature unveiled an elaborate Central Valley irrigation plan in 1933. By federal government order, the Bureau of Reclamation was cleared to take over plans for construction in 1935. Work began in 1937 on the Contra Costa Canal.

One of the key structures of the Central Valley Project was 600-foot-high Shasta Dam. The first delivery of stored water from it began in 1951. Celebrations in August that year heralded the long-awaited delivery of water through the Delta-Mendota and Friant-Kern canals, ringing in the crowning achievements of the Central Valley inter-basin system.

Other facilities that made immense impacts on the California State Water Project were the 1967 completion of Oroville Dam on the Feather River and San Luis Dam in the central part of the state. By 1968 the last contracts were signed for full project yield of more than 4,000,000 acre feet per year. The vast California water delivery system accounts for much of the state's tremendous production of fruit and vegetables for national consumption.

Reservation Reclamation Success

Administered by the Bureau of Reclamation, the Navajo Indian Irrigation Project in New Mexico and Colorado is centered around the Navajo Dam on the San Juan River. The dam was completed it 1962. It stores 1,708,000 acre-feet of water to provide irrigation to the Navajo Nation, site of the country's largest Native American reservation.

Headquartered in Farmington, New Mexico, this project delivered the first irrigation water in 1976. The water brought 110,000 acres into production, serving 33,000 Navajos.

Tragedy in a Sterling History

Countless smaller private and public irrigation projects have been built in the last 150 years across the nation. The country west of the Mississippi River includes those vast, arid lands where most of our modern irrigation industry took root, fostering varying degrees of prosperity and failure.

The history of reclamation in the U.S. is primarily one of success. Sadly, however, one of its final chapters concerns a tragic failure.

Authorized by Congress in 1964, Teton Dam, near the town of Rexburg in southeastern Idaho, was not constructed until 1972. It's 17-mile-long reservoir, designed to retain enough water to irrigate 114,000 acres, began to fill in 1975.

Without warning on June 6, 1976, the man-made earthen embankment collapsed, releasing 80 billion gallons of water that wreaked havoc on the Teton River Valley below. Eleven people died and 25,000 were driven from their homes. Property damage was more than $400 million.

The Teton Dam disaster fractured the otherwise perfect, long history of the Bureau of Reclamation in building great American irrigation projects.

A concrete diversion dam on Sand Creek, Keith County, Nebraska.

Courtesy, Department of Water Resources, Nebraska

The thrill of seeing the first great gush of water from a newly developed well in the early 1900s. A massive, flat belt powered by an early oil engine turned this deep-well, line-shaft, vertical turbine pump.

CHAPTER 5

Pumps, Pipe and Power

Pioneers in the pump business, such as Issac Newton Johnston, founder of American Well and Prospecting Company, were part of a fast moving age when inventors and industrialists, such as Cyrus Hall McCormack of reaper fame, photographer George Eastman and the Westinghouse brothers were creating indelible marks on the industrial scene.

Locating underground water for agricultural irrigation is no small feat — nor is bringing it to the surface. Early deep well pumps were powered entirely by wind. Windmill blades spun by steady breezes turned a right-angle reciprocating transmission that worked a "sucker rod." This rod actuated a submerged pump cylinder mounted at the bottom end of a drop pipe. The compact cylinder near the base of the hole pumped water all the way to the surface where it was discharged into a tank. The volume of water this system could pump was limited, but it was adequate for farmers' domestic and livestock needs in the days before the stationary engine and electric power.

Mr. R. K. Wood of Los Angeles, California, built the first vertical deep well rotary pump in 1897. Not long after, more effective vertical line-shaft turbine pumps with multiple impellers encased in a bowl assembly ushered in a new age in lifting underground water. Wood's initial pump design, however, marked the beginning of large volume deep well water pumping.

The deep well vertical turbine pump industry grew from a myriad of individual ideas. As irrigation practices became increasingly refined, the demand for more water from small diameter drilled wells rose. Two of the earliest but most

Model of an Egyptian chain of pots, by which water was pumped from the Nile many centuries ago.

The miracle of water flowing from below the ground. A 1925 Caterpillar powers a belt-driven vertical line shaft turbine pump.

Enforced safety regulations were still a way off as an International engine drove this right-angle gear head vertical turbine pump.

enduring deep well vertical turbine pump manufacturers were Byron Jackson of San Francisco, California, and Mahlon Layne of Houston, Texas. Both men offered their first pumps shortly after 1900.

Deep well vertical turbine pumps evolved into two distinct designs. The "line-shaft turbine" lifts water by driving the pump bowl assembly from surface power transmitted through a steel shaft supported by bearings contained in the discharge pipe. The "submersible" pump, as the name implies, has a turbine bowl assembly attached to a discharge pipe, but with an electric motor mounted below the bottom bowl. Power is transmitted to the submerged motor by a sophisticated watertight cable.

Power for deep well line-shaft vertical turbine pumps was first

supplied by stationary engine-driven, quarter-turn flat belts. Yet the flat belts were troublesome, inefficient, and dangerous. The development of right-angle gear drives made it possible to direct-drive a vertical turbine pump far more efficiently, either with a horizontal electric motor or a stationary engine. Pioneer pump man George E. Green of Plainview, Texas, is credited with applying his mechanical ingenuity in building the first right-angle gear drive for vertical turbine pumps sometime around 1915. Green's initial drive employed the parts of an automobile rear-end differential. In response to the increasing popularity of right-angle gear drives, electric motor manufacturers later offered hollow-shaft motors, which were mounted vertically on the extended pump shaft.

A number of companies began offering this technological advancement. Founded in 1905, Johnson Gear & Manufacturing in Berkeley, California, was noted for pioneering production of right-angle gear drives for vertical turbine pumps. A consistent manufacturer, the company is still recognized worldwide as a standard in the industry, adapting to the specifications of nearly all turbine pump makers.

Amarillo Gear Co., a division of the Michigan-based Marmon Group, Inc., was founded in 1917 as a machine shop and pump builder in Amarillo, Texas. In 1934 the company began specializing in right-angle gear drive manufacturing and dropped pump production. For many years, under the direction of Wesley Johnson, the company was considered to have produced more

Farmer-made pumping unit supplied irrigation water to sprinklers on a South Georgia tobacco farm in the 1940s.

right-angle gear drive units than any other manufacturer.

Long time builder of right-angle gear drives for vertical turbine pumps, Randolph Manufacturing Company of Lubbock, Texas, offered sizes capable of handling up to 500 horsepower. Advertising its products with the slogan, "They Run The Coolest," the factory claimed its units used a patented fan cooling system, dispelling hot air generated by the thrust bearing to the outside of the unit housing.

Stapleton Bros. Machine Co., located in Plainview, Texas, was founded in 1946. The company introduced its right-angle gear drives in 1945 as companion equipment to the vertical deep well turbine pumps it manufactured primarily for the vast southern Great Plains market.

Vertical Turbine Pump Company Development

Not all right-angle gear drive manufacturers were located in Texas. Peerless Pump Co., a division of Food Machinery Corporation (FMC), one of the most prominent vertical turbine pump manufacturers, also made right-angle gear drives for many years.

The story of the introduction, development, and manufacturing of deep well pumps is rich. It involves a number of companies and colorful characters, often intertwined with one another, who helped expand the horizons of North America's industrial and agricultural growth.

Headquartered in Glendora, California, until 1988, Johnston Pump Company was known initially in the pump business as American Well

and Prospecting Company. The company was founded by Issac Newton Johnston, born in 1853. Johnston was part of a fast-moving age when inventors and industrialists such as Cyrus Hall McCormack of reaper fame, photographer George Eastman, and the Westinghouse brothers were creating indelible marks on the industrial scene.

Johnston's early ventures included photography, farm machinery, lumber milling and well drilling. In 1909 he introduced rotary drilling to the California oil fields. The procedure caught on quickly. That year, he also became aware of the vertical turbine pump and the potential it offered for irrigation. The astute Johnston quickly made plans to build his first vertical turbine pump, which was an instant success. His son Jay soon joined him in building a new factory in Vernon, California.

Issac Johnston retired at age 85. Although under different ownership, the company bearing his name prospers today with the same philosophy of sound "attitude and quality" he initiated.

Another enduring name in agricultural irrigation is Western Land Roller Company, founded in 1908 by Mads Anderson of Hastings, Nebraska. Anderson immigrated from Denmark in 1872. As a Nebraska homesteader, his need for irrigation compelled him to build and install a 30-foot-diameter water wheel in the Platte River bordering his farm. A true innovator, he devised a land roller for seed-bed preparation using specially designed roller wheels from Denmark.

By the late 1920s, Western Land Roller Company was making its land rollers, the well-known Bearcat hammermill for grinding grain, and its first low-lift centrifugal pumps. Anderson died in 1931 but by then his sons and grandsons were deeply involved in the company he founded.

The great 1930s mid-continent drought signalled the urgent need for more irrigation water in the plains states. Western Land Roller Company began building a vertical line-shaft turbine pump in 1934. Called the "Western Deep Well Turbine Pump," the product featured a flanged column.

Anderson's great grandsons, Gary and George, carried on the family tradition of quality machinery manufacturing. The family owned the company until 1977, when it was sold to Ingersol-Rand, which continues manufacturing pumps but sold the Bearcat line to other interests.

Founded in Vermont in 1830, the E.P. Fairbanks Company probably made the first cylinder pumps for deep wells. By 1880 the firm was known as Fairbanks-Morse & Company, and was one the most prolific machinery manufacturers of its time. By 1930, the company had embarked into deep well vertical turbine pump production with the purchase of Price Pump and Engine Company of San Francisco. Fifteen years later, the firm purchased the venerable Pomona Pump Company from Joshua Hendy Iron Works, which briefly owned Pomona Pump during the war years. Fairbanks-Morse & Company remained in the vertical turbine pump irrigation field.

In 1985, Colt Industries, which for many years had been the parent corporation of Fairbanks-Morse, sold the pump assets and manufacturing to a group of investors. They renamed it Fairbanks-Morse Pump Corporation. The organization is headed by W. Jackson Letts, chairman and CEO, a longtime employee of Fairbanks Morse, and is headquartered in Kansas City, Kansas.

In 1880, Silver & Deming Company first made shallow and deep well cylinder pumps. The name of the firm was changed to Deming Company in 1890. By 1917, the famous Deming "Marvel Water Systems" were being built. Deming's earliest centrifugal pumps were made in 1929. One year later the company introduced its vertical deep well turbine pumps, with semi-open impellers and water-lubricated line-shaft bearings, to compete with the popular Pomona water-lubricated vertical turbine pumps.

Four generations of the Deming family, from founder John Deming, to Walter F., to George R. and to grandson Walter, piloted the Deming Company until 1961, when it became a division of Crane Company.

Still another prominent name in pumps — and in the history of American irrigation — is that of Henry P. Worthington of Harrison, New Jersey. An inventor of reciprocating pumps, Worthington started his company in 1841. Prior to 1900 he was making side-suction centrifugal pumps. In 1916 Worthington made a vertical deep well pump using what is termed an "Axi-flo" multi-stage propeller combination. In the 1930s, Worthington began manufacturing conventional vertical turbine pumps.

Located in the East, however, Worthington's position in the irrigation pump market lagged until the entire pump division was moved to Denver, Colorado, in 1942. The

An assembled portable irrigation pumping unit. A vacuum line from a hand-operated valve on the exhaust pipe made the Gardner Denver side-suction centrifugal pump self-priming.

New Jersey farmer proudly displays his rugged, close-connected engine-driven, split-case pump unit in 1942.

objective of the move was to be closer to the western irrigation market. In 1950 Wintroath Pump Company of Alhambra, California, bought Worthington Pump Division to broaden its position in western irrigation.

Another historic pump name, Byron Jackson, was established in Woodland, California, in 1872. For better access to materials and shipping, the company relocated to San Francisco in 1879.

The first Byron Jackson deep well vertical turbine pump was built in 1901 for the Pabst Brewery, which engaged the engineering services of

Dr. Elwood Mead, former commissioner of the Bureau of Reclamation, in whose honor the reservoir behind Hoover Dam was named.

In 1904, Byron Jackson installed the first totally submerged turbine pump and motor combination. It was the forerunner of the submersible turbine pump, not to come for another 30 years.

The devastating San Francisco earthquake and fire totally destroyed the Byron Jackson plant. By 1908 it was reestablished in Berkeley, California, where the company operated for 29 years. By then Byron Jackson had acquired the Submers-

ible Pump Company, providing it with the essential mercury seal electric motor to enhance the Byron Jackson turbine bowl assembly for well installations of excessive depths.

In 1951, Byron Jackson Company purchased the A.D. Cook Pump Company of Lawrenceburg, Indiana. The company was basically a vertical turbine pump manufacturer. Borg Warner Corporation purchased Byron Jackson in 1955, at which time Byron Jackson became a division of Borg Warner. In 1966 the division was moved to a massive new facility in Tulsa, Oklahoma, where all Borg Warner production was combined.

The Ideal Pump Company was established specifically to serve the irrigation market. It was founded in 1903 by George E. Green, builder of the first right-angle gear drive for vertical deep well turbine pumps, . By 1909 Green had moved to Plainview, Texas, where he did business as Green Manufacturing Company.

Green died in 1960. The company he founded is now operated by family members and figures prominently in the agricultural growth of the Texas high plains.

The legacy of the famous pump name of Layne and Bowler began with Mahlon E. Layne, who started manufacturing vertical deep well turbine pumps in Houston, Texas, in 1904. Shortly thereafter Layne formed a partnership with P.D. Bowler, Layne and Bowler Company was incorporated in 1907. The Layne and Bowler Company of California was incorporated next in Los Angeles.

Layne bought Bowler's interest in the company in 1916. That year, two of Layne's sons also organized a subsidiary, Layne and Bowler of Memphis, Tennessee.

Both tremendous growth and stormy business years ensued. By 1925, Layne's health was failing and he divided his assets between his wife and three remaining sons.

The Memphis subsidiary went to Layne's son Lloyd and became Layne & Bowler, Inc. Son Leslie was given the Houston operation, which he reincorporated as the Layne & Bowler Company. The Los Angeles branch retained its name and became a foundation to operate for the benefit of Layne's widow and son Ollyn. The company was managed by W.M. Mason. In 1927, Layne died.

The Layne & Bowler family contributed significantly to the advancement of American agricultural irrigation through the years. In 1966, all interests were purchased by the Aurora Pump and Manufacturing Company.

John Halstead, a former Layne & Bowler salesman, and Patrick Vaughn, started a company in 1912 called Western Well Works. It later became Western Pump Company of San Jose, California.

Western Pump Company's deep well vertical turbine pumps were uniquely constructed. In 1920 its water-lubricated column and shaft design included a redwood, line-shaft tubing bearing, a first in the field.

Halstead sold out to Vaughn in 1921. Four years later, Vaughn took in T. Bradford as a part owner. Vaughn died in 1928, at which time Bradford acquired full ownership from the Vaughn estate.

Western Pump Company was sold to Layne & Bowler, Inc., of Memphis in 1962. It continued to function as a division of the firm and was managed by Bradford until he died. His son, Taylor Bradford Jr., continued managing the division thereafter.

John Bean, a historic figure in American agriculture, invented a high-pressure positive displacement pump in 1885. His son-in-law, Mr. Crummey of San Jose, California, founded Bean Spray Pump Company there that same year. Bean Spray Pump Company purchased Caton Foundry and Machine Company in 1912. The superintendent of the acquired company, Franklin B. Waring, had developed a vertical centrifugal pump and certain designs of deep well vertical turbine pumps. The acquisition of Caton Foundry and Machine Company opened the door for Bean Spray Pump Company to get into the deep well vertical turbine business.

In 1929, Bean Spray Pump Company merged with Food Machinery Corporation. In 1933, FMC purchased Peerless Pump Company, which was well-established in turbine pump manufacturing. The John Bean Division was then formed to function as the pump and irrigation segment of FMC.

FMC's John Bean Division purchased Shur-Rane Irrigation Company in 1950. The acquisition provided the John Bean Division with a well-established line of portable, quick-coupling aluminum irrigation equipment to round out its pump line, making it a complete irrigation products manufacturer. After years of promotion and substantial successes in the irrigation industry, the Shur-Rane line was sold to Travis.

Sterling Pump Company of Stockton, California, and South Bend, Indiana, was incorporated in 1907. By 1913, single-cylinder engines and centrifugal pumps were listed as parts of its production. Everett J. Lundy, of the Peerless Division of FMC, was instrumental in the acquisition of Sterling into the Pump Division of FMC.

Sterling turbine pump design was historically significant in that the vertical pump shaft turned clockwise, whereas all other vertical turbine pumps manufactured at the time turned counter-clockwise. Of additional importance were technical studies performed between Sterling engineers and the U.S. Electric Corporation. Working cooperatively, the two organizations devised the vertical hollow-shaft electric motor and discharge assembly, which contained a built-in top motor thrust bearing to carry the entire hydraulic thrust load of the turbine pump. Unfortunately, like many other prominent pump names, Sterling was lost through amalgamation.

Frank J. Kimball, engineer and machinery salesman, operated Frank J. Kimball Company. The firm specialized in compressed air pumps to lift water from deep wells. In approximately 1914, Kimball became convinced that the newest ideas in vertical deep well pumps offered more effective ways of lifting water than compressed air. At that time he developed his own pump version, adapting the old P.K. Wood screw-propeller principal. Kimball called his creation the Kimball Direction Flow, which, despite its considerable ingenuity, was already outdated by the currently accepted vertical turbine philosophy.

In 1929, Krough Pump and Machinery Company merged with Kimball's company to form a Kimball-Krough Consolidation. A

The typical High Plains, Texas Panhandle, mid-century deep well vertical turbine irrigation pumping unit. The natural gas powered engine cooled with well water drives the turbine pump that discharges water into a vertical stand pipe.

much older firm than Kimball's, Krough Pump and Machinery had been in business in San Francisco since 1870, building pumps primarily for the mining industry.

Kimball-Krough was absorbed in 1931 by Victor Equipment Company and functioned as a division until it was sold in 1939 to the Peerless Division of FMC. The solidly established distributor organization of the Kimball-Krough Division proved to be the most valuable acquisition the Peerless Division had yet made. That merger included the transfer of two highly experienced Kimball-Krough pump men, Buford A. Tucker and Ronald Schlegel. Both contributed significantly to the Peerless Division's pump prominence.

American Well Works of Aurora, Illinois, was established in 1868. The company built well drilling machinery. By 1900 it was nationally prominent as a manufacturer of large deep well reciprocating cylinder pumps. By 1930, their first American deep well vertical turbine pump, designed with a 12-inch bowl assembly, was produced. Although well-known as a large-size deep well pump manufacturer for many years, the company

faded from the irrigation industry in the late 1930s.

Named for its founder, A.D. Cook, Inc., began business as a well service firm in 1872. However, by 1913, the Lawrenceburg, Indiana, company was well-known as a producer of deep well reciprocating steam-driven pumps.

Cook's son-in-law, Cornelius O'Brien, became president of the company in the late 1920s. The company soon added vertical turbine pumps to its product line.

O'Brien sold A.D. Cook, Inc. in a series of transactions beginning in 1947. By 1951, the company's line of reciprocating pumps had been acquired by the Red Jacket Manufacturing Company. Subsequently, its vertical pump line and facilities were purchased by Byron-Jackson Company. Thus ended 79 years of the A.D. Cook name in the pump industry.

Two former John Bean Company machinists, William F. Campbell and Frank Budlong, formed Campbell and Budlong, Inc., of San Jose, California, in 1917. The business began as a machine shop and gradually developed a line of deep well vertical turbine pumps. The pumps

employed a specially constructed inner oil tube shaft, using externally threaded couplings. It was a new concept in turbine pumps.

In 1929, Albert Greiner purchased Campbell's interest. Budlong passed away one year later and his interests reverted to his sister. Floyd A. Hanson joined the firm in 1935 and convinced the owners to manufacture orchard spray rigs. That product became known as the Robin Sprayer. In 1944, Gordon Hurst purchased the company, abandoning vertical turbine pump manufacturing and thus ended still another name that had played a significant role in the deep well turbine pump field.

Louis Bodinson of Aurora, Illinois, formally chief engineer of American Well Works, formed Aurora Pump and Manufacturing Company with others in 1920. An experienced vertical turbine pump engineer, Bodinson quickly built the first Aurora deep well vertical turbine pump in large bowl sizes. The pumps sold well in municipal and irrigation applications, mostly in the Southwest.

Aurora Pump Company, as it later was known, was sold to the industrial firm of New York Air Brake Supply in 1952. The deep well vertical turbine pump models were eventually phased out as the company focused on centrifugal and horizontal turbine-vane pumps for the building trades and marine field services.

The development of deep well vertical turbine pump manufacturing in America is intertwined with the inception and growth of the Peerless Hydrodynamics Division of the Food Machinery Corporation over the years, as well as a number of individuals and companies, some of which are previously mentioned in this chapter. Among them is John A. Wintroath, former chief engineer of Layne & Bowler in Memphis. Wintroath and others formed Peerless in Los Angeles in 1929. E.M. Smith, a prominent Los Angeles industrialist, was a principal investor in the new enterprise. After the investors operated Peerless for four years, Smith arranged its sale to FMC, whose John Bean Division was already making vertical turbine pumps. The superior Peerless turbine pump design quickly became the standard for the division's pump production.

Wintroath's tenure with Peerless was brief. In 1929 he left the company and, with others, formed Wintroath Pump Company.

In addition to B.A. Tucker and Ronald Schlegel, other pump industry notables at Peerless included Boyd Kern and W.H. Day. All of these men participated in the Peerless Division's rapid expansion across the country with branches as far east as Elizabeth, New Jersey, and Tampa, Florida.

Pacific Pump Works was incorporated in 1924 by Gaston Bastanchury and George Biglowe. For 23 years, the company manufactured deep well vertical turbine pumps. In 1947, company management decided to shift plant manufacturing to petroleum industry specialty pumps. The combine put its turbine facilities up for sale in 1947 and A.P. Shinn purchased those assets and formed U.S. Pumps, Inc. Twenty years later, U.S. Pumps was sold to Goulds Pumps, Inc., one of the oldest pump manufacturers in the industry, dating back to 1840 when it was originally known as the "Old Stone Shop." That transaction provided Goulds with an avenue for entering into the deep well vertical turbine pump field. It operated Goulds-U.S. Pumps, Inc., with headquarters in Los Angeles for several years, with some manufacturing in Texas. After more than 150 years of operation, Goulds is perhaps the oldest name continuously associated with pumps in America.

Briefly mentioned earlier in this chapter, Pomona Pump of Pomona, California, operated in the early 20th century as a manufacturer of large capacity single-cylinder deep well reciprocating pumps. In approximately 1925, George McKenna, a retired steel industry executive, gained control of Pomona Pump Company and promptly changed its

production under the direction of William H. Day. The new Pomona deep well vertical water-lubricated turbine pump became the company's featured product. Of particular significance for the industry was Pomona's semi-open impeller, which rotated in tapered bowl seats. The entire line shaft was carried on a top thrust bearing built into a hollow-shaft vertical electric motor. The line shaft, secured by an adjusting nut located above the thrust bearing, made it possible to finely adjust the semi-open impellers to the tapered bowl seats to allow maximum pumping efficiency and to adjust for wear caused by abrasives in well water. The line shaft also featured stainless-steel sleeves at the cutless-rubber bearing points in the water-lubricated design.

The McKenna years at Pomona were brilliant, as turbine pump manufacturing went. Company advertising boasted that the water-lubrication concept was so vibration-free that a full glass of water placed on the motor top would stay in place without spilling.

In 1942 after McKenna's death the Pomona Pump Company was sold to Joshua Hendy Iron Works of Sunnyvale, California, which claimed it needed additional factory space to meet World War II commitments. Joshua Iron Works sold Pomona in 1947 to Fairbanks-Morse & Company of Chicago, which continued turbine pump manufacturing in the old Pomona plant until 1963 when all facilities were moved to Kansas City, Kansas. The semi-open impeller, water-lubricated design was continued in the Fairbanks-Morse turbine pump line, although the old Pomona name faded away.

Long a household name, Jacuzzi was first known industrially in 1915 when family members formed Jacuzzi Brothers, Inc. The company made wooden airplane propellers during World War I.

After the war, Jacuzzi Brothers started building the first fully enclosed cabin, high-winged monoplane. The aircraft was powered by a specially equipped Model-T Ford engine. However, the family's plans for becoming a serious contender in

Early three-stage split-case centrifugal pump for higher pressure applications, driven by an 80 hp engine.

Modern deep-well submersible pump. The electric motor, located at the bottom, rotates the pump shaft to draw water into the suction strainer and drive it through multiple bowls.

airplane manufacturing were given up when a disastrous aircraft accident claimed the life of Giocondo Jacuzzi.

Jacuzzi Brothers searched for a new manufacturing path to travel after the accident. The company's research led to a revolutionary approach to using an injector in pressurized water pumping. In 1926 the Jacuzzi deep well jet pump for domestic water systems was introduced. It was a great turning point in the company's history.

Well-established in pump manufacturing by 1932, Jacuzzi Brothers, Inc., built its first deep well vertical turbine. Other highly marketable products that have borne the family name are the Jacuzzi whirlpool bath and hydro-marine power units. Jacuzzi still makes submersible turbines and jet pumps for home water systems. The company's vertical line shaft turbine line was sold in 1988 to Mid-South Pumps in Memphis, where they continued to be offered as "J-Line" pumps.

Wintroath Pump Company of Alhambra, California, was formed in 1929 by John A. Wintroath, Paul Carter, and Boyd Kern — all former board members of the Peerless Pump Company. The name was soon changed to Wintroath Pump, Inc. The company's seasoned engineering and manufacturing professionals accomplished all designing, machining, and production in the first year. The Great Depression years following the 1929 stock market crash took its toll on business and the company struggled.

Wintroath died in 1940. Under the guidance of Boyd Kern, the company prospered both domestically and abroad. The Worthington Corporation purchased all assets of Wintroath Pump in 1950. Although operated as a subsidiary over the following five years, the Wintroath name completely disappeared as all facilities were moved to Denver, Colorado.

J.T. Fiese and W.G. Firstenburger began manufacturing Floway deep well vertical turbine pumps in 1934 in Fresno, California. They began as a general machine shop building pumps

that were immediately accepted in the vast San Joaquin and Sacramento valleys.

All facilities were focused on military production during World War II. After 1948, the sons of Fiese and Firstenburger, Lloyd and Lowell respectively, took over the business. They operated as FloWay Pumps, Inc., and expanded production to include all turbine bowl assembly sizes from four to 24 inches.

In 1959 FloWay Pumps, Inc., purchased the hydraulic division of A.O. Smith Company to enhance the FloWay pump line. By 1968, FloWay Pumps functioned only as a manufacturer using independent sales representatives to sell its line. Eventually, all the firm's interests were sold to Barnes Pump Company.

Berkeley Pump Company was started in Berkeley, California, in 1937. It was formed by four former Byron-Jackson employees: Jack Chambers, Clem Laufenburg, Fred Carpenter, and Fred Stadelhofer. Their initial goal was to manufacture jet pumps primarily for the domestic market, and they succeeded. Three years later, the first deep well vertical turbine pump bearing the Berkeley name was built in six- and eight-inch bowl sizes.

One of the foremost names in irrigation and domestic pumping for more than half a century, Berkeley prospered largely through the efforts, talents, and expertise of Stadelhofer and Laufenburg.

After graduating from the University of California, Laufenburg worked in the Byron Jackson engineering department of Westco Pump Co., a domestic water system builder. Laufenburg became a renowned industry engineer and was a longtime supporter of the Irrigation Association. In 1982 he was honored with the IA Industry Achievement Award for his contributions to the advancement of American irrigation.

Berkeley Pump Company dissolved as a legal entity during World War II and became immersed in war-oriented production of fuel-transfer and submarine pumps. In 1948 the original group of investors and Leon Wilson re-incorporated Berkeley Pump Company. The company's ownership changed in 1982 when it became a division of Trans-America-DeLaval. Four years later all Berkeley Pump Division facilities were sold to Sta-Rite Pump Co. of DeLevan, Wisconsin, where the Berkeley label remains prominent.

Submersible Pump Development

The development of submersible pumps involved significant experimentation and research. Early vertical turbine pump manufacturers worked diligently to determine how an electric motor could be attached to the bottom end of a turbine pump bowl assembly and still function while submersed in deep well water.

The answer came in 1916, during the depths of World War I, from Russian Armis Arutunoff. He sealed an electric motor from water in an oil bath and connected it to the bottom of a turbine pump bowl assembly. The submersed combination was able to lift water from a lower level.

Arutunoff's invention was widely accepted in Russia, but he fled the country during the Communist Revolution. He found his new home, Germany, equally unstable and immigrated to the United States in 1923, where he continued the development of his "Submergible Pump and Motor" combination.

Arutunoff first settled in California, then moved to Bartlesville, Oklahoma, where he set up a factory that made pumps for the oil industry. His efforts there succeeded and he soon began developing a small diameter turbine pump and small-horsepower electric motor assembly that would fit the dimensions of a deep drilled well. In 1946 Arutunoff formed Reda Pump Company and began making small horsepower submersible pumps to fit four-inch wells.

Industry notables including Decatur, A.W. Burke, and Carl Head created multi-stage pumps with air-handling capabilities. Those entities and individuals, and the Jacuzzi Bros., were the forces that brought jet-type pump units into domestic service. Piston-type reciprocating well pumps lost popularity quickly as users learned of the simple, quiet, and vibration-free jet water system.

Centrifugal Pumps: Side Suction, Split-Case, and Self Priming

Early American surface irrigation called for low-head, slow-speed horizontal centrifugal pumps with capacities up to 5,000 gallons per minute. Pioneer manufacturers of these units included Economy Pumps, Inc., of Philadelphia, Pennsylvania; Fairbanks-Morse & Company of Chicago, Illinois; and Johnston Pump Company of Glendora, California. Other companies that followed in making centrifugal pumps were Berkeley Pump Company, Peerless Pump Company, Goulds Pumps, Sta-Rite Pump Co., Jacuzzi Bros., The Gardener Denver Company, and Aurora Pump Company.

One of the most enduring centrifugal pump companies that has had a marked impact on U.S. irrigation growth is the Gorman-Rupp Company of Mansfield, Ohio. The company was founded in 1933 by J.C. Gorman and W.E. Rupp.

Both Gorman and Rupp were experienced in manufacturing and sales. Both had agricultural backgrounds as successful potato farmers in Pleasant Valley, south of Mansfield. They had well-founded concerns about the availability of portable pumping equipment to supply water for quick-coupling sprinkler irrigation systems in periods of drought. They started building pumps in Rupp's barn during the Great Depression, and their combined talents and ideas subsequently revolutionized the pump industry with the introduction of the first self-contained, self-priming pumps.

Gorman-Rupp Company was instrumental in forming the present-day Irrigation Association, which started in 1949 as the Association of Sprinkler Manufacturers (ASIEM). The company's thorough understanding of the industry and its relations with the Irrigation Association naturally evolved into participation by two Gorman-Rupp executives. Both Donald Sanders and Paul Bohley became presidents of the IA, serving in 1971 and 1978 respectively. Going back further, Kenneth Cadigan, Gorman-Rupp sales manager, served in 1949 as one of the first board members of ASIEM.

For more than 58 years, Gorman-Rupp Company has grown and served the irrigation industry. Under the guidance of James Gorman, son of the founder, and headed by grandson Jeff Gorman, the company produces numerous specialized pumps. In addition to irrigation pumps, the company manufactures de-watering pumps, petroleum and aircraft refueling pumps, and fire and municipal waste water reuse pumps.

Another pump giant, Cornell Pump Company of Portland, Oregon, was established in 1946. Clinton Cornell Warren, founder of the firm that bears his middle name, started in the pump business in Portland as a worker and eventually became a branch manager for Pacific Pumping Company.

Warren was formally educated at the College of Idaho, Washington State College, and Oregon Technical Institute. Following World War II, he and four of his associates formed an organization known as Pump Pipe and Power. The firm functioned as a distributor representing well-known manufacturers such as A.D. Cook, U.S. Motors, Byron-Jackson, and Johnston Pumps. The company motto was, "If You Can Pour It We Can Pump It."

In the formative years of Pump Pipe and Power, Warren made substantial public relations inroads. He conducted free pump training schools and received broad industry accolades for his precision in teaching applied hydraulics related to the pump industry.

When Cornell Pump Co. began operations, it established an engineering department and test laboratory. From the beginning, the name Cornell denoted precision manufacturing and innovative design. Warren's end-suction centrifugal pumps embodied unique internal hydraulic balance features and shaft-gland advancements.

As time passed, the company expanded and became departmentalized. Pump Pipe and Power and Water Engineering Consultants, another of Warren's entities, were phased out and came under the Cornell Pump Company banner. The firm also made significant contributions in specialty fluids handling, including waste water, food processing plant materials, cannery wastes, and hot vegetable oils handling and refrigeration. More recently, the company added hydro-turbines for electric power generation to its equipment line.

In 1986 Warren was honored with the Irrigation Association Industry Achievement Award for his pump accomplishments. He is a nationally recognized pump expert credited with many industry "firsts."

When Roper Industries bought Cornell Pump Company in 1978,

Harnessing wind power for over 125 years, Flint & Walling "Star" windmills still pump water in America's vast heartland.

Glenn O. Tribe was elected president of the company. Tribe also became the 32nd President of the Irrigation Association in 1989.

Alternative Pioneer Pumping Method

While advanced pump technology prevails today, there were a number of methods early farmers used to pump and collect water. Wind power, for example, has been used for lifting water for centuries. In fact, the conventional windmill made farming possible on the Great Plains and habitable valleys across America.

Before 1919, windmill diameters ranged from 10 to 25 feet. One manufacturer's 25-foot-diameter windmill, when driven by winds of 35 miles per hour, could lift 40.7 gallons of water per minute from a depth of 100 feet. Clearly, large windmills could discharge acceptable quantities of water for limited irrigation, although system maintenance was significant.

The use of waterwheels declined rapidly as the machine age gained momentum. However, there were a number of noteworthy variations in this early technology.

The Undershot Waterwheel, as its name implies, had buckets installed on the periphery of the wheel that caught the current's flow. The device could lift water, but inefficiently because of spillage, about as high as the wheel diameter, which could be 30 feet.

Overshot Waterwheels were installed so that water flow was directed onto the buckets from the top side of the wheel. Mounted on adequate pillow-block bearings, the wheel shaft extended to accommodate pulleys or gears to transmit water energy to usable power.

The Pelton Wheel is still used in remote areas. It is a totally enclosed rotor-propeller mechanism capable of converting water under high pressure to usable power, primarily for generating electricity. Hydraulic engineering technology, coupled with early field

experiences with machines such as the Pelton Wheel, led to the development of modern-day hydro-turbines for electric power such as equipment manufactured by Cornell Pump Company of Portland, Oregon.

Irrigation Water Wells

Water well construction and pumping are a fixed part of the history of American irrigation, a phase of rural American development sprinkled with intriguing facets.

Revolutionary America was dependent on dug wells, lined or cased with stone or bricks. Water was lifted in buckets by rope and pulley. By 1800 there were only nine municipal water works. Philadelphia was the first city to install cast-iron pipe in its water works.

History indicates that the first rock-bored well in the United States was drilled by David and Joseph Ruffner of West Virginia between 1806 and 1808. To dig their well, they used the ancient Chinese "percussion" or hammering method, which simply meant raising and lowering a chisel-like tool to continually chip and thus deepen the bored hole. The Ruffner's hand-powered drilling machine consisted of a spring pole with a rope tied on the outer end to which the tool was affixed and centered over the hole. That method was used for decades for water well drilling, and was somewhat refined and modified to incorporate the use of animal power.

By 1833 the American Standard drilling rig appeared. It utilized a separate steam engine for power.

The technique of drilling for water was greatly enhanced in 1869 when the first oil well was drilled near Titusville, Pennsylvania. This first commercial well drilling accomplishment stimulated the manufacturing of percussion-type drilling rigs, which were actually improved versions of the Ruffner machine.

Within five years following the Civil War, Henry Kelley and others had formed Kelly-Morgan and Company in Osage, Iowa. The company commercially manufactured the first cable-tool well drilling rig.

In 1879 the Downie Brothers introduced their portable steam-powered drilling machine. Loomis Machine Company, later known as Cyclone Drill Company, built the first self-propelled steam-powered drilling rigs 11 years later.

Even as percussion, cable-tool drilling rigs improved, the concept of rotary drilling was frequently discussed and considered. By 1882 the Baker Brothers had built a rotary rig and began drilling wells near Yankton in the Dakota Territory.

Jerome Haas and James Manning of Stockton, California, were using efficient rotary drilling machines by 1885. The devices employed water under pressure fed through a hose to a hollow drill stem turned by gears.

Rotary drilling came into its own in 1901 when a 1,040-foot-deep hole, soon to be known as Spindletop, first bubbled mud and then, with a tremendous surge, became the first oil "gusher."

Irrigation Water Pipes

Relegated to obscurity now, wood stave pipe made of California redwood or Northwest Douglas fir was a basic water-carrying component for irrigation companies, municipalities, and power entities from 1910 to about 1970.

Perhaps the earliest manufacturer of wooden pipe, National Tank and Pipe Company, traces its beginnings to 1904 in Olympia, Washington. Founders Ralph Lloyd and Hamden Kirsch practiced a primitive procedure for making wooden pipe, which required standing an eight-foot log on end. Suspended from a steel cable, a red-hot steel ball, perhaps six inches in diameter, was then lowered into the exposed log end. The ball burned a hole through the interior length of the log. The bored log was then jigged in a wood lathe and male and female tapers were turned on alternate ends. This made it possible to connect pipe sections as they were laid in ditches

Courtesy, George E. Bartuska, Winter Park, Florida

Cross-section of pipe made with cement and crushed rock by Romans to carry water. Similar pipe was used a century ago to carry domestic water into the San Gabriel Valley of California.

to form continuous conduits, after which the ditches were refilled to secure pipe position.

National Tank and Pipe

The company's Olympia plant was destroyed by fire on July 8, 1908. The company relocated to Portland, Oregon, where better timber and transportation were available.

By 1909 Lloyd and Kirsch had perfected a method for assembling kiln-dried and treated, clear-cut Douglas fir tongue-and-groove lumber into conformed pipe dimensions.

Following World War I, a machine-banding system made wooden pipe diameters from two to 24 inches possible. Because wooden pipe had a smooth internal surface, its coefficient of uniformity was lower than

either cast iron or steel pipe. This development allowed a specific volume of water to flow, creating less friction and resulting in smaller pipe sizes.

As portable overhead sprinkler irrigation came on the agricultural scene in the early 1930s, buried wooden pipe mainlines, with vertical quick-coupling hydrants spaced at 60-foot intervals, became economical to use for supplying sprinkler lateral lines.

National Tank and Pipe Company was sold in 1926 to M & M Woodworking Co. of Portland, Oregon. Thirty years later, the complete wooden pipe manufacturing facilities were sold to Simpson Timber Company. The wooden pipe manufacturer operated as a division of Simpson Timber, but was losing its identity as National Tank and Pipe.

Sample section of four-inch Douglas fir pipe made by National Pipe & Tank Company.

In 1974 Willharp interests purchased all assets of the division and the National Tank and Pipe product identity was restored, while still operating at the original plant location. The company's facilities were relocated to Clackamas, Oregon by 1977. Although all machinery for wooden pipe manufacturing continued to be operational, regular production was suspended soon thereafter.

Many city water works of the West still serve their customers with water that flows through wooden stave pipes that have been in the ground for decades. With the advent first of asbestos-cement, Transite pipe, and the more adaptable,

lightweight, and easy-to-install plastic poly vinyl chloride (PVC) pipe, wooden pipe became yet another fading memory in irrigation water handling history.

Aluminum for Irrigation

High-purity aluminum is a soft, light, and ductile metal with excellent corrosion resistance. The first process for producing aluminum was devised in 1854.

The potential for high-volume production of aluminum can be traced to the late 1930s when the great Columbia River hydro-electric dam projects, Bonneville and Grand Coulee, went on-line to produce

previously untold quantities of inexpensive electric power. By 1941 this bountiful available power drew the big aluminum companies, Alcoa, Reynolds, Kaiser, and Harvey to construct massive reduction plants. By 1942 the inertia of this production was turned to the World War II military effort. As the war ended, aluminum production for civilian consumption burgeoned.

Aluminum tubing was soon made by several extrusion processes including drawn seamless, seamless extruded, butt-welded, formed sheet, and coil-strip welded. Initial aluminum pipe offerings were available in three-, four-, and six-inch diameters. Oaks Irrigation and Manufacturing Company of Pharr, Texas, received the first car load of extruded aluminum tubing for use in portable sprinkler systems in April of 1946.

The development of Minimum Standards for Aluminum Irrigation Tubing, ASAE S263.3, was achieved by joint committee accord of the American Society of Agricultural Engineers and The Sprinkler Irrigation Association in January 1957. That action was testimony to the importance of aluminum in irrigation applications.

The use of aluminum tubing in portable sprinkler irrigation exploded from that first shipment in 1946, with massive yearly increases through 1975. Much of this growth was due to the development of desert lands, enhanced by the Desert Entry and Homestead Acts of the U.S. Government.

Aluminum tubing is still an important part of irrigation. However, with the exceptions of center pivot and linear machines, PVC has overtaken aluminum for solid-set, drip-trickle, micro-spray systems.

RIGHT:
Lightweight aluminum pipe was a great help to the portable sprinkler irrigation industry. Three men move 120 feet of 5-inch aluminum lateral without uncoupling at a Valdosta, Georgia farm in 1949.

Early Irrigation Power Forms

The hydraulic ram, all but forgotten today, was a domestic life-saver to pioneer settlers as they carved out homesteads and farms.

The hydraulic ram was a means of raising water by induced natural available water pressure, completely independent of any other power. It functioned through a series of pipes, valves, and air chambers constructed to force a limited volume of water, induced by another water source under high pressure, to yet another higher point.

Arthur P. Davis and Herbert W. Wilson, former Reclamation Service and U.S. Geological Survey engineers, reported that a battery of hydraulic rams plumbed together in a series, and timed so that their individual pulsations did not coincide, could deliver a continuous flow of water at high efficiency ratings. Just such an early-day installation near Yakima, Washington, functioned at an efficiency of 71 percent.

Installed near Seattle, Washington, two 12-inch rams, using a water delivery head of 47.8 feet (20.78 psi) operating at 32 cycles per minute, delivered 435 gallons per minute (1.080 cubic feet per second) to an elevation of 135.9 feet. The efficiency rating was 82.3 percent.

Perhaps the strangest of all early water devices was the H.A. Humphrey "Direct Explosion" pump. In a system of very large pipes, valves, and machinery housed in a concrete pump house, air and natural gas were force under high pressure into a chamber by a two-cylinder compressor. One cylinder handled air and the other handled natural gas.

The air-gas mixture was fired by an electric spark. All valves were closed until the instant of explosion, which forced water downward into a massive discharge pipe open to the atmosphere. The column of water attained kinetic energy at the instant of explosion, when work was being done by detonated gases. Thus, a flow was energized that could be complimented by repeating the dramatic cycle.

In about 1909 one such device was installed at great cost near Del Rio, Texas. It lifted 26,940 gallons of water per minute (60 cubic feet per second) to a height of 37 feet from the Rio Grande River, downstream from the present-day site of the Amistad Dam. It was reported that the Del Rio pump installation averaged 12 complete cycles per minute, the repercussions of which, occurring every five seconds, must have seemed to someone standing a reasonable distance away like a reenactment of the Mexican and Spanish-American Wars.

Courtesy, Jack Liddell, Delta Irrigation

Reclaimed water irrigates the local zoo, parks, school grounds, golf courses and other turf areas in Santa Barbara, California.

CHAPTER 6

Wastewater Reuse

*Strong support for wastewater irrigation in the United States
returns after a century-long policy of treat-and-release.*

$\mathcal{G}$iven the world's finite natural resources, water in particular, resource recovery has become a national and international imperative. However, the study and practice of sewage wastewater reuse and recycling is anything but new. History records references to "sewage farming" in about 1800 in Great Britain. Sanitary reformer Sir Edwin Chadwick believed the sale of urban sewage to farmers would pay the costs of maintaining urban sewage systems.

Early construction of sewage systems in United States cities also prompted interest in sewage farming, or "broad irrigation" as it was called, as a means of dispersal of sewage. In the 1870s urban sewage was being treated and used to grow crops such as small grains, legumes, potatoes, and orchard trees.

The first national water pollution control act was passed in 1889. Since then, uncounted studies of the efficient use of the nation's resources have been generated. The U.S.

philosophy of resource use is one phase of a current national public trend toward the nation becoming a "recycle society" in which virtually all materials are reused indefinitely.

Courtesy, Weathermatic

Texas wastewater treatment plant
utilizes effluent to irrigate its turf.

In 1972 the U.S. Congress passed legislation that became the first strong tool to encourage recycling, including the application of sewage to the land. Five years later, the "Clear Water Act" strongly endorsed land treatment with sewage effluent.

History supports the contention that municipal and industrial wastewater is too valuable a resource to publicly disregard. From the beginning of irrigation practice, some individuals recognized the benefits of this inexpensive water and nutrient source. Others to this day remain unconvinced that the benefits outweigh the possible risks.

Although records of the practice of "soil filtration" to dispose of liquid wastes date back in the U.S. to 1900, use of the method itself dates back to Colonial times.

Sewage farming in the U.S. dates back 150 years in the this country. By 1918 more than 30 towns and cities in the West were practicing sewage irrigation.

The increasing demand for more and varied uses of a limited water supply places increased emphasis on planned reuse as one reasonable option. Wastewater reuse has become a necessity in much of the U.S. for two reasons. The first reason is that the practice is practical and necessary to meet water needs in regions where the demand has exceeded the ready supply. This is more common west of the Mississippi River, but is also becoming a reality in other regions.

The second reason for practicing water reuse is the need to curtail the pollution caused by wastewater discharged into lakes, rivers, and streams. Wastewater reuse to reduce pollution is more common east of the Mississippi River.

The combination of wastewater reuse to supplement water supplies and curtail water pollution has experienced a resurgence of interest throughout the nation since about 1960. History has a way of repeating itself, and the U.S. approach to managing wastewater is a classic example.

Courtesy, Hunter Industries, Inc.

Discharge of treated effluent into lakes, rivers and oceans is falling into disfavor as a result of environmental pressure.

Using wastewater in irrigation, a method that recycles plant nutrients, was popular throughout the world near the end of the 19th Century. In the United States, the practice fell into disfavor in the early 1900s and remained there until the environmental movement of the 1960s.

Worldwide Reuse Prior to 1890

Reports of the first wastewater irrigation system date back to the 15th century. However, substantial written documentation of this practice prior to the 1850s is scarce. To better understand the situation of the times in the latter half of the 19th century, it's important to recognize that the sewage systems we take for granted today did not exist before 1850. Sanitation practices changed dramatically by the turn of the century.

Sewage farming's popularity peaked around 1890. A book on sewage treatment by Slater, published in 1888, indicated that irrigationists and "filtrationists" (proponents of soil filtration for wastewater treatment) dominated important safety meetings of the time. Proponents of treating wastewater for discharge into lakes, rivers, and streams seemed to be supporting a less popular approach. These supporters of biological and chemical treatment of sewage waters argued their case based on economics and the ease of protecting public health with government requirements. Strong support for wastewater irrigation began to give way as more sanitary scientists agreed that treatment and discharge were better. This scientific debate was closely watched by sanitary and governmental agencies that were already on the threshold of important sanitary science decisions in the United States. Thus, as the 20th century dawned, a state of uncertainty and change prevailed regarding wastewater use.

U.S. Reuse Decline

The heated debate among many sanitary scientists in the late 1800s did not go unheeded by the U.S. Government. The newly established U.S. Geological Survey was directed to conduct a comprehensive survey of sewage disposal practices as one of its first assignments.

The results of sewage disposal practices in Europe and the U.S., which were published in 1897 and 1899, reflected the strong support for wastewater irrigation that had dominated scientific thinking in the 1890s. The principal investigator and author, G.W. Rafter, concluded that wastewater irrigation was the preferred technology because it would protect lakes, rivers, and streams from pollution while benefitting agriculture. He also believed that purification of sewage by applying it to the land was less costly to a community.

Rafter's conclusions did not hold sway with the mainstream of scientific thinking at the time. Most U.S. scientists and engineers took the position that health risks and other limitations made sewage irrigation impractical. "Treat and discharge" was to become the preferred U.S. sewage water management technology for the next 50 years.

The greatest decline in sewage irrigation was clearly in the eastern U.S., with a drop from 18 facilities in 1899 to five in 1910 and a slight increase of one per year in the next 58 years. Conversely, there was an increase in sewage irrigation in the West where the need to conserve and utilize precious water blunted the stampede for the treat and discharge philosophy. The technique of using liquid chlorine economically for killing bacteria in drinking water was just beginning to be practiced.

Rediscovering Wastewater Reuse

Renewed interest in wastewater reuse began in the 1960s, and the principal driving force behind that interest was the environmental movement. It was clear that the diminishing dilution capacity of lakes, rivers, and streams, which had seemed unlimited to mainstream scientists and engineers in 1910, was already overloaded some 50 years later. Drastic steps to rejuvenate the quality of surface water had become imperative.

The Federal Water Pollution Control Act of 1972 provided further incentives designed to prod the sanitary profession into quicker, more realistic action. The law was again amended in 1981 to extend this strong federal support for reuse through the 1980s.

The impact of revitalized, ongoing federal support of wastewater reuse in agriculture was dramatic. This support was observed by tracking wastewater management projects, which the Environmental Protection Agency listed as "land treatment" systems. The number of projects in use in 1940 was 300. By 1982 that number had grown to 1,280.

The status of wastewater reuse today, after 100 years in America, recalls that of the 1880s. In approximately one century, the popularity of wastewater reuse has come full circle. Current popularity of the philosophy is equal to the interest of 1890.

Because present-day lakes, rivers, and streams can no longer be burdened with still greater loading of sewage, modern scientific understanding points to an ever-increasing use of sewage land treatment projects. With the U.S. population currently four times greater than it was in 1900, and still growing, it is easy to foresee public demand for state-of-the-art water reuse advances.

Since 1980 the U.S. has seen a reentry into an era of conservation, reuse, and recycling. Bakersfield, California; Lubbock, Texas; Calumet, Michigan; and Lake George, New York, which have used land treatment for decades, are striking examples of communities that have reused wastewater with great success. The Bakersfield project is a study of successful use of wastewater to profitably irrigate cash crops. A Clayton County, New York, land treatment project irrigates a forest

Incentives for wastewater reuse combined with shortages of potable water, have encouraged golf course developers to use recycled water for irrigation.

with sewage effluent in the watershed of a domestic supply reservoir, thereby enhancing the dependability of that community's water source.

One of the oldest wastewater reuse agreements in the U.S. occurred in 1937 between Lubbock, Texas, then a small town, and Frank Gray, a local farmer and chairman of the Texas Soil and Water Conservation Board. Although Lubbock has grown to a city with a population of more than 225,000, even then it generated in excess of 20 million gallons per day of secondary treated sewage effluent, which is high in nitrogen, phosphorus, and potash. Gray used the effluent to irrigate approximately 5,000 acres.

Lubbock's ultimate rapid growth out-paced Gray's need for irrigation

water. Additional large, newly prepared areas on which to apply wastewater effluent were built to accommodate the city. The treated lands were used to grow worthwhile crops.

A completely biologic wastewater land treatment project near Wayland, Michigan, was started in 1968. The project was designed to accommodate the sewage water generated from a potential community of 5,000 people. The system consisted of an aeration pond and two 15-acre lagoons that received 300,000 gallons of raw sewage per day. After being held 48 hours, the sewage was transferred to 30 acres of holding ponds. Chlorine was then added, and the sewage water was pumped into overhead sprinkler

irrigation systems that constantly applied four inches per week to 130 acres. Both a center pivot machine and a traveling, large capacity sprinkler head applied the biologically treated sewage effluent to lush crops of timothy, alfalfa, and clover.

A more recent example of the cooperation between municipal and agricultural interests regarding wastewater reuse can be found in Northglenn, a suburb of Denver, Colorado. A victim of expansive urbanization, the suburb receives quality, Rocky Mountain spring snow melt water from the Farmers Reservoir and Irrigation Company (FRICO). Facing the specter of water shortages and higher water prices as its population increased, Northglenn aligned with FRICO to develop an innovative conservation program. Under the original town water company agreement, much of the water stored in Standey Lake, the FRICO reservoir, was originally released directly to irrigators in the area. Under the new arrangement, all domestic and irrigation water goes first to Northglenn for municipal use. The town then collects, treats and stores the water in a specially built winter holding reservoir until it is needed for spring irrigation.

Municipal Sewage Treatment Processes

To fully understand "sewage irrigation" and other wastewater (effluent) and land treatment practices, it's important to have a working knowledge of municipal plant sewage treatment processes.

The characteristics of wastewater are classified as:

1. *Physical* (the total solids-content including floating, suspended, colloidal, and dissolved matter).

2. *Chemical* (the degree of organic and inorganic matter contained therein).

3. *Biological* (microorganisms, which are predominantly bacterial).

Wastewater sewage plant processing is mostly classified as primary, secondary, and tertiary (or advanced) treatment. Primary treatment results in the removal of solids, those that sink or float, and approximately 30 percent of the suspended solids, which leaves a somewhat milky appearing effluent. Secondary treatment is the reduction of bio-chemical oxygen demand (BOD) and suspended solids, usually through biological action, followed by sedimentation. Both primary and secondary effluents are chlorinated to destroy pathogenic bacteria. Tertiary treatment, not usually employed when wastewater is to be applied in irrigation land treatment, is intended only to produce a higher quality effluent.

Chlorinated effluent still contains approximately 70 percent BOD. However, the bacteria count has been greatly reduced and the liquid is almost clear.

Waste-activated sludge from sewage treatment is the resultant, largely inert mass finally drained of moisture. It is classified as a sewage by-product.

Perhaps the most graphic and far-reaching example of sludge disposal is the system employed for decades by Chicago, Illinois. From this gigantic operation of sewage treatment and disposal, the city's sludge is barged some 200 miles to reclaimed, open-pit coal field land in Illinois, where it is off-loaded into lagoons. After a holding period, the sludge, in heavy liquid form, is distributed over the vast reclaimed land through conventional overhead sprinkler irrigation systems. Primary crops of field corn and alfalfa grow abundantly on the otherwise marginal land.

Sludge, as it relates to agricultural use, contains about one-fifth the amounts of nitrogen, phosphate, and potassium found in commercial mix chemical fertilizers. The values of sludge in open farming are contained in its contents — organic slow-release nitrogen and other organic matter that improves the physical properties of the soil. The most widely known sludge product, Milorganite, is a combination of sludge and other particles. It is produced by the City of Milwaukee, Wisconsin, and is sold throughout the U.S. for use on lawns, gardens and golf courses.

Public knowledge of wastewater reuse, i.e, land treatment, focuses largely on sewage products from municipal sewage plants. States that produce the largest quantity of dairy products, meat, and processed fruit and vegetable products have long practiced land treatment using sewage effluent. Nearly all farmers in Wisconsin and California, the two largest dairy product states, return animal wastes to the soil in a high crop-yield cycle that, by any standard, illustrates efficient reuse of recycling.

Wastewater reuse helps protect precious water resources from pollution and depletion. In terms of land treatment effluent dispersal through overhead sprinkler systems, it is one of America's best defined public-use technologies. The nation's clean and clear lakes, rivers, and streams mirror these advancements, accomplished by sewage handling to the land, all for the betterment of the people and their agricultural pursuits.

BELOW: Phase I pump station at El Estero Wastewater Treatment Plant in Santa Barbara, California, irrigates approximately 272 acres with reclaimed wastewater.

Courtesy, CH2M HILL

First known turf irrigation controller made and patented by
Hadden Automatic Sprinkler Company of Los Angeles in 1916.

CHAPTER 7

Auxiliary Irrigation Equipment

As the value of regulated water application to beautify lawns was recognized, equipment advances flourished.

*B*etter ways of mechanically irrigating turf areas came about as early as 1913. As the value of regulated water application to beautify lawns was recognized, equipment advances flourished. They included fixed-spray and revolving-arm sprinkler heads for large-area coverage. These products were soon followed by labor-saving controllers and remote-control buried valves for programmed watering.

Turf irrigation history studies reveal that the term "automatic," as related to lawn sprinkler systems, was used before World War I. William A. Buckner, the pioneer sprinkler manufacturer, installed the first "hoseless" overhead sprinkler system on a golf course in 1912.

By 1913, Hadden Automatic Sprinkler Co. of Los Angeles, California, advertised "Systems, Valves, and Sprinklers for Turf Irrigation." The exact date Hadden began manufacturing is unknown, but the Hadden nameplate appeared on a hydraulic-actuated controller in about 1917. A production unit of this, the earliest known irrigation controller, is part of the fine irrigation product collection of Robert Cloud's Associated Consultants of Los Angeles. Cloud is recognized as one of the city's earliest irrigation contractors, dating back from approximately 1949.

Courtesy, Bob Cloud, Associated Irrigation Consultants

Pendulum clock activates early sprinkler irrigation controller, circa 1917.

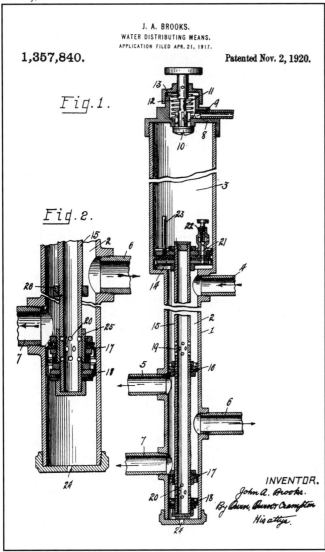

J. A. BROOKS.
WATER DISTRIBUTING MEANS.
APPLICATION FILED APR. 21, 1917.

1,357,840.

Patented Nov. 2, 1920.

Fig. 1.

Fig. 2.

INVENTOR.
John A. Brooks.
By Munn, Gunor Crompton
His attys.

Sprinkler irrigation controller designed by John A. Brooks in 1917. A controller like this still functions at the Fairlane Estate in Dearborn, Michigan.

John A. Brooks Irrigation Company of Detroit, Michigan, is listed among the earliest turf irrigation companies. Inventor and company founder John A. Brooks designed his first sprinkler system controller and applied for a patent in 1917. The patent, number 1,357,840, was granted in 1920.

Following World War I, an irrigation device known as the Burdick "Scotch Watchman" Time Valve entered the market in Anaheim, California. Undated literature describes how the product functioned: "The control cylinder governs the opening and closing of the valve.

To open, turn control key position to (0), on the indicator, this allows valve water to discharge from above the piston to atmosphere, allowing the piston to be carried to the top of the cylinder by line pressure. To close the valve at a predetermined time, turn the key clockwise to any position from (1) to (4), on the indicator. When set in position number 1, the valve will close in thirty minutes, number 2, twenty minutes, number 3, ten minutes, number 4, five minutes. The exhaust to atmosphere is now closed and the by-pass is open to the top of the piston, thus equalizing the pressure within the cylinder."

Although the description of its function was somewhat lengthy, the Burdick valve brought turf irrigation a step closer to automation.

In the early 1920s George E. Moody made his first controller. Manually started, as was the Burdick time valve, it made programming possible thereby sequencing remote controlled irrigation valves. Like the innovative products of Brooks, Moody's controller and his companion valves and sprinkler heads successfully introduced turf sprinkler irrigation to the densely populated areas across the nation, more than 20 years before real turf irriga-

tion expansion became appealing to the American public.

Superior Controls Co., Inc., of Los Angeles, California, originally known as Superior Regulator Co., was purchased and reformed by Powell and Allen Greenland in 1949. Prior to reincorporation, the company specialized in diaphragm controls for gas-fired steam boilers. The Greenlands were attracted to the developing turf and landscape irrigation market as an ideal format for applying their firm's expertise in control valve design.

A yet uninformed buying public was slow to recognize the merits of turf irrigation automation in the early days following World War II. Superior's first solenoid-equipped, diaphragm-operated remote control hydraulic sprinkler valve caught on slowly. Finding contractors capable of installing automatic electric irrigation systems was also difficult. In the earliest days of buried electric systems, the only equipment available used 120-volt AC current. Raising consumer awareness of automatic sprinkler irrigation was the Greenlands' greatest marketing challenge.

Superior made the first electric adaptor for use on manual irrigation valves in 1950. The product was a major stepping stone for the firm, as well as the automatic sprinkler irrigation industry. From that point forward, a new generation of irrigation contractors entered the field as they developed a detailed understanding of automatic sprinkler systems. Superior's electric valve adapters became an industry standard.

Powell Greenland recalled that the introduction of plastic pipe, faulty as it was, in the immediate years following the Korean War was a milestone for the turf and landscape industry. Despite rough beginnings and still unresolved problems with plastic pipe in irrigation, its successful use "fused" the industry.

Now located in Valencia, California, Superior Controls Co., Inc., is more than 40 years old. Allen Greenland's son, Richard, is an associate with the company.

Waterman Industries, Inc., of Exeter, California, is distinguished as being the oldest continuously family-owned and operated manufacturer of agricultural surface-irrigation equipment. Company founder W.A. Waterman started a sheet metal shop to fabricate small water distributing gates in 1912.

That pivotal year witnessed new advancements in land leveling, which enhanced water handling techniques for surface irrigation. It was also the year Benjamin Holt's Caterpillar tractor was introduced. Waterman chose an ideal time to enter California's imminent agricultural irrigation equipment boom.

Demand for Waterman's products increased steadily. In 1920 he expanded his shop facilities and formally adopted the name W.A. Waterman Company. He was then prepared to make brass and galvanized steel irrigation gates and valves, which were by then increasingly used in California's Sacramento and San Joaquin valleys.

Also in 1920, Waterman purchased the facilities of Red Top Valve and Argo Vine and Sill Company. These acquisitions made it possible for him to build and machine cast-iron valves and gates in addition to his fabricated models.

The company continued its strong growth. By 1940, 30 people were employed there including Waterman's three sons and his son-in-law. Waterman died in 1943, at which time his son Herrick assumed control of the company.

The firm was incorporated as Waterman Industries, Inc., in approximately 1945. Plans were made for the construction of a grey-iron foundry and accompanying pattern shop. Construction began in 1948.

In 1989 Waterman built a large modern production factory and office complex in the countryside near Exeter. The expanded manufacturing capabilities enabled Waterman to build giant water handling fixtures in diameters up to 144 inches. The company also produced a full line of air vents,

pressure-relief valves, and check and butterfly valves.

Herrick Waterman, chairman of the board of Waterman Industries, was honored in 1981 by the Irrigation Association with its "Industry Achievement Award." After Waterman passed away at age 82, his step-son Donald L. Appling assumed management control of Waterman Industries, which for more than 75 years has been an industry pioneer.

Cla-Val Co. of Newport Beach, California, has a history dating back to the first Clayton valve made in 1936. The valve came about when company founder Donald G. Griswold designed a unique float valve to improve the operation of the Clayton Steam Cleaner, made by William Clayton. The two men were so impressed with the first Clayton valve and the potential for its use in the waterworks industry that they formed Clayton Manufacturing Company, where by 1939 many automatic control valves were designed, tested and sold.

New and particularly useful controls were developed for water softeners and semi-automatic turf sprinkler irrigation systems. By 1940 valve sizes ranged from 3/8-inch to

Waterman solar-energized irrigation valve controller.

16-inch diameters. During World War II, Clayton Valves pioneered the design of controls and valves that automatically removed water from aircraft gasoline. Until then, aircraft fuel contaminated with water had been a harrowing, deadly problem for the U.S. Air Force.

In 1947 Clayton concentrated solely on his company's line of steam generators and cleaners and relinquished control of the valve business. Griswold assumed complete valve manufacturing activities and renamed his organization Cla-Val Co. in 1948. After more than 50 years, the empire Griswold developed into Cla-Val has remained a premier valve builder that serves all facets of waterworks, turf and irrigation, and specialty control segments of industry.

Fresno Valve and Castings, Inc., of Selma, California, was founded in 1951 by O.R. "Dick" Showalter. The company's history "expanded" when Showalter purchased Martin Iron Works in 1958.

Located in Los Angeles, California, Martin Iron Works had manufactured "Modern Irrigation Appliances" since 1900. The company's 1929 catalog stated, "For 30 years we have successfully solved the problems and fulfilled the needs of the

The Burdick time valve was used in the 1920s as a labor saver .

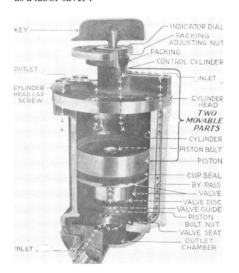

irrigators of California and the western United States. At the present time, our products are in use in 21 countries throughout the world."

Before 1917, Martin Iron Works was part of an even older company, Kellar-Thomason Co., which designed and manufactured irrigation appliances and cement machines primarily for making concrete pipe. Founder George Kellar was an irrigation equipment manufacturer who held patents that dated back to the late 1890s.

The Kellar-Thomason "K-T" trademark was cast in the top of its KT Orchard Valve for controlling water discharging from concrete pipe, and was possibly one of the earliest valves of its kind. The K-T Dumping Batch Mixer was powered by one of the first vertical single-cylinder engines.

Fresno Valve and Castings remains a primary irrigation product manufacturer.

Soil Moisture Measurement

Instrumental measurement of soil moisture has evolved into a vital requirement for planning, programming, and practicing irrigation, whether or not it is supplemental to rainfall. The earliest recorded account of measuring electrical resistance between electrodes buried in the soil, a method which is used to then extrapolate soil moisture, comes from laboratory studies and field tests performed by F.D. Gardner in 1898.

The first reference to the movement of water in the soil that proposed "capillary potential function" is from E. Buckingham, USDA Bureau of Soils Bulletin #38 dated 1907. However, Willard D. Gardner and co-workers at Utah State College in Logan, Utah, were among the first to tie this fact of soil-water physics to a method of actually measuring the force by means of a porous cup and vacuum gauge (tensiometer). Various terms used to describe this

physical force include suction, pressure deficiency, capillary tension, soil moisture tension, and matrix potential.

In 1925, one of Gardner's undergraduate students, Lorenzo A. Richards, began field-soil moisture measurement studies in the Gardner laboratory. His work focused on the tensiometer and other methods of soil moisture measurement. In 1946 Dr. Richards introduced the "Lark," the first commercially produced tensiometer, through Instrumental Development Corporation in Riverside, California. The product's name was

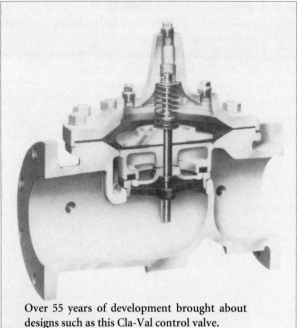

Over 55 years of development brought about designs such as this Cla-Val control valve.

derived from Richards' initials plus the letter K.

In the mid-1930s, Dr. George J. Bouyoucos of Michigan State College perfected the Bouyoucos Moisture Meter. It consisted of electrodes embedded in a cast block of porous material. The porous block improved the contact between the soil-water environment and the electrodes. The "gypsum block" concept was born and was thereafter referred to in the irrigation industry as the "Bouyoucos Block."

From that time forward, many types and combinations of materials

were experimented with and called "The Porous Body, Electrical Resistance Method." The goals of the research and development were to improve both the life expectancy of the block and its sensitivity to changes in electrical resistance, particularly in the moist soil range below 80 centibars.

The Bouyoucos Block method was only favorable for use in soils that had suction values above 80 centibars. In contrast, tensiometers functioned accurately in soils with suction values below 80 centibars.

A number of companies have produced gypsum blocks. The most prominent of these includes G.F. Larsen Co. in the West and Delmhorst and Beckman Instruments in the East.

Grower interest in detecting a crop's wilting point and related plant stress before yield and quality were affected, generated increased interest in tensiometers. The Lark tensiometer was soon followed by Richards "Hydrostat" invention. The unit was perhaps the original "switching" moisture sensor whose function was based on the tensiometer principle. The Hydrostat was designed for control of underground lawn sprinkler irrigation systems equipped with electrically actuated hydraulic valves.

Edwin J. Hunter organized the Moist-O-Matic Corporation in Riverside, California, primarily to develop the Richards Hydrostat. The device made it possible to maintain proper soil moisture for adequate plant growth, regardless of climatic conditions, simply by overriding the irrigation system.

Another extensively used moisture meter was the Irrigage, manufactured by Rayturn Corporation, a division of W.R. Ames Co., of Portland, Oregon. The Irrigage was an electrical resistance-type instrument that employed electrodes encased in a tapered cast-porous probe. A portable alternating current ohmmeter measured resistance at each probe. However, the Irrigage required several components to function, which made it unable to compete with tensiometer simplicity.

In the early 1950s another inventor in Riverside, Thomas W. Prosser, introduced the Irrometer tensiometer. His first sales manager was Sheldon G. Pooley, who later purchased the company. Pooley, now deceased, became a pillar in the irrigation industry. He presented a paper on tensiometers at the winter meeting of the American Society of Agricultural Engineers in 1973. He noted in his paper that the three greatest influences on the use of tensiometers were high water costs, the desire to improve crop yield and quality and the value of the crop.

In 1980, the Larson Company of Santa Barbara, California developed an electrical resistance type of sensor. Named "Watermark," the device was designed to increase sensor service life as well as provide accurate readings in the lower soil suction ranges. The device overcame two principle disadvantages of the gypsum block concept of soil moisture measurement. The Watermark was subsequently purchased from Glenn F. Larson by the Irrometer Company. Since Pooley's death, the Irrometer Company has been managed by William Pogue, 31st president of the Irrigation Association.

Manufacturing Expansion Continues

CMB Industries of Fresno, California, has manufactured high-quality valve products for more than 75 years. The company became a front-running irrigation name in 1980 when it purchased the entire Febco vacuum-breaker-valve line from Johns-Manville Corporation.

Charles M. Bailey incorporated the business under his name in 1923 in San Francisco, California. His firm made specialty industrial valves that quickly gained prominence, even during the Depression of the 1930s.

Bailey died soon after World War II. His widow continued control of the company with several competent managers until she passed away in 1976. In the interim, the company had moved to Emeryville, California.

In 1970 a fortuitous trade show meeting brought Carroll Wood of General Sprinkler Company, at that time owners of the Febco Valve line, together will Ralph Krogfoss of Charles M. Bailey Company. Their meeting resulted in a plan to include Febco brass products in the Bailey catalog.

In 1985, Charles M. Bailey Company purchased the Febco line of products and moved to a new property in east Fresno, California. Also that year, the company changed its name to CMB Industries to facilitate marketing of the Bailey-Febco product lines.

More than 40 years ago, the Eaton Corporation, Controls Division, Plumbing and Heating Department, of Carol Stream, Illinois, unintentionally became a supplier to the irrigation industry. The company's irrigation market entry was due entirely to layout and design plans done by irrigation specialists who devised a way of evening sprinkler head discharge pressure on steep hillside installations with Eaton's Dole Flow Control.

Primarily manufactured for the plumbing trade, the simple Dole Flow Control consists of a pliable contracting orifice contained in a metal body. It reacts to increasing pressure by reducing the orifice opening, thereby controlling the discharge pressure of a sprinkler head nozzle. The Dole Flow Control has been used for decades to control flow in fluctuating pipeline pressure conditions.

Conventional impact-drive, low capacity orchard sprinkler heads around 1950 were built with 1/2-inch male threaded bases that required a pipe coupling to join them to 1/2-inch orchard riser pipes. Although the Dole Flow Control had a 1/2-inch male and 1/2-inch female threaded body, Eaton Corporation visualized a large-volume potential for the product and eventually offered the body similar to a pipe coupling. This adaptation for

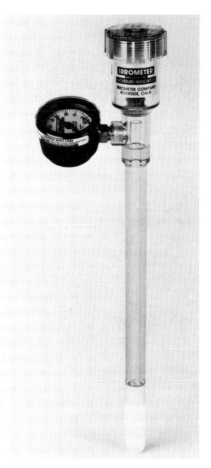

Early Irrometer tensiometer developed by Thomas Prosser.

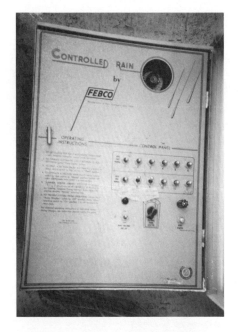
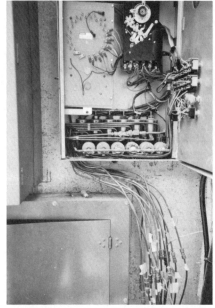

Controlled Rain hydraulic irrigation controller by Febco. An electric clock activated hydraulic valves through a network of small copper tubing.

sprinkler irrigation popularized the wide use of the Dole Flow Control, thereby providing automatic flow regulation on undulating terrain.

In the years following the first installations of the Dole Flow Control, several manufacturers offered versions using the basic contracting-orifice principal. It was adapted to sprinkler head nozzles and used widely to control flow in micro-spray, drip, and turf sprinkler head applications.

Claude Laval Corporation is distinct in the irrigation industry primarily because of its founder, Claude C. Laval Jr., whose business in water-related matters began in 1945. Located in Fresno, California, the corporation is now managed by Laval's son, Claude III.

Born in 1906, Claude Laval Jr., was a man of many talents. He first worked as a newspaper photographer for the Fresno Bee. Later, he did aerial photography work for his father's business.

An accomplished and well-established photographer at age 39, Laval was approached by a client with a unique challenge: Could he develop a camera that would take pictures in the depths of a water well interior?

Laval rose to the challenge and, despite many setbacks, was ready to apply for a patent for his underground cameras in 1950. Three years later, that patent was granted.

The Laval water well camera for underground surveys was capable of taking pictures of malfunctions in wells in which oil-lubricated, line-shaft turbine pumps had leaked up to four feet of lubricating oil, floating on the water surface. As the art of deep well photography developed, well drillers, scientists, oil field experts and others equipped mobile units, took photographs, and recorded trouble spots as deep as one mile below the earth's surface.

The Laval camera became effective in producing:

1. A closed-circuit television image.

2. A videotape recording.

3. A permanent "still" photo graphic record.

Perhaps the most productive and widely used of Laval's inventions, however, was the "Solids From Liquids" separator. Soon labeled the Laval Sandmaster, the product effectively removed solids from water without screens, moving parts, or filter elements. The first Sandmaster was sold in 1963. One of the outgrowths of its success was the adaptation of its original design for installation on the suction end of deep well turbine and submersible bowl assemblies to provide protection from abrasive wear.

Claude Laval III, avid industry proponent and the 27th president of the Irrigation Association, and his father Claude Laval Jr., who amassed 88 U.S. patents to his credit, contribute annually to educational advancement in irrigation. The Claude C. Laval Jr. award is presented to a student or faculty member of California State University, recognizing general merit, practical application, innovation and creativity in a given field of study.

Named for its founder, Frank W. Murphy Company of Tulsa, Oklahoma, manufactures engine control equipment for all types of power applications, a large part of which are in the irrigation industry.

Murphy began his career as a stationary engine salesman. He saw an urgent need for a simple means of engine protection against damage caused by loss of cooling and lubricating fluids. His concern led him to devise an electrically actuated pressure/temperature gauge that would stop an engine that was overheated or low on oil pressure. The device was the genesis of the Murphy Safety Switch Gauge, which he made in 1939 in a small machine shop in Mt. Carmel, Illinois.

Murphy and his wife moved the operation to Tulsa, Oklahoma, in 1945 to better serve the oil industry, which first used his engine protection gauges. Irrigation pump engine users quickly became aware of the Murphy switch-gauge for engine protection.

In 1952 Murphy hired Gordon B. "Sha" Schapaugh as vice president of marketing and sales. Schapaugh aggressively took charge of all sales and became one of the most admired and respected members of the irrigation industry. He was also a staunch supporter of the Irrigation Association, of which the company became a member in 1953. Schapaugh passed away at age 73 in the early 1980s.

Always family owned, the Murphy Switch Company employs approximately 465 people. Frank Murphy Sr. is still involved with the company, which is managed by Frank Murphy Jr., president and CEO.

Yardney Water Management Products of Corona, California, has served the irrigation industry for several decades. The originator of the company's line of irrigation products was Al Wilson, owner of The Engine Cooler Company. Wilson branched into sand media filters when drip irrigation gained popularity in the late 60s. His Free Flow filter has proven excellent in removing organic contaminants and particulate matter from irrigation water.

Yardney Electric Corporation purchased Wilson's company in 1973, changing the name first to Yardney Water Management Systems and then Whittaker Water Management Systems. The name was changed back to Yardney following a management buy out in 1990. Today the company, managed by Ken Phillips, offers screen filters in addition to media filters.

Founded in 1959 by Richard Gulick and Del Mariner, Richdel, Inc., started as a job shop in Burbank, California. The company's interest in turf irrigation was triggered by a Melnor Industries product known as the Model 100 Water Timer. Designed to couple to a household exterior hose bib, it employed a volumetric approach to semi-automation. This gave Gulick and Mariner ideas for further automatic devices.

In the early 1960s Gulick left the company. Mariner, with engineer Myrl Saarm, introduced Richdel Innova-tions, which expanded the operation. Early Richdel products were manual and electric irrigation valves that were privately labeled to Sears & Roebuck Co. for incorporation into its Homart line. Richdel valves, labeled "B Line," were also made briefly for Buckner Manufacturing Company.

By 1964 Richdel had announced a turf irrigation packaged line known as Lawn Genie. The line consisted of plastic sprinklers, a controller, and an anti-siphon-valve combination suited to the do-it-yourself residential market. At that point, Richdel shifted to true wholesaler-manufacturing.

Richdel located to Carson City, Nevada, in 1970. The expanding company set up original equipment manufacturer accounts with L.R. Nelson Co., Champion Manufacturing Co. and Melnor Industries.

In approximately 1980, Richdel President Mike Schwartz, who was responsible for much of the firm's industry prominence, began seeking a buyer for the company to protect the future interests of the Mariner family. Richdel was sold to Leisure Enterprises, a business group that also purchased the Drip-Mist line of irrigation products in 1983. Leisure Enterprises was renamed GardenAmerica.

Irritrol was founded in 1975 by Avram Ben-Yehuda. The company developed a dry-battery-energized irrigation controller called Cloud Nine that could be mounted on a conventional electric irrigation valve. Irritrol expanded rapidly and also developed a widely accepted line of electric irrigation controllers. The company's interests were purchased by GardenAmerica in 1986 to compliment the Richdel and Drip Mist lines.

For a relatively short time, GardenAmerica was a division of electric tool manufacturer Black and Decker before being sold to James Hardie Company of Laguna Niguel, California, in 1991.

Chemical (fertilizer) injection in irrigation water has reached high levels of efficiency. Mazzei Injector Corporation of Bakersfield, California, has specialized in high-efficiency venturi-type differential pressure units since 1976. The company's unique patented injector starts suction when the pipeline pressure is only 20 percent less than the inlet pressure.

In addition to providing auxiliary chemical injection for the irrigation industry, MIC meets exacting requirements in industrial, water treatment, washing and cleaning, pools and spas, and peristolic pumps, creating low pressure to accurately meter fluids into pipelines.

New concepts in filtering water and measuring soil moisture continue to be introduced. Some of the latest concepts in auxiliary irrigation equipment can be found in the Partners in Progress section of *Water and the Land.*

BELOW: One of the first sand media filters made by Al Wilson operating in a citrus grove in 1967.

Courtesy, Yardney Water Management Systems

Crawford Reid, (right) second president of the Sprinkler Irrigation Association, recognizes Frank W. Peikert, head of the Department of Agricultural Engineering at Pennsylvania State University for his contributions to the irrigation industry during the SIA Show in 1953.

CHAPTER 8

A Century of Irrigation Research and Development *

"*Till taught by pain, men really know not what good water is worth.*"

Byron

Much of the credit for the advancement of irrigation in America belongs to the combined efforts of state and federal agencies and institutions of learning. Without state colleges and universities and the resources of the United States Departments of Agriculture and Interior and the Corps of Engineers, many engineering achievements in irrigation would have gone unrecognized.

The earliest traces of irrigation in America were found in the arid Southwest, in the territory we now call New Mexico. Spanish institutions exerted more influence on New Mexico than on other Northern provinces of New Spain. Spanish migrants to the New World were not strangers to water problems or practices, because their European homeland is largely semi-arid.

Spanish-American colonial settlement was enhanced by Spanish rule, water and land grants. The Crown's purpose of granting land and water was to stimulate rapid and stable occupancy of unpopulated regions. The motivation behind the permanent occupation of New Mexico was the belief that the semi-civilized Indians were ripe for conversion to Catholicism.

Thus, the most primitive colonization framework was formed to

Courtesy, William Sarratt

Jack Keller, assistant professor of Civil Engineering at Utah State University speaking to the SIA Conference in Denver in 1961.

Original copy of the first sprinkler irrigation handbook, published by the Sprinkler Irrigation Association.

build significant settler activity through water and land grants and ultimate occupation of vast arid lands, from Texas to Alta California. New Mexico would live under Spanish and Mexican laws for more than 200 years before becoming part of the United States.

Shortly after New Mexico joined the Union, New Mexico State College was founded. By 1895, important changes in the curriculum emphasized training for civil engineering students pursuing careers in irrigation design and operation. The shift soon resulted in the creation of the Department of Civil and Irrigation Engineering at the school, which later attained University status.

State archives reveal the important role played by community organizations that developed and administered water resources called acquia associations. They were the principal local units of government responsible for the distribution of irrigation water. Historically, acquia associations were the forerunners of today's agricultural cooperatives.

In 1900, the New Mexico Experiment Station, allied with New Mexico State College, reported on the severity of short water supplies in the state, "The summer and fall of 1900 were exceptionally dry, with practically no water in the Rio Grande River from June 17 to November 28."

Courtesy, William Sarratt

Marvin N. Shearer, irrigation specialist with the Oregon Cooperative Extension Service, speaking to The SIA Conference in Kansas City in 1962.

New Mexico, with a longer irrigation history than any other state, has always been obliged to portion waters, even with the assistance of many Federal government issues, including water and land grants.

Irrigation Development Periods

Dr. John A. Widtsoe, an early irrigation investigator, described three periods of irrigation development in the hemisphere. They were the prehistoric, the pre-pioneer and the modern periods.

During the prehistoric period, irrigation was practiced in the West before Spanish or American settlers took possession of the land. Remnants of irrigation canals and structures in California, Arizona, New Mexico, Colorado and Utah bear witness to populations thriving near irrigation ditches.

The pre-pioneer period represents the meager attempts at irrigation made by trappers, traders, ranchers and missionaries who ventured into the West before 1847.

In Widtsoe's theory, the modern period began on July 24, 1847, when a company of Mormon pioneers led by Brigham Young entered the Great Salt Lake Valley. The pioneers spread water from City Creek over newly plowed fields in the Valley. By 1900, Widtsoe estimates that 9 million acres in the western United States were being cultivated. Irrigated acreage more than doubled during the next 20 years. He speculated that about 57 million acres of the 17 western states might be irrigated eventually.

People's Colleges

As people surged westward from the Atlantic Seaboard during the 1860s, they had strong opinions about education. They wanted "peoples colleges" that their sons and daughters could attend at minimum cost. They wanted colleges that put the emphasis on research and instruction to ultimately increase agricultural production to support the country's growing industry.

In 1862, Justin Smith Morrill, a U.S. senator from Vermont, introduced a bill allowing states to sell portions of federally owned land and use the proceeds for the "perpetual endowment" of at least one college. Under the Act, each state received 30,000 acres for each member of Congress it elected. Senator Morrill's bill, as enacted by Congress and signed by President Lincoln, became the foundation of our land grant college system.

Iowa, a new state in the fertile prairies, was the first to accept the provisions and responsibilities of the Land-Grant College Act. When Morrill's bill became law, the Iowa General Assembly was in session in the new capital of Des Moines to consider concerns of the Civil War. Three legislators quickly presented a draft of a bill for an agricultural college, which was passed and signed by the governor. Iowa State University is the product of their bill and stands as an example of land-grant institutions, each adapted to the special needs of its state.

Prior to the Land-Grant College Act, agricultural colleges had been established during the 1850s. The first was Michigan, closely followed by Maryland and Pennsylvania.

The first state agricultural experiment station in the United States was organized in Connecticut in 1875, largely through the efforts of Dr. Wilbur Olin Atwater, horticulturist and soil scientist. A decade later, the Hatch Act provided for the establishment of similar stations in all states and territories in the Union. The Office of Experiment Stations was summarily formed in the Department of Agriculture as a central agency for the stations and Dr. Atwater was appointed its first director.

Another powerful agricultural organization founded in the mid-19th century, was the Grange, the Patrons of Husbandry. William Saunders, scion of a noted family of Scotch gardeners, was called to Washington, D.C. in 1862 by the Department of Agriculture to landscape its grounds. He introduced a number of useful, exotic plant species from abroad, the navel orange among them. His interest in rural social conditions led him to join with Oliver Hudson Kelley in organizing the Grange in 1867.

Groups Lure Settlers With Water

An important benchmark in irrigation history was reached in 1903 in Bismarck, North Dakota. That October, irrigation engineers gathered in the northern reaches of the country to explore the potential of the vast Missouri River basin as a resource for agricultural irrigation. The meeting was called the First State Irrigation Congress.

The thinking of those speaking at the Congress is evident from the introductory remarks. "Do you realize the immense quantity of flood water which rushes through the state in the channel of the Missouri during the latter part of May and the first part of June? It passes on down to the Mississippi and breaks levees and floods the plantations for miles along the fertile river bottoms, destroying many millions of dollars of property each season. Competent engineers state this water can be taken from the Missouri in the northern part of North Dakota and used to enrich millions of acres of land. If this is done, it will lessen the danger from destructive floods in the lower Mississippi. In fact, the flood waters will become a valuable servant to the people, bringing wealth and contentment, instead of being a bad master. All of this will come about if the aims of the North Dakota Irrigation Association are carried out."

States weren't the only entities trying to lure farmers and Federal reclamation dollars to areas with abundant water for irrigation. The railroads wielded tremendous influence in the development of new territories. The Great Northern Railroad Company, Northern Pacific and Union Pacific utilized their resources between the 1880s and the agricultural depression around 1920 to further land reform and reclamation. Once the recession ended, the U.S. Reclamation Service joined with the railroads and beet sugar companies to promote settlement in Montana's lower Yellowstone Valley. The powerful non-profit consortium, called the Lower Yellowstone Development Association, was yet another movement to bring settlers to new farm land with ample irrigation.

These movements would have been more successful if it weren't for a succession of setbacks. The Great Depression, World War II and the

Claude H. Pair, ARS USDA agricultural engineer receiving Person of the Year Award during 1962 SIA Conference.

Korean War sapped the momentum of the farm economy in what might have been two decades of rapid development of American irrigation.

By the mid-50s, the incentive for irrigation was new technology rather than the enticement of abundant water. Derivations of agricultural sprinkler irrigation included crop cooling, low-temperature crop protection and frost control for a wide range of plants, from cranberries to orchards to row crops. Innovations in orchard spring bud retardation were introduced. The importance of irrigation for leaching soil salts and storing moisture in the soil during the winter were recognized. These expanded uses for irrigation were accepted by farmers and became part of arid land farming.

Courtesy, William Sarratt

T. W. Edminister, deputy administrator of the Agricultural Research Service, receiving SIA Person of the Year Award during the association's conference in Kansas City in 1962.

The advantages of automation and precise control over the amount of water applied, along with the development of lightweight aluminum tubing provided incentives for increased research in surface irrigation methods.

Glen Stringham and Jack Keller, two Utah State University scientists, discovered that surges of water traveled further down furrows than a continuous flow. Called surge flow, this new method of water control and application had the potential of doing for surface irrigation what center pivot machines did for overhead sprinkler irrigation. It not only made automation possible, but also decreased losses to deep percolation, a major reason for surface irrigation's low application efficiency. By increasing the application efficiency, the energy savings of surge irrigation over sprinkler irrigation became an important factor.

Electricity on the Farm

Before and during the Great Depression, more than half of America's farmers performed their early morning and evening chores by the light of kerosene or Coleman (white gas) lanterns. They pumped water from their wells with the help of windmills, oil or gasoline engines, and hydraulic rams.

Canals and gravity systems had long been used to deliver irrigation water. Development and use of electric motors for irrigation pumps greatly expanded the availability of water and farmland for irrigation from Ohio to the Pacific Ocean.

In the early 1890s, Redlands Electric Company of San Bernardino County, California, gained notoriety when it supplied power for seven electric motors to drive centrifugal well pumps. The installation of a two-mile-long line to provide power for two reciprocating well pumps in northern California made headlines in state newspapers. Replacing gasoline and steam engines with electric motors gained popularity by the turn of the century. By 1904, there were several hundred kilowatts of electricity generated to power motors in California alone.

Electric utilities have long advised farmers on getting maximum efficiency from motorized pumps. Southern California Edison started a pump testing program in 1911. Pacific Gas and Electric Company initiated a more elaborate survey and testing service in 1914. Such pump testing services continue today.

As agricultural uses for electric energy multiplied, cooperation with agricultural colleges, universities and youth groups resulted in a national movement for rural electrification by 1924. Several states developed a Committee in the Relation of Electricity to Agriculture (CREA). The power companies made grants to the committees for research and demonstration projects. Today, the only active CREA is in Kansas. However, many states have electric councils that perform many of the same functions as the old CREAs.

In 1935, Congress created the Rural Electrification Administration (REA). During the next five years, much of American farm life changed for the better as rural electric cooperatives were formed and electric lines were strung along country roads. With the flick of a switch, electric power lighted farmsteads and served agriculture in hundreds of ways.

As of 1984, irrigation pumps supplied water to 31.1 million acres in the U.S., with 66 percent of the pumps powered by electricity. It has been

Courtesy, William Sarratt

Wade Manufacturing's Mr. and Mrs. Wade Newbegin (right) and Mr. and Mrs. Ed Newbegin (left) during SIA conference in the Grand Bahamas in 1969.

estimated that 80 percent of farmstead electricity usage is for pumping.

Thirst for Irrigation Information

As the irrigation industry expanded rapidly at the mid-century mark, many innovations in equipment and techniques created the need for education from both the government and private business. Field days, seminars and conventions were created to meet this demand for information.

In 1965, the Association of Sprinkler Irrigation Equipment Manufacturers, now the Irrigation Association, stepped in to help the states of Arkansas, Louisiana, Mississippi, Missouri and Tennessee provide information on the latest irrigation techniques. Held in Memphis, Tennessee, irrigation scientists and industry leaders opened the eyes of large number of farmers. The first speaker after the invocation was USDA-ARS irrigation engineer Tyler Quackenbush. The title of his speech, nearly 30 years ago, was "Water and the Land."

Oregon State University, the ASIEM and Pacific Power and Light Company presented an Irrigation Field Day and Sprinkler Irrigation Fair in Corvallis is 1966. More than 1,500 people crowded onto the Jackson Farm near Corvallis to see how irrigation methods and soil drainage impacted crop yields. Meetings such as this became common across the country.

Another significant meeting involving the ASIEM was the first Sprinkler Irrigation Short Course of Agricultural Principles and Practices held in Pasco, in Washington's Columbia Basin, in 1974. The short course, oversubscribed by more than 50 percent, necessitated a second course in Boise, Idaho, the following year.

These short course meetings were the forerunners of today's technical evaluations for accreditation and licensing. The Irrigation Association still assists many states with these meetings.

1988 was the 75th anniversary of the University of California Cooperative Extension Service. The first farm advisor was hired in 1913. The Hatch Experiment Station Act established a cooperative bond between the USDA and land-grant colleges in 1914 that resulted in the hiring of county agents across the nation.

Indeed, Cooperative Extension has changed dramatically over the last 79 years. The late 1940s and 1950s brought both a shift toward new technology and urbanization, which greatly influenced the role of advisors. In 1949, Extension Director J. Earl Coke announced a reorganization plan which decentralized the Service.

During the 1960s, major shifts in clientele influenced cooperative extension to devote more of its energy and resources to urban agriculture, better known as horticulture. There were fewer commercial farmers and more ornamental horticultural clients seeking assistance. By 1975, 90 percent of California's population resided in urban areas.

Environmental awareness and computer literacy became two additional challenges for cooperative extension during the late 70s and 80s. It played a large role in implementation of integrated pest management programs, such as the one at the University of California in the mid-70s. The makeup of the extension service changed to reflect that of a changing society. Appointments of women and minorities increased significantly.

As Cooperative Extension rises to the challenges of the future, the needs of clients remain the driving force behind constantly changing farm advisor programs. Without the support and leadership of farm advisors, extension agents and government specialists in horticulture irrigation would not have reached its current level of sophistication or implementation. The irrigation industry owes a great debt of gratitude to these public servants of the past and present. We pay tribute to their years of service by listing them in their own section in an appendix to this book.

Jack Liddell of Delta Irrigation, 24th president of the Irrigation Association, and his wife Louise in Corpus Christi, Texas, in 1966.

Guy O. Woodward of Utah State University speaking at the 1955 SIA conference in Colorado Springs.

Robert Cloud, president of Associated Irrigation Consultants of Los Angeles (left) and Austin J. Miller, 15th president of the SIA, at the 1966 SIA conference in Oak Brook, Illinois

Desert landscapes such as the one at the Westin Mission Hills in Rancho Mirage, California, are only possible because of high-tech irrigation.

CHAPTER 9

Today's Agricultural, Landscape and Turf Irrigation

"The notion of water conservation is inherently tied to efficient water use. This means getting the most benefit — maximum yield, greatest recreational use, landscape health and beauty — out of the water applied."

—Kenneth H. Solomon
Center for Irrigation Technology

*A*s America moves rapidly toward the 21st Century, irrigation has risen to a lofty plateau in the arts of agriculture, landscape horticulture and recreation. It has far surpassed the expectations of early inventors, engineers and marketers. Irrigation is now essential to the economy of many industries and cities.

As the 1990s unfold, conservation of water has become an American priority. Irrigation planning, design and application all relate to effective, yet efficient, use of our increasingly sensitive natural resource. We can now appraise what earlier practical experiences, growing technologies and modern application have accomplished when water is appropriately applied.

Kenneth H. Solomon, director of the Center for Irrigation Technology in Fresno, California, observes, "The notion of water conservation is inherently tied to efficient water use. This means getting the most benefit — maximum yield, greatest recreational use, landscape health and beauty —

out of the water applied. To achieve water conservation, we must understand irrigation efficiency."

There are two components to irrigation efficiency, states Solomon, uniformity and water loss. Uniformity is the extent to which water is applied evenly over the irrigation

Kenneth Solomon, director of the Center for Irrigation Technology at California State University in Fresno.

Grower checking surge flow valve controller as it operates.

area. Unfortunately, he says, practical irrigation systems always apply water with a degree of non-uniformity. Some portions of the landscape receive more water than others. Consequently, some plants receive too much water while others don't receive enough. By increasing the irrigation run times to satisfy the needs of plants in the least watered portion of a zone, other plants receive more than they need. This excess water is essentially lost.

By increasing irrigation application uniformity and grouping plants by similar moisture requirements, irrigation efficiency can be dramatically improved. The ultimate goal is to apply only the amount of water plants require. But, as Solomon points out, this implies that we know how much water is needed and that we can control how much is applied. A wide range of modern irrigation equipment, sensors and control devices are available to help irrigators do this. However, knowledge is needed in addition to hardware.

"We have to know about climate, plants and soils to determine the water requirement," adds Solomon. "We also need to know about hydraulics and product performance to develop a good design."

The need for modern water-saving practices is emphasized by the warnings of impending water shortages, both in urban and agricultural areas. California, for example, the most populous state in the nation and the most productive from the standpoint of agriculture, has a water deficit. Some authorities estimate the state uses more than two million acre-feet of water more than it has during drought years.

The problem goes far beyond California. News stories during the 1990s have reported shortages in Florida, Nebraska, Minnesota and Oregon. Recent reports from the National Weather Bureau have carried the warnings...

"Water Restrictions Imposed in Florida. South Florida Water Management District imposed Phase I restrictions limiting the times when golf courses may be irrigated."

"Drought Creates Ground Water Dispute. Demand on groundwater reserves in Nebraska during drought peri-

ods causes complaints as heavy irrigation pumping lowers domestic well levels."

"**Drought Forces Minnesota to Deny Groundwater Pumping Permits. The Minnesota Department of Natural Resources suspends permits for farmers who draw irrigation water in effort to protect groundwater.**"

"**Portland Water Department Urges Conservation. The specter of impending water shortages forces Portland, Oregon, to issue pleas to conserve water supplied by Bull Run Reservoir in the Cascade Mountains.**"

We can no longer count on nature to provide all the water we need to sustain both agriculture and modern urban lifestyles. This realization has led to numerous improvements in irrigation efficiency. A few mileposts in irrigation efficiency follow.

Contemporary Surface Irrigation

Initial efforts toward increasing the efficiency of surface irrigation centered around moving the earth rather than changing the method of applying water. Surveyors as far back as George Washington had known the value of level land and good drainage to agricultural production. From the

perspective of a surveyor looking through a transit, the solution of moving earth was more understandable than creating the technology to traverse rolling terrain to cultivate, seed, irrigate and harvest.

Ironically, one of the most advanced technologies of the century, the laser beam, has been recruited to improve the efficiency of one of the most primitive forms of irrigation. With this photo-electronic concept, a single beam of light can guide mammoth, 25-yard earthmovers to precisely level large expanses of land to a gradient conducive to surface irrigation.

Guided by a laser beam, the operator of an earthmover can prepare a 40-acre field for surface

When this corn crop nears maturity, the drops of this center pivot adapted for LEPA will be just above the tassels.

Courtesy, T-L Irrigation Company, Hastings, Nebraska

Experimental center pivot that plants seed, fertilizes and irrigates with LEPA drops. The field was also prepared by reservoir tillage to reduce runoff.

irrigation in hours. Eight decades before, the same task would have taken 20 three-horse teams pulling Fresno scrapers several days. Even the Caterpillar tractor pulling a scraper relied on "eyeballing" by the operator until the introduction of the laser.

Surge Flow Irrigation

Once a field has been graded and prepared for surface furrow irrigation, water can be directed from a supply ditch or pipe on one side of the field into the furrows between crop rows. During basic furrow irrigation, water is fed into the furrows until it reaches the opposite side of the field. This type of irrigation, while simple and generally effective, has been found to be lacking in uniformity. Crops on the side of the field closest to the supply ditch, receive more water then they need while those on the far end of the furrow don't necessarily receive enough moisture. Water is also lost to deep percolation in portions of the furrow where water stands the longest.

For years, farmers had observed that stopping, then resuming the flow of irrigation water into a furrow helped the water advance further down the field. This was confirmed at Utah State University in the late 70s by Glen E. Stringham and Jack Keller in the Department of Agricultural Engineering. They were seeking ways to automate furrow irrigation. They discovered accidentally that intermittent surges of water, instead of a continuous flow, helped water move further down the furrow. Today, surge flow is both patented and registered as a trademark by the Utah State University Foundation.

Stringham and Keller determined that the negative pressure in soil actually collapses a thin layer of soil at the surface. This layer reduces infiltration of water during subsequent surges. Consequently, more water remains to travel further down the furrow, two to three times further. Research has shown that surge flow irrigation consistently saves substantial water, often 50 percent, compared to conventional furrow irrigation. It also requires less pressure than sprinkler irrigation.

The efficiency of surge flow irrigation can be increased further by automating the valves that release the water into the furrows. Given various facts, including soil type, length of furrow and the grade of the field, modern surge valve controllers can calculate and carry out surge cycles totally on their own. The cost of operation combined with the relative low cost of installation gives surge irrigation an advantage over manually operated surface irrigation systems.

Innovations in Sprinkler Irrigation

In the time line of American irrigation history, innovative concepts in overhead sprinkler irrigation have come recently. Only in the last 15 years have low energy precision application (LEPA) and reservoir tillage emerged to provide major water and energy savings in overhead sprinkler irrigation.

LEPA has emerged as one of the most notable irrigation concepts complimenting energy and water conservation. Not only is the pressure requirement significantly reduced, water is placed precisely for plant use.

William M. Lyle, USDA Extension Service Research Scientist at the Texas Agricultural Experiment Station in Lubbock, is credited with developing the concept. It is actually a modification to center pivot or linear-move irrigation machines. Instead of high-pressure conventional sprinkler heads spaced on top of the pivot lateral, low-pressure, adjustable sprinklers are suspended close to the soil surface with gooseneck drop pipes. The special sprinkler heads can be adjusted seasonally for irrigation, chemigation, frost control or cooling.

Maturing a crop with 30 to 40 percent less water, especially in water-short regions, while achieving 95 to 98 percent application efficiency is strong justification for incorporating LEPA into irrigated farm production.

Reservoir Tillage

Reservoir tillage is a companion to low-pressure mechanized overhead irrigation. This process creates basins or pockets to hold water in place so that it can infiltrate the soil instead of running off. It is especially beneficial for center pivot or linear-move applications in fields with heavy soils or contours that promote runoff.

Reservoir tillage implements have been developed to form basins in fields of row crops and small grains. Most machines use one of two basic methods for creating the basins. The first, basin tillage, employs a shovel-type tool to create small levies or basins in the field. The basin length usually ranges from two to six feet. The second, reservoir tillage, uses spades mounted on wheels to punch holes in the soil surface. The punching action creates small sub-surface reservoirs spaced two to three feet apart. Maintaining reservoir tillage through the crop life can reduce runoff during irrigation and during natural rainfall.

Irrigation Sprinkler Drop Analysis

With the aid of laser technology, researchers at the Center for Irrigation Technology have been able to count drops "on the fly" from a sprinkler spray pattern. CIT is an industry-supported independent laboratory for irrigation technology operating under the California State University system.

Ken Solomon, CIT director, explains, "Drop sizes can influence soil compaction and infiltration rates. Large drops strike the soil with greater kinetic energy than small ones. Drop sizes can also affect where water is deposited under windy conditions. This is because small drops are influenced more by wind than larger ones."

The heart of the drop measuring process is a flat beam of laser light that shines onto photo receptors. As a drop of water passes through the beam of light, it casts a shadow on the receptors. A computer records the size and speed of each drop passing through the beam. This information can then be converted by the computer into tables and graphs depicting droplet size, water volume at different distances and droplet distribution.

By utilizing this type of technology, CIT can evaluate the uniformity and pattern of water distributed by any overhead sprinkler. Improved sprinkler uniformity contributes to greater irrigation efficiency.

Infrared Telemetry Tells When to Irrigate

Advanced technology has made it possible for the modern grower to afford weather stations that collect important data at a specific location. Such weather systems enable the growers to predict crop moisture needs, warn them of potential frost damage and help them pinpoint growth stages for timing fertilization or other important management practices.

One such system is the Schedular by the Carborundum Company, a subsidiary of Standard Oil Engineered Materials Company, now part of British Petroleum. The hand-held gun uses infrared light to measure the leaf temperature of the crop. This data, in addition to air temperature, relative humidity and sunlight intensity, is recorded by a computer. From this information, plant stress can be detected 3 to 5 days before crop stress is visually observed. Data for up to 30 fields can be stored in the shoulder-pack computer. Irrigation can be scheduled based on the information gathered by the Schedular.

The company introduced a more advanced system called CropLink in 1988 that utilizes infrared telemetry to send weather and crop data from a field station to a grower's office without wires or radio. No license is required and the field station can be moved from one location to another.

Micro-Climate Control of Deciduous Orchards

A team of agricultural scientists at Utah State University has created a technique using overhead sprinkler irrigation to delay fruit bud development. By pushing the time that buds develop further into the spring, freeze damage is reduced and corresponding fruit yield improves.

The basis for the technique is using evaporative cooling to fool the plant into delaying bud development and growth. It was found that budding of apple trees could be delayed two to three weeks. This

Courtesy, Garden Way, Aptos, California.

Whether formal or informal, irrigation has vastly improved the beauty of urban landscapes.

small delay, however, prevented more than 80 percent of historical freeze damage.

The Future of Low-Volume Irrigation

Low-volume drip and micro-spray irrigation is the complete opposite of the direction taken by surface irrigators during the 20th century. Instead of changing the land to fit irrigation, low-volume takes the approach of changing irrigation to fit the land.

Early setbacks with low-volume irrigation, including clogged emitters, cost and lack of application uniformity have been resolved. Filtration, advances in manufacturing, and new technology have opened up the low-volume market to many new crops.

Turbulent-flow plastic irrigation tapes have eliminated the need for separate emitters. Emitters that resist clogging are now integrated into the tape. The tapes have two walls; one as a main flow channel and a second for emission. Manufacturers can space emitters to fit the field spacing of a particular crop. They can also control the rate of application according to the grower's requirements. Recently, manufacturers introduced tapes that are sized to permit irrigation of longer rows, thus saving on some of the costs of laterals and submains.

Turbulent-flow tape can be used economically for a single-season crop, either buried or covered by plastic sheeting as a mulch. Overall, the tapes have produced water savings, greater yields and fewer complications with foliar diseases and weeds.

Advances have also been made with emitters for hose installation. The Micro Irrigation Division of Wade Manufacturing in Fresno, California, recently introduced a flow regulator that provides a precise water discharge rate through multiple emitters and micro-spray outlets, irrespective of uneven terrain or the length of laterals. Invented by industry veteran Mark Christy, the AcuFlo has proven better than 95 percent delivery accuracy and 97 percent emission uniformity. The device brings even greater irrigation efficiency to low-flow technology.

Irrigation and Beautification of the Urban Landscape

Most Americans see cropland only infrequently. Instead, their vision is filled with the buildings and landscapes of the cities and suburbs. Shopping malls, schools, parks, residential neighborhoods and an occasional golf course make up the primary components of their quality of life.

Irrigation has contributed greatly to the quality of the urban landscape. Advanced irrigation techniques have fostered sophisticated urban beautification far beyond that of the mid-20th century. It is not uncommon today to live in the vicinity of rooftop gardens, shopping malls graced with tropical plants, streets lined with trees and groundcovers, manicured parks and verdant green home lawns. High-quality landscapes depend upon some form of irrigation and American's have come to expect high-quality landscapes.

"All in all, irrigation has greatly improved our environment, at a minimum cost," states Robert Cloud, president of Associated Irrigation Consultants of Los Angeles. During 40 years as an irrigation contractor, designer and consultant, Cloud has taken part in the "greening" of cities in the Southwest, Southeast and Texas. "As we go down the primrose path of life, remember that all the beauty and aesthetic standards we see, but take for granted, have been made possible in part by landscape irrigation."

The importance of irrigation in urban landscapes was recognized during the Third National Irrigation Symposium held in November 1990 in Phoenix, Arizona. Sponsored by the American Society of Agricultural Engineers, the significant amount of discussion devoted to turf and landscape irrigation was notable. Some studies highlighted during the program were: Management of Turf and Landscape Irrigation, Soil Effects

Courtesy, Garden Way, Aptos, California.

Property use and value in arid regions depend heavily on irrigation.

on Irrigation Management, Irrigation of Turf, Future Irrigation Strategies and the Economics of Irrigation. ASAE published the papers in book form as "Visions of the Future."

Advanced Moisture Sensing

Soil moisture sensing technology appropriate for urban landscapes is now being addressed. Companies are refining sensing devices for small to large automatic irrigation systems typical in urban landscapes.

The California Department of Transportation (CalTrans) tested several versions of moisture sensors in 1990. It observed that water savings of 44 to 60 percent were possible with moisture sensors that had irrigation over-ride capability. Moisture level adjustment, compatible sensor/controller circuitry, the sensor's ability to over-ride the irrigation schedule, and the capacity to interface with computers were considered most important to CalTrans. Not only did the sensors save water, they offered labor savings on complex irrigated landscapes.

Nutrient Feeding

In this era of fast foods, programmable video cassette recorders, and home security systems, fertilizing urban landscapes automatically through an irrigation system seems appropriate. Plants respond favorably to constant availability of key nutrients. Just as moisture sensors can pinpoint timely irrigation, fertigation with very dilute amounts of nitrogen, potassium, phosphorus, iron and other elements can eliminate the mistakes of conventional fertilization.

A new computerized turf management system by Automated Chemical Management, Inc. of Shoreham, New York, retrofits any automatic irrigation system and offers a way to optimize application of nutrients to turf. The company's controller can be directed by simple card programming. The controller

directs a proportioner/injector to provide a planned dose of nutrients prescribed for each zone.

Weather Responsive Irrigation

An irrigation system is most efficient when it supplements rainfall to supply plant water requirements. Agricultural and golf course irrigators can make practical use out of dedicated weather stations. Advanced controllers can take the data from such stations and adjust irrigation schedules on a daily or hourly basis.

Manufacturing a controller that adjusts automatically to weather data is a distinct possibility for small to medium landscape irrigation systems. However, dedicated weather stations for these systems are virtually impractical. A potential solution is the availability of localized weather data from a growing number of offices of the U.S. Weather Bureau. Accessible by computer, current and historical weather data can be transmitted by phone line to service subscribers.

Technology has advanced to the point where home alarm systems can be linked to a security service. There is little reason why an irrigation controller at residential or commercial sites can't be linked to the landscape contractor responsible for maintenance. The contractor can obtain evapotranspiration data from a weather service and then adjust his customers' controllers by phone. The same network could be used to adjust fertigation.

This chapter has touched on many of the latest advancements in both agricultural and landscape irrigation equipment. The Partners in Progress section of this history will graphically detail the latest advances in irrigation equipment.

Irrigation improved the quality and availability of American golf courses.

CHAPTER 10

Water and the Game of Golf

The practice of watering putting surfaces originated in Scotland in the 1880s. By 1894, St. Andrews in Scotland had sunk a well expressly for this purpose.

The grand game of golf is played today by one out of ten Americans on courses that rival the private gardens of monarchs in natural beauty. Irrigation has played a major role in enabling golf course architects and superintendents to elevate the sport to its current state.

Even though Americans did not invent the game of golf, they have had a tremendous impact on its current form. The first authentic reference to golf in the United States appeared in an advertisement in the April 21, 1779 edition of the Royal Gazette. The publisher of the New York City newspaper, James Rivington, was also an importer. He had become the recipient of a shipment of "Play Clubs and Feathers" from Scotland and was attempting to sell them to his subscribers.

There is no record whether or not Rivington was successful in selling the clubs and feathers. However, this simple yet rare golf equipment was available in Charleston, South Carolina, by 1786 where the game was played on a public green of a few acres. Not to be outdone, the city of Savannah, Georgia, offered the sport to winter vacationers as early as 1796.

While these two states would eventually become playgrounds for millions of golf enthusiasts, little more was recorded about the sport in the region for most of the 19th century. Golf, like other leisurely sports played on turf such as tennis, lawn bowling

Courtesy, Barrett Supply Co., Augusta, Georgia

An early Thompson sprinkler on a roller base.

and croquet, was available to an extremely small, wealthy segment of the U.S. population.

The resurgence of golf in America took place closer to the homes of the nation's wealthy. The Industrial Revolution had enlarged the ranks of the country's high society. The privileged sought recreation both at resorts and near their residences in industrial cities such as New York, Boston, Chicago, Cleveland, Philadelphia, Pittsburgh, Minneapolis and St. Louis. By the end of the century, golf was on their list of sports.

In 1888, Scotsman John Reid staked out a rudimentary three-hole course in a meadow behind his home in Yonkers, a suburb of New York City. He named the course St. Andrews Golf Club in reverence to the legendary ancient course in Scotland. Still in existence, St. Andrews most recently received the architectural flair of professional golfer Jack Nicklaus.

According to Robert Trent Jones, regarded as one of America's premier golf course architects, the first 18-hole layout in the U.S. was designed by Charles Blair Macdonald, an American who had studied at The University of St. Andrews. Macdonald, the first U.S. Amateur Champion, was so obsessed with the game and its perfection, that he was determined to build a full-fledged 18-hole golf course in the U.S. that was comparable to the famous courses in Scotland. In 1895, Chicago Golf Club in Wheaton, Illinois, opened.

Clubs began to form for the invigorating, gentlemen's sport. One such club, Shinnecock Hills Golf Club, hired Scotsman Willie Dunn to cross the Atlantic to Long Island, New York and build their course. By 1891, Dunn had completed 12 holes. The final six holes were completed in 1895.

By 1896, golfers could count 80 courses in the United States, reveals golf course architect and historian Geoffrey Cornish. By the turn of the century, the list had exploded to 982, with at least one course in each of the Union's 45 states.

Donald Ross, another Scot who emigrated to America to design golf courses, was in demand for his talents at the beginning of the 20th century. By the end of World War I, Ross had completed three new courses for soda fountain baron James Tufts at a golf resort he was building in Pinehurst, North Carolina.

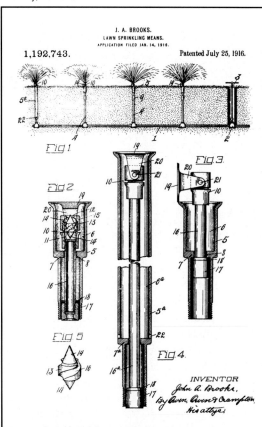

Courtesy, Marc Dutton

The first pop-up sprinkler head patented by John A. Brooks in 1916.

Irrigation Enters the Golf Scene

The Scottish influence on golf in the United States reached beyond course design. The practice of watering putting surfaces originated in Scotland in the 1880s. By 1894, St. Andrews in Scotland had sunk a well expressly for this purpose. Therefore, Reid, Macdonald, Dunn and Ross were aware of rudimentary irrigation from St. Andrews.

Man-made rain became a vital part of maintaining golf courses in the beginning of the century. Even though located in areas of abundant rainfall, courses such as Long Island's National Golf Links, Philadelphia's Merion Golf Club, and North Carolina's Pinehurst, all utilized irrigation during the growing season.

As the game of golf spread to the West Coast, the technology of irrigation took on greater importance. Golf course architects who designed western golf courses could not escape the fact that without irrigation, building and maintaining a golf course would be impossible.

Prior to World War I, a golf course architect's irrigation choices were fairly limited. During this period, inventor W. Van Thompson produced his first large rotating sprinkler head. The sprinkler was supplied with water from a hose and was generally mounted on a roller base. The Thompson sprinkler covered a large area and was frequently used for greens, tees and an occasional fairway.

This was the state of irrigation in 1912 when the Pacific Improvement Company started to plan a golf course on the craggy bluffs along the Carmel Bay in Monterey, California. Today, the Monterey Peninsula is famous for its golf courses. Pebble Beach Golf Links, Cypress Point Golf Club, Spyglass Hill and The Links at Spanish Bay are recognized around the world as spectacular American golf courses.

Pebble Beach Golf Links was designed by Jack Neville and Douglas Grant, both novices to the design field. The Del Monte Company, which owned the vast majority of the property, wanted to create a Pacific Coast resort to supplement the region's agricultural and fishing economy.

Due to the scale of the project, the Pacific Improvement Company hired a San Francisco engineering firm. One of its ideas was to irrigate the course with hoseless sprinklers.

William A. Buckner, a railroadman and inventor from Fresno, California, had just perfected such a sprinkler head in 1912. So appropriate for golf course irrigation was Buckner's new sprinkler, that the engineers contacted him. Together, they planned the installation of the first hoseless, overhead golf course irrigation system in America.

As the United States manufacturing community recovered from the production restrictions of World War I and golf gained popularity, inventors started to develop equipment that would make golf courses playable despite seasonal shortages in rainfall. They designed and built irrigation equipment that could apply water uniformly to large acreage.

By 1925, the first remote-controlled irrigation valves and hydraulic-actuated valve controllers became available from early manufacturers such as John A. Brooks and George E. Moody. Hydraulic controllers could be activated by an electric clock, which in turn activated hydraulic valves.

Hoseless, quick-coupling valves for sprinklers started to replace the large roller-mounted Thompson sprinklers as World War I ended and the Roaring Twenties began. Los Angeles Country Club was one of the first golf clubs to install pipe and quick-coupling valves for Thompson sprinklers on its fairways and tees. The valves represented a great step toward the advent of automatic controllers.

The status of irrigation during the 1920s has been aptly described by Chester Mendenhall, pioneer greenskeeper and 1986 recipient of the Golf Course Superintendents Association of America Distinguished Service

Award. He recalls that as greenskeeper of the Wichita Country Club in Wichita, Kansas, in 1928, "Water systems back then consisted of old steel, oil-field pipe laid on top of the ground in the rough along the edge of the fairways. Manual control valves were spaced at intervals along the pipe." Hoses for traveling sprinklers were connected to each valve. The sprinklers traversed the width of the fairway during the night. By morning, an entire fairway would have been irrigated by traveling sprinklers crossing the fairway side-by-side.

Word about advances in golf course irrigation spread more rapidly once the National Association of Greenskeepers of America (NAGA) was launched in 1927. Superintendents from more than 75 courses met during the International Golf Show and Country Club Sports Exposition in Chicago in March of that year. During

Automatic irrigation made development of golf courses possible in regions of low rainfall.

the conference they elected to form the NAGA, the forerunner of the GCSAA, now headquartered in Lawrence, Kansas. NAGA became the vehicle for improving golf course maintenance through the interchange of ideas among greenskeepers.

During NAGA's convention the following year, a number of irrigation suppliers exhibited. One promoted the use of "Flexible Pipe" for direct burial of lateral pipe lines for overhead irrigation. Sprinkler heads were connected to the pipe by metal saddles with threaded outlets.

The Depression did not bring an end to new developments in sprinkler irrigation for golf courses. Rain Bird introduced its horizontal impact rotary. Thompson and Campbell developed several new gear-drive,

large capacity sprinkler heads for fairways and greens. Around 1935, the first pop-up rotary impact sprinklers appeared on the market. As a result, the cost advantage of impact sprinklers over gear-drive sprinklers started to shrink. A number of pop-up sprinklers could be connected to a single underground valve. Furthermore, such valves could be operated hydraulically to open and close upon command by a clock. Block systems became the state of the art, even though most courses still irrigated just greens and tees.

Most of the hurdles to automatic control had been cleared. However, by 1940, most superintendents still managed manual or semi-automatic underground sprinkler systems with pop-up or quick-coupler heads.

Watermen were needed to run the irrigation systems during the night. At pressures in excess of 100 psi and application rates of about one-half inch per hour, human error was a considerable concern.

By the end of World War II, completely automated irrigation systems were available. Converting quick-coupler systems to automatic did not gain momentum until the 60s and 70s. In addition to supplying basic moisture needs of fairways, tees, and greens, the advanced systems were utilized for other tasks, such as flushing the frost off greens on clear, cold mornings.

One of the first golf courses to employ a fully automatic irrigation system was Brentwood Country Club in Los Angeles. The system,

Conversion of quick coupler systems to fully automatic increased during the 60s and 70s.

Courtesy, Rain Bird

Solid-state field controllers enabled superintendents to increase the number of stations and to repeat cycles as needed to match infiltation rates.

installed in the early 50s, provided wall-to-wall coverage using Buckner heads and valves and a Moody controller. The 18-hole system cost Brentwood $120,000.

Although the early systems were hydraulically controlled and had little flexibility, they offered many advantages. During the 1950s, many courses elected to use this new maintenance tool, particularly in the Sun Belt. Development of golf courses in desert resorts became more practical.

With the introduction of electrically-activated valves following World War II, automating existing quick-coupler systems became simpler. Upgrading was now a matter of converting valves, running wire and installing electromechanical controllers. The newfound ease of control gave golf course architects, irrigation designers and superintendents the confidence to add more sprinklers and zones. With so many more zones, the capacity of electromechanical controllers was stretched to its limit. Golf courses required a dozen or more field controllers to effectively schedule their irrigation

systems. Electric controllers also opened the door for moisture and pressure sensors, since these devices could be installed to interrupt the current to any valve.

The development of the transistor changed many aspects of American life during the 1960s. Once bulky tube-type radios were replaced with hand-held, battery-powered "transistor radios." Electronics were quickly miniaturized, including the irrigation controller.

The device that gained the most from the development of tiny transistors and resistors was the computer. Electromechanical switches became digital circuits. Twelve-station controllers could be upgraded to 24- and 36-station, solid-state models. The capacity of field controllers grew accordingly. A virtually infinite number of stations was now available. If need be, every head on the course could have its own identity in the controller. Manufacturers wasted no time in incorporating valves in their large, pop-up turf sprinklers.

The ultimate, the central computerized controller, surfaced in the

1970s. Now, a superintendent could change the irrigation programs of a number of field controllers from one keyboard on the desk in his office. At first, the central had to be linked to field controllers with wire. This is no longer necessary with radio and telecommunications. Today, a superintendent can operate any sprinkler head on his course either from his desk or with a hand-held remote control.

Important modern innovations in golf course management are11 computerized water management systems. With a conventional desktop personal computer and associated devices, a superintendent can link an irrigation schedule to feedback from on-site weather stations, moisture sensors and data loggers for pump energy and water sources. By using only the amount of water needed and applying it in the most economical way and at the most effective time, golf courses save millions of gallons of water and thousands of dollars each year.

Computers make calculations in seconds that could take a superintendent hours. By monitoring weather, tracking system performance, adjusting run times, controlling pump output and observing many other factors, computerized control of irrigation is extremely precise.

For example, a zone that irrigates turf on a slope might need 0.25 inches of water at a low application rate to avoid runoff. Once this information is entered into the computer program, the computer can calculate how many times to repeat short cycles until the required amount of water has been applied. The computer can store a unique set of variables for any irrigation zone and take them into account before setting the schedule.

Turfgrass managers routinely refer to "ET." This acronym stands for evapotranspiration, the amount of water that is lost by evaporation from the soil, transpired through plant surfaces and consumed by the plant's metabolism. ET is expressed as a decimal representing a daily total.

An on-site weather station can provide all of the information needed to calculate the daily ET. By accessing information in the weather station's data logger, the central computer can calculate the ET and adjust irrigation schedules accordingly.

Well documented evaporation rates for overhead sprinklers show that pressurized nozzles discharging water into dry air warmer than 85 degrees F. lose 35 to 40 percent to evaporation. This helps reveal the potential for saving water with the aid of computers. Computerized water management systems have also demonstrated time savings of 50 to 70 percent during seeding and establishment of turf grass. Such levels of conservation are attainable with properly designed and operated golf course irrigation systems.

Reclaimed Water and Fertigation

Because golf courses can consume one to two million gallons of water daily, they are perfect candidates for reclaimed water. The desirability of nighttime watering and the demand for water at one location makes for a perfect marriage. Reclaimed water is not only economical, but also provides nitrogen, which can reduce overall fertilizer requirements. During these times of scarce and expensive water, reclaimed water is a wise choice for golf courses, and in extreme cases, can make the very existence of a golf course feasible.

Modern irrigation systems also afford an efficient way to provide general fertilization. Fertilizers can be injected on a regular basis, allowing maintenance personnel to maintain a constant supply of chemicals with very little fluctuation. The result is an aesthetic standard difficult to achieve by other means.

To the modern-day golf course superintendent, sprinkler irrigation is a vital part of management procedures. It ranks in importance with mowing, fertilization, pest control, weed control, aeration and topdressing. In most cases, adjustments in irrigation can greatly improve playing conditions. How a superintendent manages an irrigation system can make or break a career.

Whether a course is located in Duluth, Minnesota or El Paso, Texas, irrigation is part of management. Golf course irrigation management is an established, year-round fact in the temperate and semi-tropical West, South and Southeast. The superb condition of golf courses in the unforgiving deserts of Arizona and California is, more than anything else, a tribute to irrigation and its management. Unproductive parched sands have been transformed into spectacular landscapes surrounding championship quality golf courses.

Modern golf course irrigation technology emulates the dedication of the originators of the game. Scientific experimentation in this broad field will soon surpass what history has recorded to date.

Courtesy, Rain Bird

A superintendent can control all field satellites from his desk with the aid of a desktop computer.

Controllers can store historical weather data and use this information to seasonally adjust irrigation schedules.

Opening of IA Exposition in 1983. (Left to right) Claude Laval, Walter Anderson, Ernest Hodas and Gary Parker.

CHAPTER 11

Tracing the History
of the Irrigation Association

*"...Combining the mutual interests of all who are concerned
with developing and increasing the use of sprinkler
irrigation systems."*

*T*he potential of portable sprinkler irrigation in crop production was clearly recognized following World War II. The catalyst was the growing availability of aluminum. The lightweight metal began to replace heavy steel tubing and fittings made of cast iron or steel.

The proponents of sprinkler irrigation saw an urgent need to form a trade association representing the irrigation industry. In 1948, they seized the opportunity to discuss the idea during the National Reclamation Congress in Oklahoma City. They realized that to represent the industry adequately, the membership would have to include distributors and suppliers, in addition to manufacturers.

The following year at the Palmer House in Chicago a group of eight industry leaders cast their votes to create an association to represent a cross-section of the sprinkler irrigation industry. They were: Fred Boyton of Reynolds Metals Company, Ken Cadigan of Gorman-Rupp Pump Company, Ray Foss of R.M. Wade &

Company, A. R. J. "Bud" Friedmann of Skinner Irrigation Company, Ellsworth Gage of Shur-Rane Company, Marion Miller of Anderson-Miller Company, Charles Race of Race and Race Manufacturing Company, and John Seitzinger of Oaks Irrigation Company. They named the new organization the Association of Sprinkler Irrigation Equipment Manufacturers (ASIEM)

Marvin Shearer speaking to the association in 1966 in San Francisco.

Robert Morgan (right) presents Industry Achievement Award to Arthur E. Jensen in 1984.

ing, Marion Miller of Anderson-Miller Company, and Ross B. Whidden with Aluminum Company of America.

The need for an association with ASIEM's objectives was quickly demonstrated in 1950 when the country plunged into the Korean War. The War Production Board, established during World War II, again went into immediate allocations of strategic materials. The officers and board of the association recognized that representation in Washington, D.C., was critical to ensure an adequate supply of raw materials for their industry.

They retained Joseph King, an attorney well oriented to the Capitol, as local counsel. His duties were to inform the federal government in general, the War Production Board in particular, of the irrigation industry's needs for aluminum and brass as they related to the production of food and fiber. King was successful in obtaining allocations of these materials for industry manufacturers.

In addition to legal representation, the ASIEM believed it was important to have a full-time industry representative in Washington. R.M. Wade & Company offered to loan the services of Robert C. Mueller to the association for the duration of

for the purpose of, "combining the mutual interests of all who are concerned with developing and increasing the use of sprinkler irrigation systems."

The first slate of officers to lead the association included Everett H. Davis; Bud Friedmann, vice president; and A. S. Marlow, Jr., president of Marlow Pumps, Ridgewood, New Jersey, secretary-treasurer. After just three months as president, Davis relinquished the office to Friedmann due to company responsibilities. In addition to the officers, there were four committee members. They were Cadigan of Gorman-Rupp, Larry Johnson of Champion Manufactur-

IA officers and board.
Back Row (left to right): Pearl Conrad, Jim Lee, Glenn Tribe, George Lockwood, LaVon Bohling, Paxton Harris, Mike Sypolt, Tom Kimmell
Front Row (left to right): Wally Anderson, John Riddering, Pepper Putnam, Claude Laval, Ray York, O.N. DiRienzo,

IA Past President Jim Wearin addresses the membership in 1980.

the conflict in Korea. Mueller went to work for the National Production Administration, a part of the Works Progress Administration.

The efforts of King and Mueller, combined with the support of Wade Newbegin of R.M. Wade & Company, Crawford Reid of Rain Bird and Marion Miller of Anderson-Miller, carried the industry through the Korean War years.

The sprinkler irrigation industry emerged as an established member of the U.S. business community. Overhead sprinkler irrigation was heralded as the greatest U.S. agricultural achievement since the moldboard plow.

In 1953, the association was officially incorporated as the Sprinkler Irrigation Association (SIA). Its next challenge was to seek relief from repressive freight rates. Because aluminum tubing was bulky, even though it was light, freight carriers increased rates on the irrigation hardware by as much as 100 percent. A committee consisting of King, Newbegin, Alfred S. Gray and J.F. Newby was successful in holding the rate increases to tolerable levels through the 1950s and into the 1960s. Their tenacious efforts saved members thousands of dollars as portable sprinkler irrigation gained importance in agriculture.

The significance of aluminum is evident in the statistics for the period. Government figures reveal that 1,250,000 pounds of tubing were installed in the U.S. in 1946. By 1955, that figure had risen to an astounding 50 million pounds.

The objectives of the Sprinkler Irrigation Association were to increase farmer acceptance of sprinkler irrigation, promote it as a supplement to rain, advocate water conservation throughout the country and to strengthen and broaden the scope of the association.

Over the next three decades it reached the following mileposts that have contributed to its rapid prominence as an irrigation trade association.

1. An educational program that eliminated prejudice and misunderstanding about sprinkler irrigation.

2. Entry of the SIA in the American Society of Agricultural Engineers Awards contest.

3. Launching of the development of "Minimum Performance Standards."

4. Publication of an Engineering Textbook on Sprinkler Irrigation by Allan W. McCulloch and John F. Schrunk.

5. Conducting of educational clinics and workshops, forerunners of today's widely heralded IA "Certified Irrigation Design Programs."

Sterling Davis proudly displays his Man of the Year Award during the IA Conference in Kansas City in 1984.

6. An early educational irrigation film, "Weather or Not," jointly sponsored by the National Fertilizer Association and the SIA. It was awarded Blue Ribbon status by the ASAE as a classroom aid.

The association's accomplishments grew as the years passed. In 1976, when the interests of the industry were no longer confined to sprinkler irrigation, the organization assumed the name the Irrigation Association. Nor is the association's influence confined to the borders of the United States. Today, through its annual exposition, seminars, committees and certification program, the impact of the IA is felt throughout world.

Presidents of the Irrigation Association

1950	A.R.J. Friedmann
1951-52	Crawford Reid
1953	Marion Miller
1954-55	Birger Engstrom
1956	Harold Lieder
1957	Robert Morgan
1958-59	Howard Janin
1960	L.H. Williams
1961-62	R.L. Burke
1963-64	A.E. Robison
1965-66	John McCavitt
1967-68	Hugh L. Williams
1969-70	John J. Oldfield
1971	Donald L. Sanders
1972	Austin Miller
1973	M.L. Rawson
1974	John H. Stevens
1975	James D. Pichon
1976	W.J. Ogle
1977	Kenneth B. White, Jr.
1978	Paul B. Bohley
1979	Taylor Ramsey
1980	Jim Wearin
1981	W.J. Liddell
1982	Gary D. Parker
1983	Ernie Hodas
1984	Claude C. Laval, III
1985	Charles S. Putnam
1986	Raymon A. York
1987	John H. Riddering
1988	William R. Pogue
1989	Richard Hunter
1990	Glenn O. Tribe
1991	Robert C. Emmerich
1992	Thomas H. Kimmell
1993	William F. Koonz

Partners in Progress

*T*his special section of <u>Water and the Land</u> features our "Partners in Progress." This important part of our history of irrigation in America presents biographies of companies and organizations whose accomplishments and contributions have been and will continue to be essential to our industry's continuing growth and success.

*W*e owe these companies, and all of their employees, a debt of gratitude. Their commitment to better irrigation practices benefits all mankind. Their participation here is a major source of funding for this book. Without the support of all of these firms, <u>Water and the Land</u> would literally not exist.

Agricultural Products, Inc.
AMS Engineering and
    Environmental
Antelco Pty. Ltd.
Bermad
John A. Brooks, Inc.
Century Rain Aid
Champion Irrigation Products
Chapin Watermatics, Inc.
Cornell Pump Company
Delta Irrigation, Inc.
Dig Corporation
DuPont Engineering Polymers
Ewing Irrigation Products
FEBCO
Frank W. Murphy Manufacturer

Golden State Irrigation Services
Griswold Controls
Hardie Irrigation
Hastings Irrigation Pipe Company
Hunter Industries
Hydro-Scape Products, Inc.
Irrometer Company, Inc.
L.R. Nelson Corporation
Marion Miller & Associates
Maxi-Jet
Midwest Irrigation Company
Naco Industries, Inc.
Nelson Irrigation
Olson Irrigation Systems
Pierce Corporation
Rain Bird International

Rain for Rent
Roberts Irrigation Products, Inc.
Russell Daniel Irrigation
Spears Manufacturing Company
Superior Controls Co., Inc.
T-L Irrigation Company
T-Systems International, Inc.
The Toro Company
Underhill International
    Corporation
Universal Irrigation Sales
    Corporation
Valmont Irrigation
Wade Mfg. Co.
Weather-matic
Weather-Tec Corporation
Western Brass

RAIN BIRD

A LEADER IN IRRIGATION

The start of RainBird... manufacturing begins in a barn in 1935.

The Beginning

It all began with U.S. Patent number 1,997,901, awarded on December 18, 1933, to citrus farmer Orton Englehart for a novel watering device described as a "spring-activated horizontal impact arm driven sprinkler". This new sprinkler was durable and distributed water farther, more evenly and much more efficiently than the existing sprinklers of the day.

Englehart's neighbors Clement and Mary LaFetra were so taken with the invention that in 1935 they arranged to manufacture the devices in their barn. Their products revolutionized irrigation. The LaFetra's son, Anthony LaFetra, joined Rain Bird in 1964 and has served as president since 1977.

Since this dramatic entrance into the industry more than 60 years ago, Rain Bird Sprinkler Manufacturing Corporation has grown into the largest manufacturer of irrigation systems in the world. Based in Glendora, California, USA, Rain Bird has extensive engineering, manufacturing, testing, sales and shipping facilities in Southern California. The company also has offices, manufacturing plants, warehouses and company sales representatives in several other states and foreign countries, and conducts business in more than 120 countries worldwide.

• Rain Bird International • 145 N. Glendora Avenue, California 91740 •

History of Innovation

Rain Bird Sprinkler Manufacturing Corporation followed one innovation with another...and another. Today Rain Bird holds more than 130 patents for all types of irrigation equipment, such as the Precision Jet (PJ ™) tube, an impact sprinkler feature that eliminates side splash, saving millions of gallons of water every year. Other inventions include a host of controller features which allow watering schedules to be tailored to specific landscape needs and to respond to changing climatic conditions. The list of Rain Bird product innovations continues, from tiny pressure compensating screens to a complete computerized central control system. Rain Bird innovations save water, save money and help plant life to thrive.

Worldwide Support Network

The rhythmic sound of Rain Bird impact sprinklers is familiar to people around the world and has become almost synonymous with the Rain Bird name. But impact sprinklers are just one element of a full line comprising hundreds of quality products. The Rain Bird line includes sprinklers, sprayheads, emitters, nozzles, rotors, valves, controllers and moisture sensors. All products are designed and tested according to strict quality standards and backed by Rain Bird's worldwide network of distributors and Authorized Service Centers.

Meeting The Needs of the World's Diverse Landscapes

Renowned landscapes around the world flourish with the help of Rain Bird irrigation products. Any fan of World Cup Soccer has seen Rain Bird-irrigated turf at such noted sites as Rome's Olympic Stadium and the Estadio Bernabeu in Madrid. In fact, Rain Bird sprinklers, valves and controllers keep life-giving water flowing to landscaping at sprawling amusements parks, sports arenas, airports, golf courses, botanical gardens and private homes across America and in more than 120 other countries.

Rain Bird... Because Every Drop Counts

At every step, Rain Bird focuses on the most efficient possible use of the planet's most valuable resource - water. This concern shows in Rain Bird's innovative products; it shows in the design aids, seminars and training programs Rain Bird provides for landscape and irrigation professionals; and most importantly, it shows in green landscapes and lower water bills. Quality products. Water-saving innovations.

BELOW: Rain Bird's first manufacturing plant with citrus farmer Orton Englehart's novel watering device described as a "spring-activated horizontal impact arm driven sprinkler", and a current watering device, a pop-up sprayhead sprinkler.

Worldwide service and support. All of these are important in the creation and maintenance of water-efficient irrigation systems, and, all are keys to Rain Bird's leadership position in the irrigation industry.

The Rain Bird Name

An ancient Indian legend tells of a terrible drought that befell the land hundreds of years ago. Crops withered and the watering holes dried up. For a generation there was no relief. Everyone but the children gave up hope.

Then, one day, a great bird overheard the children's simple, urgent prayers. The bird flew to the heavens and returned with the long-awaited, life-giving rain. The bird-like appearance of the efficient impact sprinklers, which company founders Clement and Mary LaFetra introduced to the world in 1935, prompted them to name their new company after the great rain bird of Indian legend. And so the modern Rain Bird legend was born.

TOP:1800 Series Pop-up Sprayhead Sprinklers

BOTTOM: The SSteelhead, winner of the ASAE award for one of top 50 innovative products in 1991.

• Rain Bird International • 145 N. Glendora Avenue, California 91740 •

The Rain Bird Companies

Rain Bird has separated its operations into six different Strategic Business Units. Each SBU is responsible for the manufacture and sales of products designed for a specific customer, market or application. Following is a brief description of those six SBUs.

Contractor SBU

The Contractor SBU delivers products to professional landscape and

TOP: The newest rotor in the line, the Falcon Rotor

BOTTOM: A low flow irrigation device from Rain Bird

irrigation contractors who design and install irrigation systems in residential and light commercial facilities, including private homes. The Contractor SBU offers a complete line of irrigation system products with marketing support such as its acclaimed Professional Edge program and a direct 800 service line for contractors.

Commercial SBU

The Commercial SBU, headquartered in Tucson, Arizona, targets contrac-

Rain Bird's headquarters today in Glendora, California.

tors, landscape architects and irrigation designers. Their products are installed on major commercial and public properties, including shopping centers, schools, industrial complexes, city parks and sports fields. This SBU offers state-of-the-art irrigation software and a toll-free hotline to answer customers' questions.

The Consumer Products SBU

The Consumer Products SBU sells its products

through retail stores, such as home improvement centers, hardware stores and lawn and garden shops, which sell directly to homeowners. Headquartered in San Diego, California, this SBU offers hose-end lawn and garden products as well as drip and underground watering products that can be easily installed by the homeowner. The Consumer Products SBU provides a toll-free hotline for consumers, and it is the industry leader in packaging innovations.

Golf SBU

The Golf SBU offers complete irrigation systems for golf courses to superintendents, landscape architects and irrigation consultants. This division provides thorough site analysis as well as extensive support, training and after sales service. The Golf SBU also offers its patented MAXI computer control system, the ultimate tool for effective water management.

Agri-Products SBU

The Agri-Products SBU delivers irrigation products to farmers and agribusinesses through a network of wholesale distributors and independent dealers. The SBU's products include sprinkler systems and low flow systems designed to save water and energy while providing superior crop production.

International SBU

As Rain Bird's marketing and sales arm for overseas, the International SBU delivers a complete line of Rain Bird sprinkler and drip irrigation products to more than 120 countries around the world. This division's customers cover the entire range that the other SBUs service separately. These include contractors, landscape architects and irrigation designers, golf course superintendents and retail store buyers.

Manufacturing

Rain Bird's products are manufactured in the company's numerous Southern California area facilities. Rain Bird also has manufacturing plants in other locations: Arizona, which produces items for the Commercial SBU; Mexico, which is utilized by the Agri-Products, Contractor and Consumer Products units; and France, which manufactures products for the Agri-Products and International SBU's. The company also manufactures products through exclusive arrangements with off-shore sources.

Sales and Distribution

The Contractor, Commercial, Agri-Products and International

SBU's distribute their products through a network of wholesales distributors to reach customers such as independent contractors, irrigation designers and small farmers. The Consumer Products SBU employs its own sales force in addition to using independent manufactur-ers' representatives. The Golf SBU employs regional sales managers to target a network of exclusive golf distributors.

The Legend Continues

In 1990, Rain Bird impact sprinklers joined Eli Whitney's cotton gin as an American Society of Agriculture Engineers (ASAE) historic engineering landmark, the society's highest honor. The legend continues as the SSteelhead, the world's first stainless steel impact sprinkler, received an ASAE award for being one of the top 50 innovative products in 1991. Recent other ASAE top 50 innovative products included Rain Bird Rain Tape.

Today, Rain Bird maintains its position as the world's leading manufacturer of irrigation products.

BELOW: New developments in the Golf Line...the MSC controller and the Eagle rotor.

VALMONT IRRIGATION

Valmont Industries is the largest manufacturer and distributor of mechanized irrigation systems in the world. In fact, through an inspired fusion of foresight, merchandising, and $5,000, Valmont quite literally created the entire industry.

Valmont's Origins

Nobody could possibly have envisioned this in 1946, when a young ex-Marine named Robert Daugherty was looking for a good business opportunity...and found one. Daugherty recognized the potential of a small manufacturing company owned by an inventor named Sam McCleneghan. After careful consideration, he invested virtually his entire savings — $5,000 — in the

**Robert B. Daugherty
Chairman of the Board,
Valmont Industries, Inc.**

company and soon brought in his uncle, Frank Daugherty. The company, which was situated on a farm just west of Valley, Nebraska, was named **Valley Manufacturing** and began by building farm elevators. (In 1967, the name of the company was changed to Valmont Industries, Inc., to avoid confusion with other companies using Valley in their name. The name Valmont is a combination of two Nebraska communities located on either side of Valmont headquarters, Valley and Fremont.)

Eventually the new company contracted with Sears, Roebuck to supply 1,000 elevators. They soon added speed jacks, wagon hoists, universal joints, hay rakes, stalk cutters, minimum tillage tools and a front-end loader to their product list. When recession hit the farm industry in 1952, Valley Manufacturing began looking for ways to diversify. That search led down the road to Columbus, Nebraska, where a visionary was struggling to breathe life into a revolutionary idea: the center pivot.

Development of the Center Pivot

Frank Zybach, part-farmer and part-tinkerer, had hammered together the prototype center pivot in 1947 after viewing a demonstration of hand-moved pipe. During the next several years, he continually modified and refined the basic design to improve its operational efficiency. Unfortunately, it proved difficult to market a system that always seemed to be undergoing changes. Finally, frustration at having failed to capture a significant market segment led the inventor to sell his patent rights to Bob Daugherty in 1953.

Like many great inventions at their birth, the early center pivot wasn't pretty. As Daugherty recalls, "It was a contraption — a great, long piece of pipe mounted on wheels every 100 feet or so. It sprayed water on crops, and it moved around in a circle so slowly that it looked as though it moved not at all. And it didn't work very well."

Nevertheless, he judged the center pivot "a brilliant idea" with the potential for making fundamental changes in irrigation. In fact, Scientific American (June 1976) named the center pivot "perhaps the most significant mechanical innovation in agriculture since the replacement of draft animals by the tractor." Valmont believed that, if the center pivot could be made stronger and more reliable, farmers would realize enormous benefits through reduced use of water and time, leading to improved land and crop management. But for Valley Manufacturing to succeed with this "contraption," two critical objectives had to be met: they needed to perfect the irrigation system's structure and mechanics, and they had to establish an effective marketing organization.

Early Challenges for Valmont

To say that Valmont faced an uphill battle at this point is to seriously understate the situation. Valmont's engineers took Zybach's unit apart and rebuilt it again and again over the next several years to make it sturdier, taller, and more reliable. Even then, the agricultural experts remained critical.

"When we installed our first systems, we always had farmers and other folks gathering to watch: 1,200 feet of pipe, 10 or 12 towers, steel wheels, all kinds of cable holding up the pipeline and cable holding up the towers. All in all, it did not look too promising," Daugherty recalls.

At one installation-in Texas-one of the locals called over to ask, "What does this Rube Goldberg machine do?" After Daugherty's careful explanation, the farmer responded, "Well, mister, that may be, but if it doesn't work, it sure will make a great buzzard roost."

The Valmont team concluded that the labor- and water-saving attributes of the center pivot were not the only marketable features. "The fact that it could irrigate light, sandy soils became the economic driving force that eventually brought many sales. A farmer would buy cheap land, $50 an acre, and then raise better crops than on land costing ten times as much," Daugherty said.

They also found that fertilizers and insecticides could be mixed with the sprinkler water and that rolling land could be irrigated, thus opening thousands of additional acres to irrigation.

Marketing Organization

While Valmont engineers were engaged in improving the efficiency and reliability of the center-pivot, the company was skillfully developing an effective marketing organization. The first dealers were five successful, mechanically inclined farmers who had purchased center pivots. By 1965, the sales force had mushroomed to 25 dealers, selling in a dozen states. The dealer organization, marketing systems under the Valley trade name, sold nearly 900 units in 1968. This positioned Valmont for dramatic growth in the early 1970s.

Meanwhile, the system's fame spread to the general public in a unique way. The strange green circles that passengers saw from the air prompted a raft of questions, so Valmont sent letters to all the airlines. Soon, in-flight announcements were being made about Valmont, center pivots, and mechanized irrigation.

Today's network of more than 200 value-added Valmont dealerships is widely acknowledged as the best-trained and most knowledgeable in the industry. Each dealership is evaluated annually on professionalism, product knowledge and customer service.

Re-engineering the Center Pivot

By the early 1960s, according to Daugherty, Valmont had overcome most of the design and production problems. A basic improvement was conversion from the original water hydraulic power system to electric drive. Most machines were running on electric power by 1975.

Other "firsts" followed, each reinforcing Valmont's leadership role in this dynamic, young industry. Hot-dip galvanizing was begun in 1966, providing long-term corrosion protection. The company also extended the

FRANK ZYBACK'S CENTER PIVOT, C. 1953
The pipeline on early center pivots was barely three feet above the ground. Propulsion was supplied by water flowing into the main pipeline and then into the hydraulic cylinder.

• (402)-359-2201 • FAX (402)-359-4429 •

VALLEY CENTER PIVOT, MID-1960s
Valmont re-engineered the center pivot extensively to provide greater system reliability and irrigation efficiency. Crop clearance was 7 1/2 feet, wheels were larger, and a porcelain-coated drive cylinder reduced wear on drive train components.

life of each system with the introduction of high-quality drive train components, the most expensive part of the system. Since 1974, Valmont has built its own gearbox - the only company in the industry to do so— which many other pivot systems utilize as a replacement part.

Valmont introduced corner systems in 1975 to assist in irrigating square, rectangular and odd-shaped fields. This addresses the frequently asked question of how to irrigate valuable corner acres. The corner system is simply a regular center pivot system with an articulated arm attached at the outer end. Following a low-frequency signal emitted from a buried cable, this arm is guided by a steerable drive unit so that it extends into corners and retracts around buildings and other obstacles. The first system was installed in Wray, Colorado, and drew the rapt attention of Valmont's competitors, who overflew the field to take photographs. "A sort of U-2 affair," Daugherty said.

Another development was the linear system, which Valley pioneered in 1977. Unlike the center pivot, the linear travels straight down the field, making it the preferred mechanized system for long, rectangular fields and heavy soils. It has been particularly successful with the irrigation of grains, forages, fiber crops, vegetables, and vines.

With the energy crisis of the mid-1970s came concern about the cost of operating high-pressure mechanized systems. Consequently, Valmont developed a series of low-pressure systems capable of reducing energy costs by up to 80 percent. The company also installed computers in its dealerships to assist sales representatives in designing energy-efficient systems based on an individual farmer's energy costs, crops and terrain.

C:A:M:S

Valmont's integration of computers into modern farming practice led to another significant break-through in the 1980s: the Computer Aided Management System (C:A:M:S) pivot panel. Named to the prestigious "Agricultural Engineering 50" for 1991, C:A:M:S enables farmers to quickly, easily and confidently program and monitor their center-pivot systems to accomplish a full range of irrigation, chemigation and fertilization functions, all based on time, date, field position, crop grouping, soil type and other variables.

Once the information is programmed in, the panel ensures that the correct amount of water (or chemicals or fertilizer) is delivered to each section of the field, automatically making adjustments as the span passes over different crops and soil types.

The C:A:M:S panel features on-screen prompts to guide operators smoothly through programming steps. Irrigation programs may be scheduled for periods exceeding three months at a time. C:A:M:S stores up to nine different programs, which may be recalled again and again for different cropping patterns or changing seasons.

A C:A:M:S Windspeed Monitor was introduced shortly afterwards, allowing C:A:M:S users to program the system to shut down automatically when a predetermined wind speed is detected. This provides irrigation uniformity by limiting drifting and has proven invaluable in helping to accurately apply chemicals.

Another innovative enhancement was the C:A:M:S Flow Meter. Its purpose was to simplify the grower's task of accurately tracking and reporting water usage.

By 1992, C:A:M:S panels were employed on farms from coast to coast, managing the irrigation of cotton, corn, wheat, soybeans, potatoes, and a variety of vegetables and specialty crops.

C:A:M:S BASE STATION

The extraordinary in-field savings in time and resources available with the C:A:M:S panel firmly reinforced Valmont's role as the industry pacesetter, but there was more to come. In 1991, Valmont unveiled the C:A:M:S Base Station. The ease and efficiency of computer programming was thus moved from the field to an office, den or living room. Armed with an IBM-compatible 386 personal computer, a mouse, a color monitor, and a radio modem and transmitter (for sending signals to individual C:A:M:S panels), the grower could now control and monitor dozens of center-pivot systems from one location when a modem and radio transceiver are attached to each panel. Not surprisingly, Agricultural Engineering magazine included the Base Station as one of

its 1992 list of honorees.

Valmont also developed special software to enable computer operators to view a colorized diagram of their fields. At a glance, a farmer can tell if a pivot is running with water, running without water, or is not running. If there is a problem, the farmer uses the computer to isolate the problem before dispatching someone to put the pivot back into operation.

The base station is a natural outgrowth of technology that has been proven in industrial monitoring and control applications worldwide and further developed by Valmont in the early 1980s, according to John Chapman, Valmont's Director of Research and Development. In coopera-tion with United States Department of Agriculture experts, Valmont tested a number of radio-controlled units on a farm near Sterling, Colorado. More than a dozen projects still use this early technology. Valmont also developed a highly successful wastewa-ter system for Duncan, Oklahoma, using radio telemetry. "It's fair to call C:A:M:S a descendant of this pioneering system, and it's important to note the years of in-field experience that stand behind it," Chapman said.

Additional Lines of Business

Over the years, Valmont's success fostered the growth of additional business lines. Pipe and tubing were added out of necessity. "We'd found that it wasn't always easy to get the pipe we required when we needed it and at the right price. So we decided to make our own," Daugherty said. As they found other markets for their pipe, they gradually established a ma-jor niche in manufacturing light poles. Today, Valmont's **Industrial and Construc-tion Products Division** (ICPD) organization is the world's leader in supplying pole structures for traffic and lighting applications and is a major supplier to the electrical transmission and communications indus-tries. In 1989, Valmont ac-quired Sermento, a leading producer of steel and alumi-num poles in France.

VALLEY CORNER SYSTEM, 1976
Valmont pioneered the corner system in 1975 for irregularly shaped fields. The initial investment in a center pivot is leveraged by bringing incremental acres into productive use.

VALLEY LINEAR SYSTEM, EARLY 1980s
Introduced to the market in 1977, the Valley linear is particularly well suited for high-value crops where total field coverage offsets the additional labor required.

VALLEY CENTER PIVOT, EARLY 1990s
As it has from the very beginning, the Valley center pivot, the ultimate labor and resource management tool, continues as the standard by which all other systems are measured. More than 9 million acres around the world are now being irrigated by Valley systems.

Valmont Electrical, another offshoot, manufactures and distributes lighting ballasts and controls to the construction and renovation markets.

Overseas Sales

Valmont began developing overseas markets in the early 1970s, forming Valmont International. Licensing agreements were established in Saudi Arabia, Brazil, Yugoslavia, Austria, and the Soviet Union. Valmont translated and printed brochures and product literature in several languages and participated in key trade shows throughout the world.

By the mid-1970s, Valmont had begun to capitalize on opportunities created as foreign governments sought to convert less efficient irrigation systems and develop arid regions. In time, substantial numbers of pivot and linear move systems were sold in Europe, the Middle East, Africa, Australia, the People's Republic of China, Thailand, and Latin America. There were even a few in Switzerland and a handful just outside London.

Long-term efforts frequently paid off dramatically. For example, following two decades of irrigation technology sales to the Soviet Union, Valmont subsequently was authorized to construct a $28 million facility for the production of drip irrigation components. In 1989, Valmont signed a five-year agreement valued at $25 million with KITE, a Hungarian cooperative. This contract capped three years of successful irrigation assistance in Hungary.

In 1988, the company purchased a fifty percent interest in Rudolf Bauer, A.G., an irrigation company based in Voitsberg, Austria. The two companies entered into cross-licensing agreements, and Valmont assumed the manufacturing and distribution of Bauer products in North America. Bauer was later bought by a European company, and

Valmont relinquished its interest in 1991.

The North American Irrigation and International Irrigation segments were combined to form **Valmont Irrigation** in 1990, creating a single management structure for all aspects of sales, marketing, manufacturing and distribution. In addition, closure of a manufacturing facility in Spain, where center pivots and linear moves as well as a system designed for small- and medium-sized fields were produced, meant consolidation of all manufacturing at Valmont's headquarters in Valley.

In 1991, the European dealership was broadened. Eastern European operations, based in Budapest, grew in profitability despite widespread political and economic uncertainty throughout the region. Increased sales to the Middle East and Latin America the following year strengthened Valmont's dominant worldwide position.

Today, Valmont distributes its mechanized irrigation systems in more than 70 countries.

The Future

And what were the results of nearly four decades of innovative engineering and sophisticated marketing? After surviving the anemic sales of the first decade, Valmont tallied as many as 900 systems annually in the 1960s. By the 1970s, annual sales of center pivot and linear move irrigation units had increased well into the thousands.

The 25,000th mechanized system was sold in 1979 and the 50,000th in 1984. Projections indicate that, by the end of 1993, more than 80,000 Valmont irrigation systems will have been sold worldwide, a number that far exceeds that of any competitor and, according to many observers, surpasses the combined total of most rival companies.

Valmont recognizes the irony by which mankind's efficiency in harnessing natural resources to provide for the welfare of present and future generations is often simultaneously blamed for the very depletion of those resources. Thus, while food and fiber production races to keep pace with global population growth, now inexorably approaching 6 billion, we find ourselves engaged in a delicate balancing act, mandating that each individual and every corporation becomes environmentally responsible.

At Valmont, conservation of resources has been, and remains, the cornerstone of success. The savings in time and water, combined with the precision application of fertilizers and chemicals, enable farmers throughout the world to develop land and harvest crops to satisfy an increasingly high demand. From the rugged center pivots of the 1950s to today's computer-run systems, all painting green circles visible from hundreds of miles above the earth, Valmont continues to set the standard for engineering and environmental excellence.

TOP: C:A:M:S PIVOT PANEL
Valmont made the advantages and benefits of computerized technology available to irrigators with the award-winning Valley C:A:M:S pivot panel.

BOTTOM: C:A:M:S BASE STATION
Just as the Valley center pivot transformed irrigation forever, so the Valley C:A:M:S Base Station has initiated a revolution in how future irrigators will interface with, and manage, our most precious resource: water.

GOLDEN STATE IRRIGATION SERVICES

Golden State Irrigation Services, headquartered in Stockton, California employs a staff of water application experts. The firm designs, installs, provides materials and parts for sale and rent in six Western States, Latin America and Canada.

The founders, James Clare, Bonnie Bunyard and Michael Conrad worked together for several years before starting Golden State in November of 1985. The firm installed over 125 irrigation systems that first year. Jim and Mike each qualified for California State Contractors Licenses and hold Certifications by the

> "We know irrigation equipment because we own it and use it ourselves. We know what works and what doesn't."

© Rich Turner

Farmington, California grower Larry Togninali germinates his processing tomatoes and peppers with sprinklers then irrigates through harvest with drip. Over the last twelve years Togninali Farms has realized an increase in production and quality of 2 1/2 times while reducing use of pesticides, fertilizers, electricity and diesel fuel. Steven Sanguinetti (pictured at right) is a Golden State designer and field man.

Jim Clare, Bonnie Bunyard and Mike Conrad (pictured left to right) founded Golden State Irrigation Services in November of 1985.

© Rich Turner

Irrigation Association in Agricultural Sprinkler, Drip, and Surface Irrigation. Those first few years "the boys" designed and sold while Bonnie ran the Store, sold the parts and loaded the trucks. According to CEO Clare: "From the beginning, our mission was to provide first rate service and timely response to each customer large or small. We strive to stay abreast of new developments in water application technology."

The diverse agriculture of the San Joaquin Valley and the Delta Region, the Coast Range and Sierra Foothills, the variety of crops, climate and soil type challenged the company to incorporate a wide range of expertise coupled with a variety of good equipment as their irrigation package. By offering an array of services, from design and construction of "turn-key" projects, rental equipment, hard to find parts, pumps and pipe for any crop any place, the company grew in size and reputation. From the beginning, Golden State has participated in partnerships and joint ventures with manufacturers and irrigation professionals to develop and improve irrigation equipment and application. The conversion from aluminum to plastic surface pipe which does

• Golden State Irrigation Services • 1648 North Shaw Road • Stockton, CA 95215 • (209) 943-7774 •

This 1946 Dodge hauled first loads of irrigation pipe to customers in the Nebraska area.

Washington, Idaho, Utah and other states.

With the addition of the Madera plant, Hastings Irrigation is now the largest manufacturer of seam-welded aluminum pipe and tube in the United States. From its beginning in 1949, Hastings Irrigation Pipe Company has always had one goal in mind, "to continually strive to be the leader in irrigation equipment design, manufacturing and distribution." Proof of the company's philosophy can be seen in the manufacturing and technological "firsts" credited to the Hastings Irrigation Pipe Company.

❖**FIRST in the nation to weld aluminum irrigation pipe.**

❖**FIRST to roll-end reinforce aluminum irrigation pipe.**

❖**FIRST to develop and manufacture a self-sealing coupler for aluminum surface irrigation pipe.**

❖**FIRST to design and manufacture self-sealing gates for further row irrigation systems.**

Innovations in manufacturing equipment and techniques are the reasons behind the quality products that make up each Hastings Irrigation System. Constant striving to improve quality control assures Hastings customers of systems that will give maximum performance year after year.

Although the manufacturing of irrigation products has been and still is today the bread and butter of the company, it was apparent for many years that to be able to continue to grow, while spanning some of the lean years that

the irrigation market has seen, the need for diversification was a must.

To some companies this would have been a major undertaking, but with the imaginative skills of highly qualified employees who had built Hastings Irrigation into the leader of the irrigation industry, the task at hand was not a difficult one. Recognizing the need for a diversification of product lines to cope with a cycle when irrigation needs were down, a search began for a product — preferably of aluminum, with welding involved. Recreation (in particular, boating) seemed to be on the upswing so the first step, then, was to design an aluminum boat that could be made from the same aluminum sheet being used for irrigation pipe. A number of boats were made and marketed in two sizes — 14-foot and 16-foot, and two models — the open fishing boat and the Runabout.

One of seven company owned tractors dedicated to making on time deliveries coast to coast.

With the successful entry into markets other than agriculture, Hastings Irrigation Pipe Company has since designed and manufactured a multitude of products from architectural fabrications, which built solar screens, handrails and other decorative items, to satellite antennas, picnic tables and, perhaps the most successful diversification, floating internal covers and geodesic domes for the petroleum industry.

Over the years, with the ever-expanding aluminum tubing business, not only for agriculture, but also for the industrial and international market, coupled with the diversified products coming out of the production lines, it was necessary to form two new corporations to handle some of the unique problems. The first company formed was Hastings Transportation, Inc., which solved the problems of handling aluminum tubing and assured on-time deliveries of quality systems to the dealer network. The pursuit of foreign customers led to the formation of Hastings Pipe International, Inc.

Since the birth of the company in 1949, the customer has been the most important key to the success of Hastings Irrigation Pipe Company. The management team of the company has dedicated themselves to making these customers feel confident that the service they experienced in the past will continue in the future.

•   Hastings Irrigation Pipe Company   •   (402) 463-6633   •   FAX — (402) 463-4355   •   1-800-759-8823   •

JOHN A. BROOKS, INC.

Canadian born John A. Brooks never had any formal schooling past the third grade. Yet, he became one of the most prolific innovators ever known in the turf irrigation history.

Today, his legacy lives on, over 75 years after he first installed his first sprinkler system. Still headquartered in Detroit, John A. Brooks, Rain's Only Rival, thrives on his tradi-

> John A. Brooks became one of the most prolific innovators ever known in the turf irrigation history.

tion of providing quality and excellence in both irrigation system and fountain installations.

The Brooks name is renowned in the industry. His installations can be found across the world with such diverse residential clients as the King of Siam to auto baron Henry Ford.

His history of civic installations spans the country, including the Capitol Building in Washington, D.C. in the early 1930s; Grant Park in Chicago in 1937 and his earliest civic installation,

Roosevelt Park in Detroit in 1921. This installation, which was the grand entrance to the Michigan Central Train station, became a revered model upon which other cities in future years would base plans for their own systems.

In 1927 for example, when planners were developing Central Park, the New York Times noted the successful demonstration of Detroit's irrigation system, which was providing uniformly beautiful turf. With each new installation came testimonials. One such satisfied client, the superintendent of parks in Atlantic City, New Jersey, commended Brooks in 1927 for setting the sprayers "only 18 to 20 feet apart," even though this was obviously much more costly. A neighboring city, it seemed, had a system where the sprayers were 25 to 30 feet apart, and as a result, the superintendent wrote, "there were brown spots all through their lawn."

Brooks was a masterful planner of systems designed to the specific needs of his clients, in part, because he designed most, if not all, of the sprinklers he installed. A persistent engineer (it is said he continued tinkering with his inventions well into retirement in the 50s), Brooks applied for some 27 patents over the span of some four decades,

John A. Brooks, as viewed in his office, built in 1929. In the late thirties, he sold the building to Packard Automobile Company. Along with Rolls Royce engineers, the Packard employees created airplane engines for the war effort.

The Brooks building, 14528 Second Avenue, Highland Park, was literally in the shadow of the smoke stacks of Henry Ford's Highland Park assembly plant where some 28 million Model-T automobiles rolled off the line. Also at this time, a few miles down Second Avenue, the Durant (General Motors) building was just being built. Today this is the world headquarters of General Motors.

receiving 11 patents in total. His Brooks flip-top brass mist head and the Brooks 'Bazooka' (single action control) valve would become standards in the business.

Other patents ran the gamut from rubber covered heads (1927) and vacuum breaker valves to the first frost-free sprinkling system, which had a draining mechanism to prevent frost damage.

For all of his accomplishments, Brooks was not a young entrepreneur in the irrigation business. In fact, he began his business relatively late in life, in 1915 at the age of 44. Until then, he had been trained as a master plumber and for most of his early working life, he ran a plumbing business that he called "The Hustling Plumber."

But all along, he had been toying with irrigation ideas. Even in the early 1910s, he was convinced that the early methods used for watering streets to keep dust at a minimum could be applied to gardens and lawns.

Then, in 1913, a wealthy plumbing customer complained to Brooks about the cumbersome method of having gardeners hauling hoses about to water his spacious lawn. The simple inquiry was the spark which converted Brooks' drawings into actual sprinklers.

Two years later, Brooks had installed his first underground, pop-up sprinkler at a residence in Toledo, Ohio. By 1916, he had been granted both a Canadian and U.S. patent, which he called "Lawn Sprinkling Means." The following year, he applied for his "Bazooka Valve."

In 1915, Brooks moved his family from Toledo to Detroit, where he was to become the head of an established plumbing firm. His first jobs, for the prestigious Detroit families of B. Siegel, S.S. Kresge, the Dodges, the Fisher brothers of Fisher Body, and Henry Ford earned him the nickname of "a plumber with spats."

In three years time, Brooks felt confident enough to abandon his plumbing business and

> Brooks installed his first underground, pop-up sprinkler at a residence in Toledo, Ohio in 1915.

opened John A. Brooks Irrigation Specialists, located on Second Avenue in Highland Park. It was the Roaring Twenties and the Brooks building was literally in the shadow of the smoke stacks of Henry Ford's assembly plant where some 28 million Model-T automobiles rolled off the line. A scant few miles down Second Avenue at West Grand Boulevard, William Crappo Drurant was assembling the world's largest corporation as he bought out Louis Chevrolet, David Buick, Random Olds, and David Leland (Cadillac).

Brooks was draped in the wealth of the auto industry, which brought a constant flow of money and business into the state. And, as the only irrigation company in the Detroit area when he first opened, manor estates with acres of lawns that needed to be green and well-watered were at his disposal.

Detroit was also an ideal location at the time because Brooks was smack in the center of the malleable iron manufacturing industry, which turned out castings, springs, and copper and brass parts and fittings. In addition, there was the immeasurable supply of fresh water from the Great Lakes.

With Detroit on sound footing, Brooks began to expand and develop out-of-state offices in Philadelphia, New York, Chicago, Maryland, Florida and California. Brooks of California would later go on to become today's leading vacuum breaker manufacturer, Febco. Eventually, Brooks entered into marketing and sales agreements with Nibco (Northern Indiana Brass Co.). Other notable men to start at Brooks were Max Snoddy (Weathermatic), Fred Reinecke, Sr. (Febco), Ned Rowland, Ray McCallum and Austin Miller, Sr.

Instinctively knowing the importance of good marketing, Brooks would artfully solicit endorsements from customers and create in-office displays of photos and letters. He established a company newsletter called "Babbling Brooks," with which he kept his employees and branch

Now expanding into the fountain installation business, the company continues to adapt and change to meet the needs of the future.

offices up to date on new products. He published pamphlets for his salesmen to carry to prospective customers. He began mail order advertising that touted his new products in a time when general mailing was almost unheard of.

However, like any company, Brooks was not without its low points. The Depression was so severe that his installers, faced with such high prices for supplies, had to cut 1/2-inch couplings in half to make two.

But, when the war was over, Brooks rebounded and once again began to manufacture and install Brooks watering systems. As the years brought new concerns, Brooks would become well-known ;for his work in conservation, drip irrigation and vacuum breaker valves.

In 1951, Brooks retired to Florida, placing John Sydenstricker in charge to keep the company on course. Never one to retire, Brooks kept in constant contact with the Detroit office, always suggesting new ideas up to his death in 1958. During the 60s and 70s, business continued to

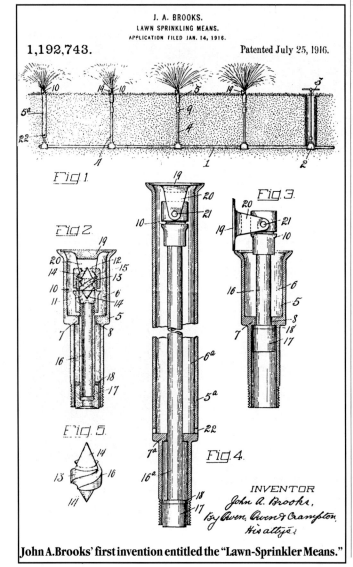

J. A. BROOKS.
LAWN SPRINKLING MEANS.
APPLICATION FILED JAN. 14, 1916.

1,192,743.   Patented July 25, 1916.

INVENTOR
John A. Brooks,
By Owen, Owen & Crampton
His attys.

John A. Brooks' first invention entitled the "Lawn-Sprinkler Means."

• John A. Brooks, Inc. • Rains Only Rival • 20114 Livernois • Detroit, Michigan 48221 •

Marc Dutton, owner of John A. Brooks, Inc., and Al Couck, field supervisor, working on the historical sprinkling system display at Fairlane Estate, once the residence of Henry Ford. Circa 1926, thousands of Brooks' pop-up sprinklers were installed on the estate by Brooks' company. Part of the original sprinkling system has been restored. The original pop-up brass heads still operate in the Jens Jenson meadow.

flourish and in the 80s, John A. Brooks, Inc. began to specialize in fountain installations.

In 1988, Marc Dutton, president of Marc Dutton Irrigation, bought the company. Dutton was thrilled to run his own full-scale irrigation company and welcomed the chal-lenge to steer John A. Brooks Inc. into the 21st century.

Today, the company reigns among the leading irrigation companies in Detroit. As in the past, the business is very tied to Detroit's auto industry. In recent years, the combined companies of Dutton and Brooks have installed irrigation at the Ford Rouge complex, General Motors Poletown and Lake Orion assembly plants as well as the G.M. New Center area at the World Headquarters, Chrysler's Jefferson Avenue Jeep assembly plant, the Dodge City Truck Complex, the newly opened billion dollar Chrysler Technological Center and Toyota's Technological Headquarters.

Now expanding into the fountain installation business, the company will continue to adapt and change to meet the needs of the future, just as John A. Brooks would have intended.

• John A. Brooks Inc. • Rains Only Rival • (313) 863-9650 • FAX (313) 674-3091 •

L. R. NELSON CORPORATION

The L. R. Nelson Corporation delivered a world-class performance at the 1992 Summer Olympic Games. The Nelson team designed, manufactured, and supported 64,000 sprinkler heads and more than 500,000 square yards of irrigation systems for the Olympic Village in Barcelona, Spain.

Whether they're serving customers in Spain or one of the other 22 countries with whom they do business, Nelson employees always "go for the gold." They share a common work ideal: Customers Always Receive Excellence (CARE).

"Nelson people CARE," says Chairman David Ransburg who bought the company from the Nelson family in 1972. "Our goal is— and has always been—total customer satisfaction. We're committed to providing a steady stream of innovative, high quality, high value products and services."

The company's commitment to customers dates back to 1911 when Lewen R. Nelson invented a small metal repair device that extended the useful life of garden hose. Realizing that such a device could save customers time and money, he patented his invention, then began manufacturing it in a plant in Peoria, Illinois.

Nelson continued to innovate. His company endured two World Wars, the Depression, and a tornado that severely damaged the plant. But through it all, Nelson people kept their focus on the customer, designing and building time-saving, economical lawn and garden products. Nelson's son Russ succeeded his father as president in 1952. His grandson Bart was with the company until 1972 when he left to form Nelson Irrigation Corporation of Walla Walla, Washington.

When Ransburg took the helm in the early 1970s, the company continued on a course of quality, value, and innovation. Investing heavily in research and development, Nelson expanded its product line rapidly and began to serve a broader customer base. The 1980s brought a worldwide recession and a global competitive threat, but Nelson withstood the challenge.

Today the L. R. Nelson Corporation holds the leadership position in the U.S. lawn and garden business and is a successful entrant in the commercial irrigation industry. Operating from a 240,000 square foot administration and manufacturing facility in Central Illinois, Nelson provides a full line of products related to the controlled application of water.

The L. R. Nelson Corporation 240,000 square-foot administration and manufacturing facility in Peoria, Illinois

The line includes:

• Oscillating, impact, stationary, and whirling lawn sprinklers;

• Nozzles, repair couplings, timers and other hose accessories;

• Gear drives, impacts, pop-ups, controllers and valves for residential and light commercial applications

• Low volume watering systems including bubblers, sprayers, misters, tubing, connectors and accessories

The Nelson plant features new manufacturing technology, automated materials handling systems, and efficient manufacturing processes. This technology, when put to use by a highly motivated work force, yields higher quality, lower cost, flexible production.

Nelson products are distributed from three locations in Illinois, Florida, and California. The distribution centers support customers' needs for just-in-time, service.

Nelson is aggressively pursuing worldwide markets. Exports as a percent of sales have doubled in the last five years, and will likely continue to grow at a rapid rate. Competition is intense in the world marketplace, but Nelson is well positioned to capitalize on emerging opportunities in Europe, Canada, Australia, South Africa, and Latin America.

Four basic principles will drive the L. R. Nelson Corporation as it strengthens its long-term

• The L. R. Nelson Corporation • Peoria, Illinois • (309) 692-2200 •

competitive position at home and abroad.

1. Put technology to work for customers.
Research and development will continue to be a Nelson priority. The engineering team will explore new applications, evaluate new technologies, test new materials, and develop new processes — all in an effort to provide differentiated products and services to customers worldwide.

2. Provide lightning fast service.
It isn't enough to design and build premium quality, premium value products. Service excellence is also vital. Nelson employees work to ship all orders on the day the customer requests shipment. Speed is the watchword in everything Nelson people do. Whether it's providing product information, or following up on an order, or just answering the tele-

phone, the Nelson team puts customers first.

3. Respect the environment.
Water is a precious resource, and Nelson is committed to conserving it. Recent additions to the product line offer greater irrigation precision, eliminating soil erosion and delivering the lowest possible volume of water exactly where it's needed. Future products will offer even more precise water control.

Nelson people also care about conserving forests and preserving landfill space. That's why packaging is kept to a minimum , and wherever possible packages are made of recycled material and can be recycled themselves.

4. Create a climate in which all Nelson employees are motivated to continuously improve the quality of the work they do.

The L. R. Nelson name has always been synonymous with quality. But in today's competitive environment, no one can rest on a quality reputation. Manufacturers must demonstrate continuous quality improvement.

Nelson employs close to 500 men and women during peak season. All are critical to the continuous improvement effort. Working together on teams and trained in statistical process control methods, Nelson people are rewarded for contributing ideas for quality improvement, cost reduction, and safety. Using the talent and expertise of the entire Nelson team not only improves quality. It makes the work place more productive and the work experience more positive for everyone.

As the twenty-first century approaches, the

L. R. Nelson Corporation will continue to "go for the gold" —in Barcelona and around the world. Pursuing a strategy in which *Customers Always Receive Excellence*, Nelson will set new standards of quality, performance, and value in the irrigation industry.

CHAPIN WATERMATICS INC.

Left to right: Dick Chapin and Norm Smith at Old Westbury Garden, September 18, 1993. Dick Chapin was honored along with Norman Smith with a historical plaque denoting the first installation of plastic mulch and drip irrigation in the United States. It is located in the Old Westbury Gardens, on Long Island, New York.

In 1960, Chapin Watermatics was founded and the first greenhouse watering system was marketed. The roots of the company, however, go back to 1929. Richard D. "Dick" Chapin, Chairman of the Board and founder of the company, was still a schoolboy when, with his father's help, he started growing flowers as a business.

During the next thirty years Dick saw his flower business grow to employ as many as 25 people during busy seasons and fill ten greenhouses to serve his customers. Dick became increasingly aware of the need for automatic watering systems that would deliver a precise amount of water to each plant. Such systems would, he believed, save labor and water, and ensure even growth to entire greenhouses of plants.

In 1959, he came up with the idea of using small plastic tubing to meter out water to individual plants. This system, which worked well, was seen by several salesmen who called on Chapin's Flowers. Some coaxed him to display the method at the Ohio State University Short Course in January, 1960, held in Columbus, Ohio.

The idea got many laughs with all that tubing spread out looking like a snarl of spaghetti. A few took the idea seriously, however, and very soon the newly formed Chapin Watermatics was shipping tubing all over the country. The business incorporated in 1962 with Dick Chapin as President, and his wife, Ruth, as Vice President. The company had nine full-time employees at that time. Mr. Chapin improved his "spaghetti tubes" by adding a weight to hold it in the container and then developed an on/off version for hanging baskets and retail nurseries where the tubes could be individually shut off when the plant was sold.

During the early 60's, Norman Smith, extension agent from Nassau County, Long Island, New York, worked with Mr. Chapin experimenting with the tubing. They wondered why the idea could not be applied to row crops. A friend of Norm's asked if tropical melons couldn't be grown in the north. Norm felt this might be possible with the use of plastic mulch which was also just getting its start. Mr. Smith contacted Dick, who hand slit some round tubing for the initial experiment, which was at Old Westbury Gardens on Long Island. The experiment was a tremendous success. Mr. Smith reported that the crop was excellent.

Dick then developed the first thin wall drip hose, sewing a seam in plastic film which lay flat on a reel and was packed in a minimum of space. This worked much better than the first experiment. This product was named "Dew Hose" and sold for several years.

> Dick Chapin, who owns 15 patents, designed and patented Twin- Wall® tubing which has become an industry standard.

An improved product was needed for use on long row lengths. Dick, who owns 15 patents, designed and patented Twin-Wall hose, which became an industry standard. The product was a giant breakthrough and came to be the leading design in the world. Several generations of improvements led to today's turbulent flow "Twin-Wall" design which is the staple of the industry.

> **The Twin-Wall® hose helps the farmer produce more and higher quality crops at lower cost.**

This new product offered greater uniformity over long runs to help the farmer produce more and higher quality crops at lower cost.

Corporate growth was substantial and the company outgrew the greenhouse facilities. The move to the present Water Street facility was completed in June, 1978. Eighty-five employees helped set new production records that year.

While Mr. Chapin spent much of his time in product development and sales around the world, he also recognized that he must find better and faster ways to produce the products to get the cost down so that it would be more economically viable for a greater variety of crops. He developed some very ingenious methods of production for the thin wall tubing. Some of those ideas are patented and some have been kept proprietary.

Dick and Ruth had each personally dedicated their lives to Jesus Christ as Savior and Lord, and had seen Him enrich their lives over the years. It was natural that they dedicated the company to Christian principles with the stated purpose of helping to feed a hungry world and using a portion of the profits for Christian work. The foundation of the company has remained the same and will continue under the leadership of Dick's son William A. "Bill" Chapin, now President and General Manager.

In 1986, Dick Chapin was named to the Floriculture Hall of Fame by the American Society of Horticulture. He was further honored by the American Society for Plasticulture with their Pioneer Award in September, 1991.

More recently, he has received two honors of great significance. He was honored along with Norman Smith with a historical plaque denoting the first installation of plastic mulch and drip irrigation in the United States. It is located in the Old Westbury Gardens, on Long Island, New York.

The second, made by the Irrigation Association, for Industry Achievement, was presented at the 1993 Irrigation Association Expo in San Diego, California.

Chapin Watermatics Inc. has enjoyed tremendous growth working from the foundation set by Dick and Ruth Chapin many years ago. On this foundation, the future builds.

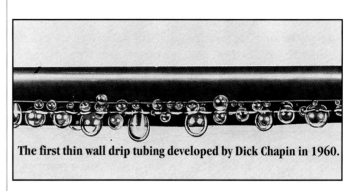

The first thin wall drip tubing developed by Dick Chapin in 1960.

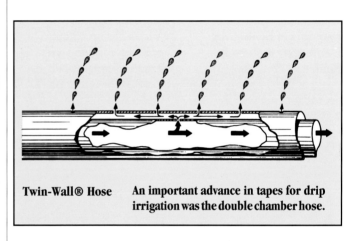

Twin-Wall® Hose — **An important advance in tapes for drip irrigation was the double chamber hose.**

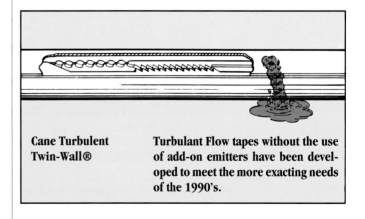

Cane Turbulent Twin-Wall® — **Turbulant Flow tapes without the use of add-on emitters have been developed to meet the more exacting needs of the 1990's.**

Chapin WATERMATICS

• Chapin Watermatics Inc. • (315) 782-1170 • FAX (315) 782-1490 •

REINKE MFG. CO., INC.

In the heartland of America, on what once were seemingly endless prairies in what is now Nebraska, a product was developed and refined, which has been heralded as the greatest breakthrough in agriculture since the invention of the tractor. That product is the center pivot irrigation machine.

A true pioneering spirit and American ingenuity were manifested in the founding of Reinke Mfg. Co., Inc., by Richard F. Reinke in 1954. The early years of the company were spent fabricating structural steel and wood trusses for commercial buildings, as well as various short-line items for the farm.

Attention was initially focused on center pivot irrigation by the young company in 1966. From these humble beginnings, the first reversible, electric, gear-driven center pivot irrigation system with an undertruss support was developed. With a product trade name of Electrogator, various design patents were applied for in 1967 with numerous patents being awarded for center pivot system design. In succeeding years, a significant number of primary features for center pivot and lateral move irrigation equipment were developed, which have since become industry standards.

The company is still headquartered in Deshler, Nebraska, and manufactures a complete line of center pivot and lateral move irrigation systems which include the Electrogator, Alumigator, Maxigator and Kwik-Tow models.

In the mid-1980s, a successful entry into the flatbed semi-trailer market was made with the all-aluminum "Silver shadow" designed at Reinke Mfg. Co., Inc. In the early 90s, a combination aluminum/steel flatbed was added to the line. In addition, large numbers of steel container chassis trailers and flatracks are produced. Diversification has accelerated Reinke's growth into a major Midwestern manufacturing operation.

Reinke Mfg. Co. markets its products through a national and international dealer and distributor network. In addition to its position as a dominant manufacturer and marketer of center pivot and lateral move irrigation equipment domestically, the company is also a leading exporter to numerous international markets worldwide.

Through on-going research and development, Reinke Mfg. Co., Inc., has made a significant contribution to water saving techniques and the improved efficiency of irrigation. This contribution includes the development of Reinke's patented Energy Saver Package (ESP) sprinkler option for cornering systems. Improved irrigation efficiency, plus improved application design, have allowed today's growers to be better stewards of their natural resources.

The employees and management at Reinke Mfg. Co., Inc., represent over 40 surrounding rural communities and take pride in the contribution the company has made in the developments of irrigated agriculture. The company looks forward to building on its successful past toward continued growth and development in future years.

ABOVE: Reinke lateral-move irrigation system.

BELOW: Aerial photo of Reinke plant in Deshler, Nebraska.

•   Reinke Mfg. Co, Inc.   •   101 Reinke Road, Deshler, Nebraska   • 68340,   •   (402) 365-7251   •

NACO INDUSTRIES, INC.

Since 1974, NACO Industries, Inc., has been setting standards of excellence in the fabricated PVC fittings industry. Today, irrigation is easier, more reliable and more cost-effective than in the past. That's good news for growers and NACO deserves a lot of credit. After 20 years of innovation and leadership, NACO Industries has earned a prominent place in the irrigation market and its success is now being marked by a company-wide expansion of manufacturing facilities.

NACO President and CEO Verne Bray attributes the company's success in a challenging and competitive marketplace to one word — quality. "At NACO we've always focused on quality in three areas," Mr. Bray says. "Engineering and product design, quality control and testing, and customer service. If we've succeeded over the past 20 years, it's because of our high standards in all three."

NACO's commitment to quality products and service is well known. Prior to NACO's 1983 purchase of Valor Division in Lodi, CA, Valor had established itself as a leader in the manufacture and distribution of quality PVC fittings to growers in California and the West. NACO has since built on that reputation.

But NACO's tradition of engineering excellence didn't start with Valor. In

Home Office and Manufacturing Plant in Logan, Utah.

1976, under the direction of Larry Cox, NACO entered the irrigation business and began production of the patented triple-wall fabricated pressure tee. Over the next several years, NACO introduced several more important innovations, including the one-piece 45° elbow, PIP fabricated and gasketed fittings, the IPS fabricated line, air and heat fittings, the Surface line, PVC inline valve and the PIP injection molded tee's introduced in 1990.

Each of these developments had a significant impact on the industry as a whole and helped establish NACO as a major force in the irrigation market throughout much of the country.

"The key to the success of our fittings is testing," Mr. Bray explains. "From the research lab to the production line, all of our products undergo rigorous performance tests under both simulated and real-world conditions." NACO quality control laboratories routinely test products for bursts, sustained pressures, heat inversions and impact.

NACO also prides itself in its ability to keep customers happy. NACO's nationwide network of manufacturing plants and warehouses ensure customers fast product delivery and immediate response to special needs. "We're just not satisfied until our customers are," Bray says. The recent company expansion is just one more indication that they are. Verne Bray sums it up another way: "For us, quality and service isn't a business strategy. It's simply a way of life."

Manufacturing Plant in Garden City, Kansas.

• NACO Industries, Inc. • 395 West 1400 North • Logan, Utah 84321 • (801) 753-8020 •

T-SYSTEMS INTERNATIONAL, INC.

T-Systems International was founded in July of 1977 in San Diego, California, by Davies Allport. His goal was to provide row-crop growers with a more reliable, less expensive, more effective solution to their drip irrigation needs. Mr. Allport succeeded with his mission.

In 1979 T-Systems designed and patented the first T-TAPE®. Over the years the original T-TAPE® was continually improved through T-Systems' dedication to research and development. T-TAPE® was first introduced to the market with laminar flow technology.

In 1987 T-Systems introduced a turbulent flow feature into T-TAPE® and initially called it Turbo-Tape®. This product provided better regulated pressure at the outlet, resulting in improved water application uniformity. The new product was also less susceptible to plugging if problems developed with filtration.

Today this product is known worldwide as T-TAPE®.

In 1991 T-Systems introduced T-TAPE 700™, a 7/8-inch diameter product, which allows the grower to save money by eliminating submains or lateral supply lines because the T-TAPE® could be installed to run up to a quarter of a mile. T-Systems is still the only supplier of this product in the world.

Today T-TAPE® is offered in over 45 different models of wall thickness, outlet spacing, flow rates, and packaging options. Growers can be assured that no matter what the crop or growing conditions, T-Systems will have the right drip irrigation system for their individual needs. Billions of feet of T-TAPE® have been successfully installed on tomatoes, strawberries, peppers, pineapple, sugar cane, and a variety of other crops worldwide and is rapidly expanding into new areas and new crops.

T-Systems is proud of its ability to respond quickly to the market's demand. T-Systems has established strong worldwide distribution channels which growers have learned to depend on for the fastest delivery and unsurpassed quality and service in the industry. Qualified T-Systems dealers work to provide expert service and advice to supply growers with the best solutions to their drip irrigation needs.

In 1984 T-Systems Australia was established and is now operating in Brisbane to serve Australia and the Pacific Rim region. T-Systems Europe was established in 1987 to serve Europe, Africa, and the Middle East out of Toulouse, France. In 1992 T-Systems International headquarters relocated to a new, larger facility in San Diego, California.

T-Systems' success can not only be attributed to its continuing dedication to research and development,

service, and delivery, but also to quality control. T-Systems' people are continually working to supply the most technologically advanced and highest quality product for its customers. T-Systems' quality control has evolved to a very sophisticated, computerized system which tests virtually every roll of T-TAPE® before it's shipped to a customer.

While T-Systems has been fortunate to enjoy continued growth over the years, the company prides itself in carrying the same

> Providing row-crop growers with a more reliable, less expensive, more effective solution to their drip irrigation needs.

entrepreneurial spirit with which it began. This spirit is a drive to continually work with our growers in the field to improve the product and technology, provide prompt, helpful service, and to conduct all business dealings with the highest level of fairness and integrity. T-Systems is committed to building partnerships with its growers and dealers and to remain the world's leading choice for drip irrigation technology.

SUPERIOR CONTROLS CO., INC.

The manufacture of automatic controls for landscape irrigation did not become a serious occupation until after the close of World War 11 and remained in its infancy until the early part of the next decade. It was during this pioneering period that Superior Controls Co., Inc. entered the field.

Originally incorporated in 1926 as Superior Regulator Co., manufacturers of steam pressure controls for the boiler industry, this company was destined to become one of the first to enter the fledgling industry. The Greenland brothers, Allen and Powell, joined the firm in 1945 and later bought out the original shareholders, re-incorporating as Superior Controls Co., Inc. in 1949. The following year, in a program of diversification, the new company began experimenting with early models of sprinkler automation; at the same time making market studies to learn how best to enter a completely new industrial field.

With limited capital for such an ambitious undertaking, the early years marked a period of slow but sustained growth. Marketing was difficult because distributors were few or non-existent and, in the absence of trade journals, advertising was confined to consumer media such as the "Home and Garden" section of the <u>Los Angeles Times</u> and <u>Sunset Magazine</u>. Without trade shows, it was their practice to display at the Los Angeles County

> ### Superior Controls has the most extensive line of brass control valves and adaptors on the market today

Fair, (a 17-day run) and follow the "Do-It-Yourself" show circuit, popular at that time. The first big breakthrough in this area was the organization of the Southern California Turfgrass Council with its annual show at Brookside Park.

The advent of plastic pipe, for sprinkler systems in the early 50's was a most significant innovation in landscape irrigation and was the real beginning of the industry as we know it today. By the 1955, Superior Controls was firmly established as a participant in this exciting new field having introduced the first diagram operated remote control valve in the industry (all previous automatic sprinkler valves were piston operated). However, it was the invention of the Superior "Adaptor," (sometimes called actuators by its imitators), that made Superior Controls Co. unique in the field with

sales, to date, in the range of 2.5 to 3-million units and most still in the ground today.

Superior Controls has the most extensive line of brass control valves and adaptors on the market today and has augmented its adaptor line with plastic models greatly increasing its market potential. It also produces a complete line of mechanical and "state of the art" electronic controllers with a wide variety of

models ranging from 4 through 36-stations.

To increase its production capabilities and to keep in the forefront of new technological advances, Superior Controls Co., Inc. in 1986, moved to its beautiful new facility in Valencia, California where it remains, the oldest manufacturer of automatic sprinkler controls, under the same ownership and management, in the industry today.

HYDRO-SCAPE PRODUCTS, INC.

In a small warehouse in Santee, California, Bob Tiglio and his brother John opened the doors of the first branch of Hydro-Scape Products during the summer of 1975. Within a few months of operation, they needed a larger facility to house their rapidly expanding inventory and moved to their Kearny Villa Road location in San Diego, which is now the corporate headquarters as well as their largest branch warehouse outlet. By 1993, the company had expanded throughout Southern California to its current 12 branches located in the cities of Orange, San Bernardino, Carlsbad, Encinitas, Escondido, El Cajon, Lake Forest, Rancho Cucamonga, Riverside, Chula Vista and San Juan Capistrano.

The original concept of the company, which continues today, was *to provide full service and supply facilities for irrigation and landscape contractors* who often found it difficult to locate a broad range of products from *one supply source.* Hydro-Scape Products inventories over 19,000 irrigation and landscape products.

Several specialized divisions operate within Hydro-Scape Products which include commercial turf, golf and international sales and a technical service department which builds Hydro-Scapes' Hydro-Safe Irrigation Controller Assemblies and provides warranty and non-warranty repair for all irrigation controllers. In-house educational training programs for all levels of **Hydro-Scape Products** employees are emphasized to maintain the highest degree of customer service possible.

Over the years, Hydro-Scape Products has won numerous awards from manufacturers for their outstanding sales and service performance including both the Rain Bird Turf and the Rain Bird Golf Distributor of the Year Awards.

HYDRO-SCAPE PRODUCTS MANAGEMENT TEAM FROM LEFT TO RIGHT:
Frederick R. Larsen, vice president, general marketing manager; Kevin S. Hall, vice president, chief financial officer; Robert Tiglio, chairman, chief executive officer; Dale A. Tiglio, vice president, general operations manager; and Archie V. Humphrys, president, chief operating officer.

• Hydro-Scape Products, Inc. • 5805 Kearny Villa Road • San Diego, California 92123 • (619) 560-6611

MARION MILLER & ASSOCIATES

In 1971, when Marion Miller created Marion Miller and Associates, Inc., the irrigation industry's first factory rep business, he was determined to offer his clients only the very best equipment and service. That philosophy still holds. "I hate to have anything but the best," says Miller. *"Only the best will help our clients survive. Only if they succeed, can we succeed."*

Over the years he has introduced new products for:

❖ **Senninger, Inc.**
❖ **Weather-Tec, Inc.**
❖ **Hydro-Engineering, Inc.**
❖ **Cloudburst Mfg. Co.**
❖ **Irrigation Industries, Inc.**
❖ **Vanmar Plastics, Inc.**
❖ **Agri-Fertigation, Inc.**
❖ **Irrometer Company, Inc.**

When Miller saw a problem, he helped the manufacturer improve his product, or he did it himself.

Farmers devised the first pivot drops to avoid heavy ice loads that built up on center pivot machines during freezing weather. They were made of 3/4-inch galvanized steel or PVC plastic with elbows and nipples. When dealers complained about the labor necessary to install these drops, Miller came up with a one-piece gooseneck made from galvanized steel or plastic pipe, which eliminated several costly fittings.

The goosenecks and drops enabled farmers to replace the old sprinkler heads, which required an average of 75 lbs. pressure

Marion Miller, with nearly 50 years in the industry, is the oldest active founder of the organization that became the Irrigation Association. He has been president, vice president, director and historian of the organization.

to operate, with spray heads that required only 20 to 25 lbs. of pressure or less. They also reduced the 30% to 35% evaporation loss that was common with overhead sprinklers.

Miller had established Irrigation Industries, Inc., in 1974 to produce galvanized steel goosenecks and drops. When he semi-retired in 1986, he sold the company.

But erosion was still a problem on irrigated land. So Miller began work on a new line of plastic drops that had the desirable features of both steel and plastic. Through an arrangement with Vanmar Plastics, Inc. of Denver, he was able to participate in the further development of his goosenecks and drops.

Because of their strength, rigidity and U.V.L. and corrosion resistance, these new super strong PVC 80 goosenecks and drops are well adapted to the new

Low Energy Precision Application (LEPA) system developed by Bill Lyle and Jim Brodosky of Texas.

Those first 3/4-inch galvanized steel goosenecks moved the industry forward. But, in the 100 mph wind tests Miller demanded, the coating on galvanized drops cracked and corroded and the drops failed after 1,640 flexes. Lighter weight thin-wall drops failed after 4,380 flexes.

Early PVC goosenecks and drops weighed only one-fourth as much as galvanized pipe. But drops failed after 8,440 flexes. So Miller added strength stainless steel inserts inside the drops and goosenecks. Only after 64,795 flexes were engineers able to break the reinforced drops. And the reinforced special formula Schedule-80 PVC goosenecks survived more than one million flexes and never did fail!

To further reduce failures and speed coupling of goosenecks and drop tubes, Mark Schellinger of Vanmar Plastic tapered the PVC pipe threads.

Miller sought experienced associates who share his own dedication to quality and service. They include:

❖**Jack Look & Associates**, Clovis, CA (209) 323-4432;

❖ **Universal Irrigation Sales Corp.**, Eugene, OR (503) 344-4650;

❖ **Steven Driewer,** Cibolo, TX (210) 659-5065;

❖ **Farmland Irrigation, Inc.,** Grand Island, NE (308) 381-1509;

❖ **Pipe-USA,** Denver, CO (303) 296-9594.

"Our aim is to introduce and sell only the best," says Miller. "Only the best will help our clients survive."

With Art Schellinger, founder, and his son, Mark, president of Vanmar Plastics, Marion Miller developed super PVC-80 drops and goosenecks to cut water losses and save time and labor.

AGRICULTURAL PRODUCTS, INC.

Agricultural Products, Inc., was established in 1973 in Burbank, California when Lon Schultz, founder of the company, realized that a better drip tube fitting could be made to service the then fledgling drip irrigation polyethylene tubing industry. Early drip tubing stretched laterally and split when standard barbed insert fittings were used as connections. Lon conceived the idea of a compression ring that would encircle the outer diameter of the tube. Acting much like the Chinese handcuff toy, the tubing inserted into, rather than over, the fitting. After insertion, the tubing expands slightly inside the fitting, generating a tight mechanical lock which creates a strong leak proof connection that holds the tubing in place without harmful stretching.

Schultz began his business with an assortment of four different fittings that fit the most commonly sized tubes used at the time. As drip irrigation became accepted nationally and internationally through the years, Ag. Products added the sizes demanded by an expanding industry. Today, connecting polyethylene tubing via the compression fitting is a worldwide industry standard.

As the use of drip (now referred to as Low Flow) irrigation grew, so did the proficiency of system designers and installers, and their need for special fittings and accessories unique to this changing technology. It was only natural that technicians in the field would turn to Ag. Products as these needs surfaced. The company responded by developing such products as Loc Sleeve fittings for tapes, Spin Loc fittings for thin wall drip tubing, the 4E-Spin Clean filter line, extruded PVC and Poly-ethylene hose and micro-tubing in addition to a myriad of other specialty items. Today's Ag. Products' line of drip/low flow irrigation fittings, accessories, tubing and filters exceeds 650 cataloged items and the research and development process necessary to satisfy the changing needs of a growing industry contin-ues non-stop.

During the last 19 years, Ag. Products has expanded several times from its original produc-tion location at a card table in the back of a molding plant in Burbank. Manu-facturing facilities have been added in Florida as well as warehouses in Texas, Georgia and Penn-sylvania. In mid-1992, Ag. Products-California relocated into a new, larger custom-built facility in Ontario, California.

> **Ag. Products' line of drip/low flow irrigation fittings, accessories, tubing and filters exceeds 650 cataloged items**

Agricultural Products Inc. Headquarters in Ontario, California.

FEBCO

FEBCO, the leader of backflow prevention valve sales to the Irrigation Market, has its roots in the Irrigation Industry. FEBCO began in 1924, when Fred Reinecke Sr. of Los Angeles secured a franchise for irrigation products manufactured by John A. Brooks Co. of Detroit. Reinecke's operation sold spray-type lawn sprinklers and hydraulically operated irrigation valve sequences throughout the western United States under the name of Brooks of California.

Reinecke formed FEBCO, Inc. when the 25-year franchise agreement ended in 1949. He continued the irrigation products specialty he had established. History records the name FEBCO was derived from the first-name initials of Reinecke's children who were active in the business: Fred Jr., Ed, Bill, Charlotte, and the "Old Man." Automatic sprinkler controllers were developed in the mid-1950s. During this period, FEBCO worked with Robert Trent Jones, a well-known golf course architect, to create the master/satellite golf course control system. Further development was also made on the FEBCO line of backflow prevention valves, used to protect the drinking water from contamination.

The mid-1960's was a period of change for FEBCO and the Irrigation Industry. General Sprinkler Co. purchased FEBCO from the Reinecke family in 1965 and moved it to Fresno, California, where the FEBCO corporate headquarters are today. The Johns-Manville Corp. purchased General Sprinkler in 1972 and split off the backflow prevention product line from the other sprinker related products. This allowed FEBCO to concentrate on backflow prevention, which is their focus even today.

The Charles M. Bailey Co. bought FEBCO in May, 1980, and began development of improved backflow prevention valve designs. The resulting "Y" pattern double check and reduced pressure assembly set new industry standards in backflow preventer design and performance. FEBCO's share of the Irrigation Market sales continued to grow and established FEBCO as the Irrigation Industry leader in sales of backflow preventers. In 1983, both FEBCO and Charles M. Baily Co. were sold to the Michael Coyne family and were made part of CMB Industries.

During the 1980's, FEBCO became very active in education and training on backflow prevention. They expanded their market share in the Irrigation and Water Works Markets and helped establish backflow prevention awareness and code development in the Fire Sprinkler Market. However, FEBCO's strength and commitment continued to be in the Irrigation Industry.

THE BACKFLOW PREVENTION SPECIALISTS

TOP: FEBCO's innovative Model 870 MasterSeries Backflow Preventer.

BOTTOM: FEBCO's corporate headquarters in Fresno, California.

Today, FEBCO specializes in backflow prevention and leads the Irrigation Industry in sales of those products. Their innovation in design and performance has set the industry standard. FEBCO's newest line of large diameter backflow preventers, the MasterSeries, was introduced in 1992.

This line of valves was developed based on the needs and features requested by the industry. The revolutionary new designs offer substantially shorter lay-lengths, a choice of valve configurations to meet specific application needs, improved flow characteristics, greater corrosion resistance, and lower "total installed cost".

FEBCO is continuing its leadership in design and industry education to help promote clean drinking water through backflow prevention. Sales and training now extend around the world, providing education and support to many backflow prevention training schools and industry associations; and providing seminars to industry groups and end users on backflow prevention and water quality.

FEBCO is committed to protecting our drinking water in the 21st century and beyond.

FEBCO • 1550 N. Peach • Fresno, CA 93727 • (209) 252-0791 • FAX (209) 453-9030

IRROMETER COMPANY, INC.

The history of the Irrometer Company represents the vision of two personalities — Thomas W. Prosser and Sheldon G. Pooley, both of Riverside, California. Tom Prosser was an inventor, oriented toward products development. Shel Pooley was an expert marketing man, oriented toward the concept of managing irrigation functions to enhance crop production.

The T.W. Prosser Company of Arlington (Riverside), California, began development of a commercially available tensiometer in the later 1940s. This simple, yet scientific instrument, traces its beginning to the field of soil physics in the 1920s. The tensiometer was developed and used in soil and plant science over the decades of the 1920s, 1930s and 1940s. Tom Prosser noticed it at the Citrus Experiment Station in Riverside. His curiosity was piqued by the researchers' use of this homemade instrument to manage the timing of irrigation in order to enhance production of citrus fruit. Examining the

Shel Pooley — Mr. Irrometer.

tensiometer, Prosser saw the possibilities for refining the product design to enhance its usefulness and function as well as its ability to be effectively manufactured.

Tom Prosser and his son-in-law, Cal Callender, got together with Bill Hawkins, a Riverside ceramist, and began development of the ceramic cup to be used. The "IRROMETER" was born in 1951.

Besides the Citrus Experiment Station at U.C. Riverside, one of the first customers for the new Irrometer was George C. Pooley, a Riverside area citrus grower and friend of both Prosser and Callender. He installed many of the instruments in his Moreno grove and started experiencing the very profitable benefits of correct irrigation scheduling.

Prosser and Callender realized that they needed a hard-hitting salesman to spread the message and generate sales. They asked George Pooley if he knew of anyone who could help. Pooley recommended his son, Sheldon, who was a sales representative for National Cash Register in Phoenix, Arizona. Shel was contacted. When he visited Riverside, his

father, Tom and Cal convinced him that the future was bright to sell the new Irrometer. So Shel moved back to Riverside and became the Sales Department for the T. W. Prosser Company.

In a Nash Ramble station wagon with a box full of Irrometers in the back, Shel began his "mission." He traveled all the roads of central and southern California, plus Arizona, talking to citrus and avocado growers, installing Irrometers, and showing the farmers how to use them. From this humble beginning, the Irrometer Company grew and prospered.

Cal inherited the company upon Tom's death in 1961 and formed a partnership with Shel. Cal took care of the office and shop, Shel did the selling. In 1969, Shel bought out Cal's interest and incorporated in September of that year.

The Irrometer went through its major evolutions in the 1950s — the Model "A" (1951), Model "B" (1953) and finally the Model "R" (1956). This final version was the result of Prosser's patent 2,878,671 and incorporated a sure seal and a fully submerged, air-free gauge chamber for accuracy, sensitivity and reliability. Except for an enlargement of the reservoir in 1980, the Model "R" remains today as it was in 1956. The sealed gauge (Prosser's patent 2,773,388) provided for long operational life in the field, where

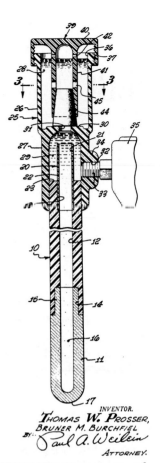

INVENTOR.
Thomas W. Prosser,
Bruner M. Burchfiel
BY: *Paul A. Weilein*
ATTORNEY.

ABOVE: T.W. Prosser patent for the Model R Irrometer.

ever-present moisture is the biggest enemy of a gauge.

In the late 1980s, Irrometer jumped into an additional soil moisture sensing technology, the WATERMARK, acquired from its inventor, Glenn Larson of Santa Barbara, California.

From the days when Tom Prosser "couldn't give them away," to today, the Irrometer Company has seen its instruments used on literally millions of acres of irrigated crops and landscapes throughout the world. Wherever on this planet irrigation is practiced, you will find the Irrometer or the Watermark, used by the grower to produce better crops and save water, energy and fertilizer by practicing effective irrigation.

Irrometer Company, Inc. • P.O. Box 2424 • Riverside, California 92516-2424 • (909) 689-1701

MIDWEST IRRIGATION COMPANY

Midwest Irrigation Company was founded in the agriculturally rich farming community of Henderson in the south-central Nebraska county of York in 1954 by Gustav Thieszen. Gustav took advantage of the areas abundant underground water reservoir forming a company to manufacture aluminum pipe. With the purchase of two of the first Gordon Morgan roll forming mills in Nebraska, Midwest Irrigation had its beginning.

Midwest Irrigation Company was off and running, manufacturing and supplying aluminum pipe to dealers and distributors across the Midwest. Midwest Irrigation Company has progressed in the last 39 years to become known for its high quality products and excellent customer service across the country.

In servicing the changing needs of the irrigation industry, Midwest Irrigation Company continues to develop its own product line allowing its dealer organization to be able to rely on them for all their customers' needs from mate and female couplings, elbows, tees, chemigation and check valves, underground fittings, to custom made items that meet their specific requirements.

Midwest Irrigation Company is dedicated to providing products for it's customers that they can depend on and buy at competitive prices. We are proud of our company's history in the irrigation industry and look forward to the future as an opportunity to serve our customers with new and better products.

Midwest Irrigation has remained a family owned company and is presently owned by Carl C. Buller; Carl purchased Gustav Thieszen's well drilling company in 1970 and operated it until 1985.

Supplying aluminum pipe to dealers and distributors across the Midwest.

TOP: Where it all began, Gordon Morgan Tube Mill.

MIDDLE: Office at Midwest Irrigation, built in 1954.

BOTTOM: Fittings inventory to readily service our customers.

Midwest Irrigation Company   •   Box 516, 701 South 17th Street   •   Henderson, Nebraska   •   (402) 723-5374

AMS ENGINEERING AND ENVIRONMENTAL

In the twelve years since its inception, AMS Engineering and Environmental (AMS) has emerged as a leader in providing quality engineering designs and professional consulting services to the Florida agricultural industry.

AMS grew out of Agricultural Management Services a corporation established in 1978 to supply professional on-site managers and timely financial reporting to agricultural landowners in the southeastern U.S. It soon became apparent that AMS required in-house engineering and environmental services to reduce the dependence on outside consulting services for agricultural land development.

The Engineering Division was formed in 1982 and soon became a leader in providing the Florida agricultural industry with surface water and irrigation designs, permitting and construction engineering services. In 1986 the Environmental Consulting Division was formed and likewise soon became a leader in providing quality environmental consulting services. Turner Foods Corporation (TFC) , acquired Agricultural Management Services in 1987 and soon afterwards the two Divisions were combined and expanded services in hydrogeology and water quality were offered to the industry.

With the expansion of citrus into the Flatwoods of South Florida came a need for new and innovative surface water management and irrigation designs. The Flatwoods soils and a seasonally high water table in this region provided AMS an opportunity to develop specially tailored designs for the citrus producers. These site specific designs have

> **AMS uses a multi-disciplined approach to provide state-of-the-art, cost effective designs for agricultural development**

resulted in considerable savings in development and operational costs for the agricultural industry.

The design and operation of an efficient irrigation system is an integral part of these unique agricultural developments in South Florida. With the massive expansion of urban developments in the past ten years, a growing public concern has developed about the use of water for crop irrigation. New state water regulations are now using irrigation efficiency as a incentive or disincentive in the allocation of water. Even before this time AMS engineers were involved in the conversion of irrigation systems from the less efficient overhead

sprinkler systems to the newer, more efficient drip and micro-jet under-tree spray systems. In the early 1980's, TFC's existing Highland Citrus grove was converted into an efficient operation with the installation of an improved irrigation system designed by AMS engineers. In 1986, the TFC 4,300 acre Gator Slough grove in Hendry County was planted. This grove was one of the first in the area to employ the latest computer assisted irrigation controls and the new high efficient micro-jet spray system. The advanced drainage design and irrigation system enables Gator Slough to cope with more than nine inches of rain during a Florida summer storm or weeks of drought during the winter dry season. The system design provides the grove manager with a tool to not only manage the application of water but also manage the use of fertilizers, pesticides and other agrochemicals.

The design of the Gator Slough and other groves in Southwest Florida provided AMS engineers and scientists with projects that demonstrated the capabilities of the Division to other citrus and vegetable growers in South Florida. The reputation of the AMS soon began to spread over South Florida. Today, AMS engineers and scientists have designed irrigation and drainage systems for over 200,000 acres of crop land. Their staff of four

engineers, one hydrogeologist, three ecologists and ten support people provide the client with a team approach to agricultural land development. This multi-disciplined approach to design enables AMS to provide the client with a competitive, cost effective design.

With a growing need to conserve groundwater resources, AMS engineers now incorporate surface water irrigation storage reservoirs and water reuse into their agricultural development designs.

These new designs depend on the use of blended water from two aquifers and from surface water storage reservoirs, a new concept for Southwest Florida agricultural developments. This requires expertise in plant water use, groundwater hydrology and hydrogeology.

The design team uses the latest groundwater and water use models to determine irrigation needs. Hydrologic engineers design surface water management and storage systems and the ecologists ensure that the designs meet Florida's stringent environmental protection requirements.

WESTERN BRASS WORKS

Western Brass Works has played an intricate and important role in the history of irrigation. Its roots go back to the dreams of a young man who came to California in 1932. Walter V. Storm arrived as a young entrepreneur in the midst of the Great Depression. In exchange for his savings, hard work and dedication, Storm learned to be a foundryman. Walter learned his craft well and both he and Western Brass prospered. During the forties, the foundry provided many castings for the war effort. Later, he helped his pattern maker and good friend Tony Pejsa, Sr., create the beginnings of Champion Irrigation. In turn, he began to pour more brass irrigation parts, which included pump parts for Berkeley and castings for Rain Bird and Champion. In the fifties and sixties, Western Brass machine shops churned out tens of thousands of line shaft bearings and impellers for turbine pump manufacturers, such as Peerless, Fiese & Firstenberger, Floway, Byron Jackson, Soults, Whitten and many others. Some of these majors have come and gone but, each of them have pumped millions of irrigation gallons and earned their place in the history of irrigation.

Walter Storm's skills and devotion allowed him to develop other businesses and branch out into the irrigation field further. In the early sixties, he started Western Raintrol, Proven Pumps and, for a brief time, Sturdy-Jet. In the beginning, Raintrol distributed its own brand and later it provided private-label brass pop-ups, quick coupler valves, keys, hose swivels and impact sprinklers for other OEMs. Although the Proven Pump product line was used primarily in the home and marine markets, both companies became large consumers of brass castings for the foundry.

Throughout the eighties and nineties, Western Brass and Western Raintrol have continued to produce, sell and distribute irrigation products worldwide. The products are used in many applications of irrigation, including agricultural, turf, commercial, along freeways and in homeowner systems.

Western Brass division continues to manufacture line shaft bearings, along with water lubricated bearings, foot valves, and sight feed valves. Solid growth has occurred with new products, extensive private labeling for other irrigation majors and through the distribution of its line of West Ag Irrigation Products.

As the demand for food and water continually strive to pace population and need, Western Brass Works, Western Raintrol and West Ag Irrigation Products will continue in their tradition of quality, innovation and leadership.

Today, Western Brass Works continues to be a leader in the irrigation industry. Its products can be found throughout the world. Walter Strom has extended his dream to the Storm family as they continue to operate the business. Even though Mr. Storm has gone on to other facets of manufacturing and founded many successful companies, his roots and love still remain with Western Brass Works.

Western Brass Works • Western Raintrol Corporation • West Ag Products • Est. 1932 • (213) 223-3101

BERMAD, INC.

Over a quarter of a century of proven expertise and measurable results have made the name Bermad synonymous with control valves used in water management systems throughout the world. Begun in 1964, Bermad has always placed an emphasis on innovation, quality and service. Now, in this last decade of the 20th century, with products specified, sought, sold and serviced in nearly every country of the world, Bermad is acknowledged as the international leader in irrigation control valves.

Widely diversified within our field, Bermad designs and manufactures dozens of different products for thousands of applications. The versatility and reliability of our products, along with our highly qualified engineering and service capabilities, have con-

Begun in 1964, BERMAD has always placed an emphasis on innovation, quality and service.

vinced numerous engineers, consultants, agricultural organizations, water supply authorities and government agencies to specify Bermad products.

The product groups developed, refined and produced by Bermad for irrigation systems include:

❖ **200 SERIES** —
The unmatched combination of hydraulics and engineered plastic technology in these 3/4-inch through 2-inch hydraulic control valves provides long, trouble-free operation. Coupled Bermad-designed and engineered reducing and sustaining control pilots, electric solenoids and related accessories, these valves provide superior control, flexibility and excellent value in both landscape and agriculture irrigation systems.

❖ **300 SERIES** —
In 1-1/2-inch through 3-inch sizes, these valves combine rugged brass, cast iron and plastic materials in high flow Y-pattern bodies with flexible single or double

chambered actuators. Utilizing Bermad hydraulic and electric control accessories, the 300 Series valves are the ideal choice for many agricultural irrigation and pump station pressure control applications.

❖ **350 SERIES** —
This patented compact 3-port filter backflush valve minimizes the unwanted mixing of supply and waste water. The short travel of the diaphragm plug assembly guarantees smooth changes of flow direction, conserves water and prevents filter site flooding.

❖ **RAM HYDRANT SERIES** —
Characterized by simple design and durable construction, these specialized 3-inch hydrant valves are available in angle, single tee and double tee configurations. They have long been successfully used as "field" valves and more recently have been applied as angle pattern quick-acting pressure relief valves for system protection.

❖ **400 SERIES** —
Only the innovative combination of Bermad's irrigation and control valve expertise could produce the unequaled simplicity, reliability, performance and economy of the 400 Series Hydraulic Control Valve. With only five components — body,

400 SERIES for simple reliable control.

Bermad • 4070 Leaverton Ct. • Anaheim, CA 92807

bonnet, spring, spring retainer and diaphragm/seal — the 400 Series promises years of trouble free operation. Available in 2-inch through 10-inch sizes and in virtually any control function required. The 400 Series is destined to become the standard in irrigation control valves.

❖ 700 SERIES —

This unsurpassed benchmark for high performance, high quality control valves incorporates a high flow, energy efficient "Y" pattern body, standard double chambered unitized actuator assembly and Bermad's exclusive V-port throttling plug. Primarily installed at large pump and filter stations to accurately control pressure and flow, the 700 Series is increasingly being specified for use in any critical and demanding application.

❖ 900 SERIES —

Combining an accurate

> **BERMAD is acknowledged as the international leader in irrigation control valves.**

turbine type water meter and a diaphragm actuated control valve in a single body makes the 900 Series one of a kind. The unique Hydrometer can be configured to deliver a preset quantity of water and then automatically and smoothly close, needing only line pressure to operate. This particular model is used extensively throughout the world to simply automate irrigation systems to volumetric control. Adding an electric solenoid and a pulse transmitter, the Hydrometer becomes a state of the art flow sensor and transmitter fully capable of interfacing with computers and controllers to provide water and energy saving volumetric control to both landscape and agricultural irrigation systems.

More than just a manufacturing company, Bermad provides total solutions to specific client needs. Our philosophy requires the integration of engineering, manufacturing, quality and marketing personnel dedicated to quickly and efficiently meet our clients needs. Bermad employs highly trained professional design and application engineers and technicians who utilize the latest computerized design techniques and technology. Production personnel make use of internationally recognized and approved materials that are machined

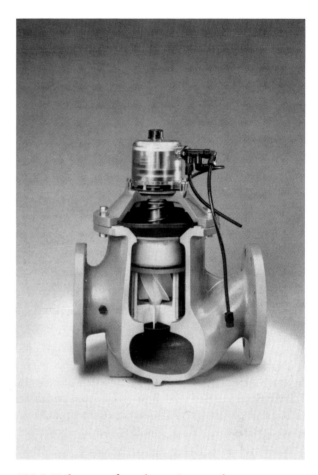

900-D Hydrometer for volumetric control.

in fully automated and computerized machining centers. Meticulous and rigorous inspection and testing in the framework of a quality assurance program that is certified to ISO 9003 assures high quality reliable products. In the field, comprehensive design, installation and maintenance guidance and assistance is furnished by Bermad experts who travel the world to provide timely and qualified support to our customers.

The entire Bermad organization is proud to be a Partner in Progress and a part of the History of Irrigation in America. As a pioneer in water management and control systems, we look forward to being a continuing part of that history and pledge to continue to provide innovative, efficient, high quality products and services for all water distribution systems.

EWING IRRIGATION PRODUCTS

Beginning above a plumbing contractors shop in downtown San Francisco, King Ewing started his irrigation supply company with little more than a notebook, a knowledge of sprinkler installation, a strong desire to succeed, and a commitment to provide honest service for his customers, King began laying the foundation for what would become one of the largest wholesale providers of professional quality landscape and irrigation materials in the Western States.

Ewing Irrigation Products traces its beginnings to a small irrigation company, Atlas Lawn Sprinkler. Started in 1922 by Barney Butler in San Francisco, the company was purchased by Thad Binkley, a hydraulic engineer and contractor, in 1926. When King Ewing moved to California from St. Louis during the depression in 1938, Atlas was engaged in

Ewing Bakersfield, California Branch.

sprinkler installation and supply in the San Francisco Bay Area. King went to work for Atlas

King Ewing, company founder

selling and installing home irrigation systems door to door and running the field crews for Atlas, installing among other projects, the first sprinkler system around Fleishacher pool in

McClaren Park in San Francisco

After World War II. King became a partner in Atlas Lawn Sprinkler. However, he was more interested in the distribution and design portion of Atlas than in construction and in 1948, he purchased that division from Binkley and renamed it Ewing Turf Products.

King wanted to give his customers a consistent supply of quality products so he persuaded Buckner Sprinkler Company to appoint Ewing Turf Products their exclusive irrigation distributor in Northern California. This Manufacturer-Distributor partnership became a pattern for distribution agreements for much of the industry into the 1990s.

One of the greatest reasons for King's substantial influence on the industry — and one of the strengths behind the company — was his nearly legendary loyalty to customers, employees, and the industry. He maintained a simple but powerfully effective business strategy! "Treat your customer right. The best advertising you can have is a satisfied customer." This principle helped guide him and his company — it still does today.

In 1963, King turned the daily operation of the business over to his daughter and son-in-law, Sue and Ray York. With the expansion of the irrigation construction market outside of San Francisco, and the need for larger offices, the company relocated in 1965 to its present location in San Leandro. In 1967, to better reflect its services, Ray renamed the company, Ewing Irrigation Products. Under this name and Ray's leadership the company has prospered, expanded, and kept pace with the irrigation industry's constantly changing products and business methods.

Ray and Sue developed an ambitious business goal - to be the industry's most efficient supplier of landscape and irrigation products and customer services. Their strategy was to provide customers with irrigation products more quickly, accurately, and with reasonable prices. To do this, they embarked on an ambitious plan of expanding into various landscape irrigation markets.

Starting late in the 1960s Ewing Irrigation had two branch operations, one in San Leandro and one in Sacramento. Four more locations around the San Francisco Bay area opened in the 1970s. In 1973, Ewing installed its first computer system and began developing the

Ewing Irrigation Products   •   2462 Polvorosa Avenue   •   San Leandro, California   •   (510) 357-9530

Left to right: Richard York, Susan York, Ray York and Doug York breaking ground for the construction of a new corporate office in Phoenix, Arizona.

software that enabled its rapid growth. During the 1980s, Ewing opened three stores in the central valley of California six stores in the Los Angeles basin and five stores in San Diego. In 1987-88, Ewing ventured outside of California to open two stores in the greater Phoenix area. In the 1990s it has continued to grow its service area throughout California and Arizona and has added Las Vegas, Nevada and Salt Lake City, Utah. In June, 1993, Ewing broke ground for the construction of a new corporate office in Phoenix, Arizona. The new facility will have 28,000 square feet of office and warehouse and is planned to serve the company's growth for the next twenty-five years.

The growth and success of the company can be attributed to many factors. Ray York's long range vision and business strategies have brought modern distribution business practices into the company to develop a professional approach to landscape irrigation distribution. Excellent product blend and inventory management have provided the foundation for customer service. The multi-location distribution computer network has been a model for the industry.

Ewing Irrigation Products understands the value of, and has a strong commitment to, improving the company through education and training. The company holds bimonthly management training meetings and has recently embarked on an ambitious training program for its warehouse staff.

Ewing also has a commitment to service to the irrigation industry. King Ewing was one of the founders of the Northern California Turfgrass Council and served as its president for 9 years. He helped establish the Turf Research Test Plot at the University of California Davis and represented the turf and horticultural industries on the University of California Agricultural Council.

Continuing this tradition of service, many of the Ewing staff have been active in industry organizations! Ray York has been active in the Irrigation Association since 1970 serving several years on the board, and then as its president in 1986. During the 1990s Sue York has been responsible for the business seminars for the Irrigation Association's annual meeting and has served on the board. Doug York has served as chairman of the turf distributors committee and the subcommittee chair for turf distributors standards. In addition to the York family's contribution, other

Ewing staff are active and have held offices in the California Landscape Contractors Association (CLCA), the Arizona Landscape Contractors Association (ALCA), and the Northern and Southern California Turfgrass Councils (NCTC and SCTC).

Over the years, Ewing has become "more than just an irrigation supply house." As it continues to grow in branches, so too does its commitment to helping grow the success of its customers, its employees, and the irrigation industry.

Ewing Phoenix, Arizona (Deer Valley) Branch

Ewing Irrigation Products • 3441 East Harbor Drive • Phoenix, Arizona • (602) 432-9530

CHAMPION IRRIGATION PRODUCTS

It is in the nature of companies to diversify their products and services as they grow and prosper. The origins of many older, familiar firms are in fields light years away from their current business activities. Champion Brass Manufacturing Company was founded in 1937 in a business entirely unrelated to the irrigation industry. The only common thread, in fact, is water.

Champion Brass Manufacturing was founded by two brothers, Anton and Ralph Pejsa. The brothers moved from Ohio to Alhambra, California in 1917. Anton went into the business of importing and selling tropical fish when he was 21, near the start of the Depression. Seeking more lucrative work, he moved into the pattern business; renting space from Western Brass Works, across the street from the site that would later be headquarters of his own company.

Ralph also entered the tropical fish business becoming a manufacturer of aquariums. Anton joined forces with his brother and in 1937, the two opened an aquatics garden in Alhambra. During the Second World War, the firm went into wartime production, manufacturing torpedo parts for the U.S. Navy. The end of the war brought with it the baby boom and an enormous influx of families into the largely arid West. This precipitated an explosion in the construction and landscape industries.

The Pejsas were among the first to realize that irrigation systems, formerly limited to the wealthy, would become standard equipment in the yards of the middle class. With new homes popping up at a dizzying pace and the demand for irrigation equipment growing, the Pejsa brothers saw an opportunity and quickly started their own irrigation business. They continued to make aquariums until the 1950.

Anton Pejsa began making patterns for brass sprinkler products and in 1956 the Pejsa brothers opened their own foundry in El Monte, California. The Pejsas performed all machining and assembly of sprinkler heads themselves. Irrigation products produced by Champion were inexpensive and easy to install; ideal for the blossoming residential market. Today, Champion is one of the few sprinkler brand names that the average consumer recognizes. This is due to the company's strong presence in both the retail and contractor markets.

Tony Pejsa became chief executive officer in 1970, at the time his uncle passed away and Anton, his father, went into semi-

> **The Pejsas were among the first to realize that irrigation systems would become standard equipment in the yards of the middle class.**

retirement. Today, Champion employs 200-300 people at peak operation. In 1985, the company started using the name Champion Irrigation Products to convey its commitment to the irrigation industry.

Champion recently began strengthening its turf sales with several new lines of inline valves, sprayheads and controllers designed for professional applications. While the company has long been a participant in Irrigation Association events and conventions, in 1993, Champion unveiled its new Professional Division products and services at an International Golf Industry show. If history is any indicator of the future for Champion, this is only the beginning of another new and exciting business adventure.

Anton Pejsa at his desk sprinkled with castings in the early 1950s.

GRISWOLD CONTROLS

Established in 1960 and headquartered in Irvine, California, Griswold Controls has become known for its outstanding quality line of irrigation products. The irrigation controllers and valves makes up only one division at Griswold. Griswold also has a Water Quality division specializing in Centrifugal Separators and Media Filters, and a Flow Control division with a full line of fluid handling products.

Griswold was the first company to introduce Automatic Flow Control Valves which balance flow distribution for hydronic applications. In their Corona, California plant, they manufacture gas valves that are used in kitchen appliances. Besides their Irvine and Corona locations, Griswold also has a machine shop in Santa Ana, California where all of the machining and tooling for the flow control and irrigation product lines is done.

David Griswold, founder and president of Griswold Controls, has a background of involvement in the valve, control and irrigation industry that started before World War II.

Griswold Controls entered the irrigation market with a valve that was slow-closing and self-cleaning. The slow closing prevented water-hammer, which could damage an irrigation system, and self cleaning was achieved without internal filters or screens, simplifying the maintenance of the valve. Add to that a low-wattage solenoid, allowing long wire runs from the controller, and the 2000 Series valve line was born. Still viable today, more innovations have been added such as pressure regulation, internal bleed and even several types of surge anticipation valves. Over the years, two more valve series were added, based on the same principles of slow closing and self cleaning, completing a valve line that is ideal for any application, including the use of reclaimed water.

Along with the valves, Griswold has created a host of innovative irrigation controllers. The 2400, an electro-mechanical controller was the first to offer individual station control. Griswold offers a full line of solid-state and hybrid controllers, and produced the first controller

> **Griswold was the first company to introduce Automatic Flow Control Valves which balance flow distribution for hydronic applications.**

ABOVE: Griswold Controls Corporate Headquarters in located in Irvine, California and is staffed with over 50 employees. There are a total of 12 other branches and sales offices throughout the United States.

BELOW: David Griswold, founder and president of Griswold Controls.

with moisture sensing built in. Today Griswold is one of the leaders in Computerized Central Irrigation Control, offering the most flexible and cost-effective system available.

As for the future, Griswold Controls is committed to its major objectives — that of offering a unique product line that solves problems and features superior quality and high performance.

Griswold Controls • 2803 Barranca Parkway • Irvine, California 92714 • (714) 559-6000

SPEARS MANUFACTURING COMPANY

In 1969, with a strong background in plastics injection molding, including machining, mold design and hydraulics, Wayne Spears formed Spears Manufacturing Company. The company initially produced such items as hose and sprinkler fittings and adapters and flow control devices for agricultural irrigation.

During the early years, Mr. Spears spent much of his time traveling to meet his customers gaining a personal understanding of what it took to service their needs. It was in response to these personal meetings, that Mr. Spears developed a wide variety of specialty irrigation products, laying the groundwork for an ongoing committment of responding directly to customer needs. Over the years, PVC Schedule 40 pipe fittings, PVC and CPVC Schedule 80 pipe fittings, additional turf irrigation

Wayne Spears, founder and President of Spears Manufacturing Company.

specialties and industrial valving products were added to the line.

Considered a light industrial manufacturer, Spears Manufacturing Company has developed its operations from modest beginnings into one of the world's finest and efficient manufacturers of plastic piping products. The company has embarked on an ambitious program to continually develop and manufacture products to meet the needs of the many different industries that use PVC/CPVC plastic piping systems.

Spears products are for use primarily in pressurized fluid handling systems, such as agricultural and landscape irrigation, chemical processing, industrial, food and pharmaceutical, semiconductor, municipal water distribution, sewage treatment, and residential wet fire sprinkler systems.

The company takes pride in having one of the most accepted comprehensive line of fittings in the industry. This reputation was achieved through an ongoing commitment to produce high quality products, with strict use of virgin PVC and CPVC materials from nationally known producers. The Company's integrated program of Quality Assurance maintains a high level of control through all phases of product design, tool construction, production, and distribution.

Today, specialized state-of-the-art Computer Aided Engineering (CAE) capability for design and analysis, allow product designs to be tested long before products are actually produced. Full in-house mold making capabilities utilize the latest in Computer Aided Manufacturing (CAM) to produce precision tooling and mold components. As a result, a new product or product modification can literally go from concept-to mold manufacture - to production, testing, and final shipment in a much shorter time than when outside services with long lead times are utilized.

Corporate headquarters, a manufacturing facility, an international sales office, and a Regional Distribution Center are located in Sylmar (Los Angeles), California. Spears has an additional manufacturing and fabrication plant in Jerome, Idaho, and a manufacturing

facility in Caney, Kansas. Nine regional locations make up the Spears National Distribution System for making product readily available to a multitude of wholesale distributors. All Spears Manufacturing Company distribution centers have established an unprecedented reputation for providing the fastest delivery service combined with high fill rates and error free shipments.

Spears Manufacturing Company has enjoyed a consistent and solid growth pattern over the last twenty-four years, contributing greatly to the overall success of the plastic piping industry and its growth into many new markets. The personal service given customers by Mr. Spears during the company's formative years, is carried out today by a network of highly competent employees servicing customers worldwide.

ANTELCO PTY. LTD.

Sue and Bill Antel, owners of Antelco Pty. Ltd., which produces innovative products like the adjustable emitters, the Shrubbler and the Vari-Jet.

Antelco Pty. Ltd. continues to produce innovative products:
• adjustable emitters
• the Shrubbler
• and the Vari-Jet

Antelco is a privately owned Australian company which specializes in developing, manufacturing and marketing a complete line of top quality low volume irrigation products.

The Company has maintained a position at the forefront of product research and development with substantial re-investment of profit being committed to the future development of innovative and functional products.

The Owner and Director, Bill Antel, originally formed a company in 1970 as an irrigation dealer. Before long the company developed into a successful manufacturer and a pioneer of plastic low volume irrigation products, like the original Waterbird mini sprinkler. It was designed to meet the unique needs of the under tree market. The company was eventually sold and became a part of Hardie Irrigation with Bill remaining under contract as the group's Research and Development Manager.

At the present time Bill is once again heading up his own company, Antelco Pty. Ltd., with his wife, Sue. Bill Antel continues to produce innovative products; like adjustable emitters, the Shrubbler and the Vari-Jet. In the Fall of 93 the Spectrum range of vortex spray jets was added to an already full line of low volume irrigation products.

Success for Antelco has come quickly due to strategic alliances with major manufacturing marketers. Finding new markets was the only way in which to grow. We found the U.S. to be a viable market and one that had a need for products like ours. Therefore, Antelco Corporation was formed in Florida early in 1989.

The objectives of Antelco are to design or refine products to respond to the changing market needs. We also strive to facilitate the manufacture of quality, long lasting products at the lowest possible cost while still utilizing modern manufacturing practices, facilities, tools and equipment.

Antelco has grown to be a dynamic and innovative company. We incorporate a team of commit-

In the Fall of '93 the Spectrum range of vortex spray jets was added to an already full line of low volume irrigation products.

ted staff, designers, engineers and marketers. Their combined wealth of experience and knowledge within the irrigation industry is second to none.

ANTELCO.....
Putting water where it counts!

Antelco Corporation • 450 Commerce Way, Suite 104 • Longwood, Florida 32750 • (407) 331-0699

UNIVERSAL IRRIGATION SALES CORPORATION

Universal Sales Corporation, a manufacturers' representative company, was formed on April 1, 1978 by Ron Pallin, current owner and president. Although formed on April Fools' Day, Universal Sales was to be no joke. Based on the sound principles of being service oriented, representing high quality products, and providing those products at a fair price, Universal Sales was sure to be a success.

Universal Sales currently represents 20 different manufacturers of irrigation, plumbing, and waterworks products. Based in Eugene, Oregon, and employing 10 people, Universal Sales markets to the Pacific Northwest and western Canada as a manufacturers' representative.

The driving force behind the formation of Universal Sales was the need for manufacturers to have their products represented to dealers and distributors in an affordable, effective way. Due to the high cost of traveling, manufacturers have had to limit the use of in-house sales personnel. Manufacturers simply cannot reach the market efficiently. With the use of external sales companies, like Universal Sales, the manufacturer can increase

> Universal Sales represents manufacturers of irrigation, plumbing and waterworks products and can distribute these products quickly from their large warehouse.

sales and profit. For sales in the Pacific Northwest and western Canada, Universal Sales has distinct sales managers in Ellensburg, Washington; Springfield, Oregon; and Boise, Idaho.

Universal Sales is unique in that it warehouses a large quantity of products. It maintains 16,000 square feet of warehouse, 43,000 square feet of yard storage, and 2,000 square feet of office space. Warehousing was determined as necessary three years after Universal's founding. Because of the fact that Universal Sales has inventory on hand, it can distribute products faster, in more convenient quantities and with better service.

On November 1, 1987, Universal Sales bought out Tuf-Skin Valve Corporation (one of the manufacturers Universal Sales was representing). Universal Sales now manufactures and distributes this product line to North American markets from Eugene, Oregon. The expansion of this line led to the growth of the Eugene-based warehouse. The warehouse grew from 10,000 square feet to its present 16,000 square feet. Universal Sales uses other manufacturers' representative companies to market this product outside the Pacific Northwest.

Universal Sales' five-year plan projects good growth using the same marketing ideas as in the past. Universal Sales' management believes that the distributors need faster service and the manufacturers need more efficient direct sales calls to the distributors. A manufacturers' representative group, such as Universal Sales, can provide both.

BELOW:
The Eugene-based Universal Sales office is unique in that it maintains a 16,000 square feet warehouse of inventory, plus 43,000 square feet of yard storage, in addition to the 2,000 square feet of office space.

Universal Irrigation Sales Corporatation   •   1045 Arrowsmith   •   Eugene, Oregon 97402   •   (503) 344-4650

Hydrostatic drive carries T-L's momentum into the future.

Since its origin in 1955, this Hastings, NE based manufacturer has developed, manufactured and installed hydrostatic drive (continuous movement) irrigation systems worldwide. LeRoy Thom, farmer, ag-engineer, inventor and owner of T-L Irrigation Co. states that "continuous movement" fits best, when talking about the company's history OR the most important feature of his hydrostatic drive design.

"Continuous movement is definitely the key to a good irrigation system," Thom stated. "We first looked at hydrostatic drive for its design simplicity and because farmers are familiar with hydraulics. Those reasons are still important . . . but continuous movement really sold us on the concept."

As a farmer himself, Thom knew first-hand the problems irrigators face, and as an ag-engineer, he knew the advantages of hydrostatic drive could better answer a farmer's need. After much research, the first two T-L hydrostatic drive systems were produced for testing — each being chain driven. One model utilized a webbed track, much like those used on a snowmobile. The other unit used inflated rubber tires. More importantly, both moved continuously, the result of hydraulic drive and T-L's exclusive guidance system.

Thom's engineering instincts pointed to the gearbox as the heart of any center pivot and in 1972, T-L introduced planetary gear drives and in 1982, added worm gear models to expand options available for various applications. Continuous movement, provided by hydrostatic drive, has proven so successful and cost-efficient, that T-L offers the longest warranties in the industry.

T-L has come a long way since Thom developed the first chain-driven hydraulic irrigation system. A full line of hydrostatic drive models is available, including center pivots in several lengths and designs with a variety of sprinkler packages to meet modern irrigation needs. Ditch feed and hose drag linear systems fit long, rectangular fields on level terrain. Linears may be center or end fed and pivoting models are available. A corner system irrigates square or irregularly shaped fields while the Quick-Tow system is easily moved from field to field.

Thom pointed out, "Farmers are looking more and more at center pivots as a tool to help them cut production costs. Pressure for more efficient crop production has helped to introduce chemigation and seedigation . . . which in turn points to the clear-cut advantage of continuous movement." Thom continued, "Hydrostatic drive's smooth motion provides a more uniform water application than the repeated start-stop-start movement of electric systems. That makes a T-L look better and better to the farmer who irrigates." concluded Thom.

Linear Systems

Pivot Systems

Corner Systems

Quick Tow Pivot Point

T-L Irrigation Company
P.O. Box 1047/Hastings, NE 68901
(402) 462-4128   FAX: (402) 462-4617

The choice is simple.

OVER **35** YEARS
of Irrigation Excellence

Legendary Quality,

From The Company That's Dedicated To The Irrigation Professional

For more than 40 years, the Hunter name has been associated with major advances in irrigation technology.

As industry history buffs know, Ed Hunter introduced the first plastic gear-drive sprinklers, the first plastic valves, the first controller with both a clock and a moisture sensor…and many other irrigation firsts.

Today Hunter Industries is the world's leading manufacturer of gear-driven rotary sprinklers, and we are proud to continue a tradition of innovation and quality that started so many years ago in Riverside with the Moist O' Matic Company.

Hunter now has two manufacturing centers, the main plant in San Marcos, California and a second facility in Cary, North Carolina, where gear-driven rotors, spray heads, valves, and controllers are produced. Hunter products are sold in 35 countries through an exclusive network of professional distributors.

Richard Hunter
Chief Executive Officer

Irrigation Association President, 1988-1989

From our earliest days, Hunter has been dedicated to supporting the people and programs of the irrigation industry.

We have advocated new standards of professionalism, and worked to promote continuing education and an increased public awareness of water conservation.

We are also dedicated to forging strong ties with the irrigation professional. We rely on the specifier's knowledge, the contractor's experience and the distributor's marketing expertise as we introduce innovative products that meet new conservation standards around the world.

The PGP World's Best-Selling Gear-Driven Rotor

Hunter®

Dedicated To The Irrigation Professional

1940 Diamond St. ☐ San Marcos, CA 92069 ☐ 619-744-5240 ☐ FAX: 619-744-7461

Innovative Products

The PGM
For Close-Range Coverage

Model I-40s At Work in Chicago

At Hunter, education is an important part of our business philosophy. The Hunter Sales Education Department has recently produced a new series of irrigation instruction modules for universities and colleges around the country.

We continue to present up-to-date training classes for Green Industry personnel, and have started a unique College Fellowship program for promising young men and women.

It is our belief that the future of the Green Industry depends upon the involvement of educated professionals, and the development of products that help us conserve our most valuable natural resource.

The HPV Longer-Life Valve

A Commitment To Continuing Education

The ETC
Evapotranspiration Controller

Member
The Irrigation Association

Bringing new

ndustry leadership begins with an idea, evolves into a blueprint, materializes as a product and, only then, is conferred by the marketplace. Those companies that today comprise Hardie Irrigation have earned a reputation for leadership by bringing innovative ideas to the irrigation industry for more than three decades.

Created through the careful assemblage of these quality companies (Hydro-Rain, RIS, Rain Jet, Richdel and Irritrol), today's Hardie organization is a full-line manufacturer of products for the turf, agriculture, and retail domestic and international markets. The company is a member of the James Hardie Industries family of companies, a worldwide leader in the manufacture and marketing of building products and services.

deas to irrigation...

The Hardie heritage of innovation, established by the introduction of irrigation's first plastic valve, also includes the development of the first solid-state and hybrid controllers, and drip irrigation's newest and most advanced tape product. This commitment to innovation continues today with a skilled team of engineers planning the next generation of water management tools.

The Hardie heritage — bringing new ideas to irrigation

Hardie Irrigation

A James Hardie Company

Hardie Irrigation
27631 La Paz Road
Laguna Niguel, CA 92656
(800) 634-TURF
Fax: (714) 831-3212

Agriculture Division
1588 N. Marshall Ave.
El Cajon, CA 92020
(800) 333-8125
Fax: (619) 258-9973

International Division
1588 N. Marshall Ave.
El Cajon, CA 92020
(619) 562-2950
Fax: (619) 258-7960

European Office
Loc Prato Della Coarte
Lot Scirocco 0065 Fiano Romano
Rome, Italy
39-76-5455-201
Fax: 39-76-5455-368

The World's Most Innovative
Continue To Come

HERB MADSEN
V.P. Finance

SKIP HARROLD
V.P. Manufacturing

BART NELSON
President

LARRY MEYER
V.P. Engineering

BOB RUPAR
V.P. Marketing

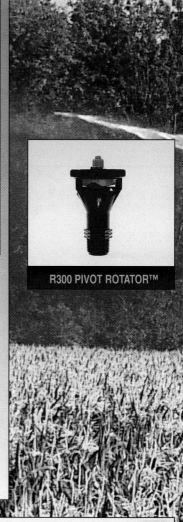

R300 PIVOT ROTATOR™

Nelson Irrigation Corporation is headquartered in Walla Walla, Washington. It plans, designs, manufactures and sells proprietary products for the agricultural irrigation equipment market. It is focused on doing things that improve the state of the art of agricultural irrigation...saving water, saving energy and doing a better job of irrigating. We believe that irrigated agriculture is absolutely essential to sustaining and improving the standard of living of a growing world population.

As we go into the 21st century, we feel that water will be the most precious element on the face of the earth. We will have to produce more food and fiber on less land with less water. We feel that we have a relevant product line at this time and that the new products that we are working on will make us part of the solution rather than part of the problem. We are always interested in your input so we can come up with the things that you need and that are cost effective.

innovation in irrigation • innovation in irrigation

Olson Plant in Santee, California

Drip Emitters

Micro-Spray

Specialty Fittings

OLSON
IRRIGATION | when water counts®
SYSTEMS

10910 Wheatlands Ave
Santee, CA 92071
(619) 562-3100

Olson Irrigation Systems
A Company Profile

Background

Donald Olson's extensive background in plastics manufacturing and mechanical design brought him into the irrigation industry as a consultant in 1966. His earliest drip irrigation emitter designs became the nucleus of a new firm, DRIP-EZE Company. Incorporated and taken public in 1972 as Controlled Water Emission Systems, the company pioneered drip irrigation technology with Olson's DRIP-EZE emitters and fittings.

Controlled Water Emission Systems was acquired by Reed Building Products of Australia in 1973, and Olson became the company's president. He left Reed in 1976 to start Olson Irrigation Systems.

Don Olson is an innovator. He holds some of the earliest drip irrigation patents issued in the United States. Just a few of those patents cover: the DRIP-EZE emitters, the Olson turbulent-flow emitter, the O-Jet, Hydro-Jet, Ultra-Jet™, and the EH-12 multiple outlet emitter head.

Current Products

Today, the company's product line is considered state-of-the-art.

Pressure-Compensated Emitters. The patented Vibra-Clean® valve provides a unique method of controlling flow without a startup hydraulic "spike", thereby eliminating the need to overdesign a system to satisfy a startup surge. The Vibra-Clean® valve is the heart of Olson's single-outlet and multiple outlet emitters. VIBRA-CLEAN® PRESSURE-COM-PENSATED SINGLES feature a patented self-punching barb which allows attachment to the tubing as it is extruded, saving costly field installation. Olson pioneered the multiple-outlet emitter with the EH-12 VIBRA-CLEAN® SYSTEM. This "drip system in a head" contains 12 pressure-regulated emitters, a 150-mesh internal filter/fertilizer applicator, and on-off plugs. It has made drip irrigation practical in commercial landscaping.

Micro-Spray Systems. The newest addition to Olson's micro-spray line is the ULTRA-JET™ — a one-piece jet, available in a variety of concise spray patterns and featuring the Olson quick-lock connection which allows installation with a simple quarter turn.

Specialty Fittings. The company supplies a line of adapters, stakes, bug caps and other ancillary items for use with its micro-spray and drip lines.

The Olson E-Z ELL® is a flexible swing joint used extensively in landscaping.

Russian Project

Olson's drip irrigation product line was selected in 1986 when the USSR's Ministry of Land Reclamation and Water Management wanted to construct a drip irrigation manufacturing facility in Simferopol in the Ukraine. Working with Valmont Industries, coordinator of the overall project, Olson was selected because of its excellent drip technology and automated manufacturing. Working hand-in-hand with Valmont, Olson handled all aspects of the micro-irrigation design and manufacturing. The $30 million project was completed on time and is housed in a 250,000-square-foot factory and adjacent 10-story office building.

Company Philosophy

Olson Irrigation Systems places great emphasis on new product development, product improvement, and quality. Relatively small in size, Olson designs and develops innovative irrigation devices, and has the ability to develop and build the equipment necessary to manufacture those products. This allows the company to turn ideas into products in a relatively short period of time. According to company president, Don Olson, "Good ideas for irrigation design don't come from studying the ceiling in an air conditioned office, they come from meeting the needs of the users, and you find out about their needs by getting out and meeting them and discussing their requirements. Many products manufactured here were designed to fill the specific needs of one customer, but were appropriate for many others."

RUSSELL DANIEL IRRIGATION

45 Years of Irrigation History

1956 RDI Dealers' Meeting

In 1948, Graham Daniel and H. L. (Bubber) Duke, both AG Engineers from the University of Georgia, had a vision of selling farmers agricultural irrigation. Hauling in Studebaker trucks pumps, aluminum pipe, sprinklers, etc., they held irrigation demonstrations in cooperation with county agents and ASCS men. Having limited success in central and north Georgia, H. L. Duke envisioned and built an irrigation market for the shade tobacco (cigar leaf) production industry in north Florida/south Georgia. Bubber opened an office in Havana, Florida, thus, the beginning of southeastern agricultural irrigation.

In 1951, Russell Daniel Irrigation Inc. (RDI) formally became a partnership. RDI evolved into the first southeastern agricultural irrigation distributor in Georgia, Florida, and Alabama, manufacturing portable pumping units, pipe trailers, special fittings, etc.

Southeastern ag irrigation in the late fifties and early sixties was often unprofitable; sales depended solely upon a dry spring and fall season. During this period, RDI introduced to the southeast automatic irrigation systems in turf, golf, and container nursery industries. Since the mid-fifties RDI has designed/installed hundreds of nurseries, ball fields, recreational areas, and over 400 golf courses from Guam to Portugal and Chicago to Venezuela.

From a southeastern historical perspective, RDI was the first to:

- Demonstrate and promote sprinkler irrigation
- Design/install electric motors in AG applications
- Design/install ag. aluminum solid-set systems
- Establish engine specifications for irrigation pump units
- Design/install fully automatic golf course irrigation
- Design/install automatic nursery irrigation
- Help start and promote the SIA, now IA
- In business "rain or shine" for 45 years

H. L. Duke

RUSSELL DANIEL IRRIGATION

Athens, Georgia • 706-543-0168   Havana, Florida • 904-539-6136

Even after 30 years, helping you create new products still turns us on.

DuPont Engineering Polymers has been a source of innovative products and services for more than three decades. You'll get unequaled technical expertise and experience with every product we make. Products that

IF YOU WANT TO GET TECHNICAL
To tap into more of what DuPont has to offer, call Janice Geipel at (714) 263-6233.

enhance performance and reduce manufacturing and assembly costs. By working as partners with our customers, we create value that helps them succeed. And that's something we can all get excited about.

Engineering Polymers

A COMPANY WELL AGED IN AGRICULTURE SINCE 1934

When Charles P. Lake arrived in Bakersfield, California in 1934 to begin the fledgling Western Oilfields Supply Company (WOSCO), little did he realize that the business would grow to be an international company with 25 divisions in 11 Western states and New Jersey.

Initially involved in selling used oilfield equipment, Lake believed in providing a quality product with top-notch services; and his business grew right along with the West.

Lake believed in providing quality products with topnotch services and his business grew right along with the West.

Even during the Depression of the 1930s, Lake's ingenuity carried the company through.

WOSCO dealt in used pipe, both oilfield products and used boiler tubing. The company manufactured water well casing, handled drill pipe repairing and resleeving threaded oilfield tubular products. The company even experimented with manufacturing clothesline poles in order to weather the tough economic storm.

While the California oilfields boomed during the 1940s, WOSCO also began to focus its attention on the thriving agricultural industry that was sweeping California. Its first agricultural product was irrigation pipe. Boiler tubing was cut into 30 inch lengths to be inserted through ditch banks. Hundreds of thousands were sold.

Lake's vision of the potential for irrigated farming was right on target; and in 1948, the company made its first sale and rental of aluminum irrigation pipe. In 1950, Rain for Rent was formed and a period of rapid expansion began.

In 1977, Lake received the coveted Irrigation Asociation's Industry Achievement Award for developing the irrigation equipment rental industry.

As the company continued to grow, it became clear that the best way to provide a reliable product

was to manufacture it. The WOSCO Foundry began producing its first aluminum couplers in 1956; and by 1969, WOSCO acquired an aluminum tube mill for the manufacturing of six and eight-inch aluminum mainline and gated pipe. Through the years, WOSCO acquired companies and tube mills to manufacture tubing from 1 1/4 inch through 12 inches. The later acquisition of West Side Pump Company of San Joaquin, CA. and Gifford Hill's tube mill division in Visalia further expanded the company's operations.

After World War II, Lake's sons, Don and Jerry Lake joined in the business full time and the company began additional expansion. Markets for WOSCO products were found in the Middle East, Mexico and South America. The company began working in other industries such as construction and waste water reclamation.

As agriculture continued to grow, Rain for Rent dealt with a variety of irrigation products, enabling the company to service growers of various crops from cotton to apples. Branches all over the western U.S. were opened in order to service agriculture in those areas.

The year 1974 was a boom year for aluminum irrigation equipment

As water supplies became scarce, farmers turned to Rain for Rent for equipment that was highly efficient.

and company officials worked day and night to keep up with the constant demand. However, the 1977 California drought brought a change to the irrigation industry.

As water supplies became scarce, farmers turned to Rain for Rent for equipment that was highly efficient. In 1980 the company sold its first major drip irrigation system consisting of 13 million feet of drip hose. That demand for water conservation products has remained, especially during the recent California drought.

Charles P. Lake passed away in 1988 but his family continues his strong commitment to the business. His grandson, John Lake, is currently company president and many other family members work in various areas of the company. The entire Lake family remains dedicated to Charles P. Lake's vision of quality products and first-rate service.

From left to right: Jerry Lake, C.P. Lake and Don Lake

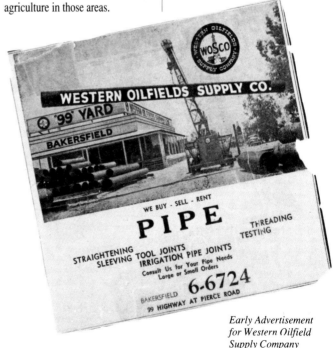

Early Advertisement for Western Oilfield Supply Company

FROM BRAINSTORM TO MAINSTREAM IN JUST 20 YEARS:

 **LOW-VOLUME IRRIGATION**

Low-volume spray-jet irrigation was discovered and brought to American growers when Tom Thayer attended a conference field tour in South Africa in 1972. Thayer was fascinated by a unique "under the tree" method of irrigation he witnessed being used on a macadamia nut tree. Intrigued, he returned to Florida with micro-jet samples and a head full of ideas, ready to experiment with the concept in his own working groves and the test fields of the University of Florida's experimental station, IFAS, at Lake Alfred. After extensive testing, the University's Dr. Robert Koo and Thayer concluded this new system offered a far more efficient and superior method of irrigation than conventional overhead impact sprinklers.

* * *

FROM HIGH-VOLUME TO LOW-PROBLEM

The advantages of spray-jets over conventional high-volume systems proved immediate. Reduced water consumption. Lower maintenance. Less expensive installation. Lower water pressure requirements. Improved tree growth. Improved yield. Lower labor costs. The new spray-jet system even distributed herbicide, nematicide and liquid fertilizer with a minimum of labor.

It didn't take long for citrus growers to switch to the new system Thayer distributed. Within just a few short years, many Florida growers relied entirely on Thayer's system. Soon, groves and orchards across the U.S.A., Canada and South American relied upon it, too.

* * *

FROM IRRIGATION TO FROST PROTECTION

In 1977, a hidden benefit of spray-jet irrigation surfaced in the field: Excellent frost protection. Growers contacted Thayer following a night of freezing temperatures to say the spray-jets helped them successfully fight the damaging effects. Research into the physics of the phenomenon revealed the reason: The fine mist emitted by the jets raised the dew point — or moisture in the air surrounding the trees — thereby decreasing any dehydration around these cold-sensitive trees.

From Tom Thayer's point of view, the spray-jet concept — with some refinement — had the potential to solve some of the most troublesome problems growers routinely faced in the field. He decided to apply his enhancements to the spray-jet system and manufacture a new and specially improved version. And **Maxijet** was born.

* * *

FROM FATHER TO DAUGHTER

Today, **Maxijet** is known throughout North and South America as the standard of quality in low-volume irrigation. The Company continues its commitment to advancing the science of irrigation under the management of Tom Thayer's daughter, Susan, now President of **Maxijet**.

At **Maxijet** 's manufacturing facility and headquarters in Dundee, Florida, ongoing research seeks out new and better ways to help growers wherever they may be. In a true case of "like father, like daughter," Susan personally innovates and develops new jets and other low-volume products for the agricultural, commercial and do-it-yourself home users.

* * *

FROM A TO Z

The Big Idea behind the original **Maxijet** spray-jet appears deceptively simple considering it formed the foundation for one of the greatest improvements in modern irrigation. Today, **Maxijet** produces a wide variety of spray pattern caps and gallonage bases. This versatile jet permits a variety of caps to snap into the same base, each producing a different spray pattern.

A Deflector Jet was developed which also snaps into the original base allowing another 13 spray patterns. The design and shape is sturdier and more permanent than earlier caps. **Maxijet** also manufactures a series of single-piece jets . A further improvement on these was the unique Max-One series available in three spray patterns with eight gallonages. The new Swap Top series attaches to the Max-one Fan and Max-cone (patent pending) for two additional spray patterns.

Originally, risers were used to attach jets to poly or PVC pipe and are still used in commercial and retail applications. Stake assemblies were since developed which provide more flexibility in the field. This 13" stake supports spaghetti tubing from the lateral poly line to the jet and is hammered or pushed into the ground. **Maxijet** produces a trademarked orange-

Riser   Stake Assembly   Landscape Stake Assembly

colored stake for the agricultural market and a trademarked green stake for the landscape market.

The most recent **Maxijet** innovation is the patent-pending Tree Clip which attaches directly to a lateral tree limb. A simple turn of a 3-way valve lets you choose to supply water to either the Tree Clip for frost protection (also ideal for cooling apples in summer) or to the stake assembly for normal irrigation and fertigation.

For landscape contractors seeking to reduce water usage, **Maxijet** developed a patented flow controlled adapter for Rainbird® and Toro® style pop-ups. A flow-controlled 1/2" shrub adapter is also available.

Maxijet rounds outs its product development with a line of low-volume products for the retail do-it-yourself market under the brand name **mister** landscaper.

For further information, call (813) 439-3667 or write **Maxijet** at P.O. Box 1849, 8400 Lake Trask Road, Dundee, FL 33838.

W E A T H E R · T E C
C O R P O R A T I O N

THE PREFERRED CHOICE OF AGRICULTURE!

In Fresno, California during the year of 1970, seven men with 90 years of combined talent in agri-business and sprinkler irrigation, formed Weather-Tec Corporation. In a time when many in the irrigation industry thought all new ideas had been exhausted and new companies were not needed, these people, with a great deal of dedication, began in a building of 18,000 square feet that had previously housed chicken incubators. Less than three months after formation of the company, the first sprinklers came off the production line and went into field service. Actually those first sprinklers produced in September, were considered test models. The first production models came off the line in October, 1970 with the initial major production run commencing the next month.

In 1974 they moved into a 30,000 square foot plant on Clinton Avenue as the business continued to grow. In 1991 a 5,000 square foot addition was added to provide even more production capabilities. The initial product line consisted of four basic sprinklers, designed for use in agriculture. The dealer network existed primarily in California and the Pacific Northwest. Today, the firm manufactures a full line of irrigation equipment for not only agriculture, but golf, turf, and landscape markets as well, with distribution and representation world-wide.

Engineering has always stressed durability, uniform water distribution and product innovation. Over the years these innovations have made good products even better. The list of those improvements and accomplishments is long, but several stand out as industry firsts. Examples are: a bellows bearing cover to protect the bearing from wear, which enclosed the spring and upper bearing area in a rugged two-piece blue vinyl housing for complete protection from wind blown or splashed sand, silt or mud. In recent times, the development of tighter seals and closer manufacturing tolerances have rendered the "Blue Bellows" unnecessary. The stainless steel spindle has always been an exclusive feature of the Weather-Tec line of equipment. Its use will smooth the rotation, cause less drag and significantly reduce the wear factors connected with other similar products on the market. Working directly in the field, the engineers developed sprinklers for use on nearly every crop grown. Every conceivable type of nozzle, lever, bearing and sprinkler angle was designed to deliver the most efficient application of water to the crop and produce maximum yields. This work proved to be invaluable for growers as they provide food and fiber for our own people and the people of the world. Most important, every product is individually water tested before shipment, a requirement of the company since its inception.

As the years have gone by, Weather-Tec continues in its quest to provide the best products to do the job. A recent example is the "Genesis" Series "G" agricultural sprinklers. The design is a complete departure from traditional impact sprinklers. The entire water passage is now stainless steel, with the head assembly die cast around it. The new lever is lighter and the die casting method used to produce both the head and lever insures a more consistent product. Another example is the new Valve-in-Head rotor for use in golf and turf areas. It is an industry first with the use of all brass and stainless steel construction, plus other features not presently found in competitive units.

In another effort to ensure superior product performance, Weather-Tec has been a subscriber to CIT (Center for Irrigation Technology) at California State University, Fresno to conduct all testing for performance to provide an independent and certified endorsement for the entire product line. CIT provides additional confidence in our products for our customer.

In the irrigation business, like most businesses, people buy from people and not companies. Products like ours, coupled with experienced customer service, are prime reasons for our success. We will continue that high degree of service. If the user, dealer, or distributor needs our help, we will provide it, anywhere in the world.

In the future, our primary focus will continue to be on agri-business. We will continue to improve existing products and to design and develop new products. We intend to maintain a prominent respected position in the industry. If Weather-Tec finds a need in the field, we will fill that need. We are proud of our 23 year history and look forward to the challenges that lie ahead.

5645 E. Clinton, Fresno, CA 93727 • Phone (209) 291-5555 • FAX (209) 294-8802 • Toll Free 1-(800) 835-7836

WADE RAIN

Manufacturing quality Irrigation Products since 1936

In 1936, R. M. Wade & Co., a long-established farm equipment firm in the Pacific Northwest, decided to bring the new concept of sprinkler irrigation to the farm fields in their area. With a factory already part of their organization, they were able to both manufacture and market their Wade'Rain sprinkler irrigation equipment. The early years required selling the concept of irrigation; but later when the value of irrigation was realized, growth was rapid, especially after World War II.

Wade'Rain Poweroll has been watering fields around the world since the 1950's. This labor-saving system allows one person to move hundreds of feet of connected pipe from one part of a field to another.

As they did with sprinkler irrigation, Wade engineers began looking for ways to improve on micro irrigation technology. With many new patents, they brought out novel products to revolutionize the micro-irrigation industry. Some of the new products include the Acu-Flo, a regulator that equalizes water pressure throughout the line. Acu-Flo was awarded the AE-50 Award by the American Society of Agricultural Engineers for being one of the 50 outstanding innovations in agriculture in 1990. The Pulsator was another new innovation from Wade'Rain. It was designed for orchards and citrus that combined, for the first time, the benefits of drip irrigation with micro-sprinklers and enabled the grower to irrigate in large diameters with less than one gallon per hour.

Pulsator

The Wade'Rain Coupler Evolution

The first Wade'Rain coupler in 1936 was made of cast iron with a bolted lock.

1938 model was redesigned to the famous Wade'Rain knob and latch that with some refinements is still used today.

In 1946 Wade'Rain introduced a lightweight steel coupler with the patented knob and latch.

By 1947 Wade'Rain was making aluminun alloy couplers, and in 1950 introduced the patented Wade'Rain gasket.

Today's Wade'Rain couplers include bolt-on, press-in, weld-on and ring-lock.

By the 1950's Wade'Rain, with its export partner, Irridelco, had become an active exporter of irrigation equipment around the world. Brazil was an especially good market, and Wade people were claiming, "All Brazilian coffee is Wade'Rain irrigated!"

Wade'Rain introduced mechanized pipe moving in 1956 with its Poweroll system. Using Poweroll, one man could mechanically move four or five inch pipe a quarter of a mile long. This was a tremendous labor saver and made sprinkler irrigation efficient for large farms.

In 1972, Wade'Rain once again introduced an innovative sprinkler system — the first self-propelled automatic lateral move system. It was called the "Squarematic." The following year, Wade' Rain also introduced a water drive and electric center pivot system.

Drip and Micro-Irrigation

The 1980's ushered in a new technology to Wade'Rain. Seeing the need for a different type of irrigation for many crops and for some arid and semi-arid lands, Wade'Rain moved into the new technology of micro-irrigation by purchasing a drip irrigation equipment manufacturing firm in Fresno, California. With this move into drip and micro-irrigation, Wade became the only company to manufacture all types of irrigation equipment. Today, Wade'Rain can offer growers a complete choice of water delivery options from hundreds of gallons per minute to less than one gallon per hour!

During the past decade, Wade'Rain has participated in several large irrigation projects in Third World countries that have enabled individual farm families to greatly improve their standard of living by growing crops on land not previously considered farmable.

In his history of R. M. Wade & Co., Wade Newbegin, long-time leader of the company wrote, "Nothing in my career fills me with such pleasure and pride as the knowledge of the very significant contribution Wade'Rain has made in increasing the world's food supply and also in conserving water."

WADE RAIN   **Wade Mfg. Co., Sprinkler Irrigation Division**
P. O. Box 23666, Portland, Oregon 97281-3666
Phone: (503) 692-5353 • Fax: (503) 692-5358

Wade Mfg. Co., Micro-Irrigation Division
3081 E. Hamilton Ave, Fresno, California 93721
Phone: (800) 695-7171 • Fax: (209) 485-7623

Toro Irrigation: Better Systems —

PRINCEVILLE GOLF COURSE — KAUAI, HAWAII

Beneath these beautiful outdoor environments, you will find Toro Irrigation – the leading manufacturer of automatic irrigation systems.

Toro Irrigation's reputation for engineering finesse began during the early sixties with its pioneering use of plastics technology for irrigation products. Engineered plastics — especially well-suited to irrigation requirements — offer a more economical means to provide a high-quality sprinkler with proven strength as well as corrosion resistance and all-weather flexibility.

"Our mission is to deliver innovative, environmentally-sound water management products and services that meet the needs of our worldwide customers and help them beautify and preserve the outdoor environment."

Anyone who plays the magnificent greens of Princeville, views a sporting event at the Rose Bowl or visits Claude Monet's elegant country home outside Paris, will see some of the most spectacular landscapes in the world.

WATERIDGE — SOUTHERN CALIFORNIA

Smarter Solutions

Toro revolutionized golf course irrigation in the late sixties by introducing central satellite irrigation systems and pressure regulated valve-in-head sprinklers.

Toro's highly sophisticated systems provide the ultimate in operational simplicity combined with maximum control.

In 1969, another irrigation success story was born with the introduction of the innovative Stream Rotor® sprinkler. Uniquely designed, it is easily recognized by its graceful "fingers of water".

Our committment to water management and conservation is evidenced by the introduction of such products as the Rain Switch® and soil moisture control systems. High flow shutoff valves, another Toro first, disrupt flow to damaged sprinklers — significantly reducing water waste.

ROSE BOWL STADIUM
PASADENA, CALIFORNIA

As we move toward the 21st Century, Toro continues to set the pace by offering products and services that meet the irrigation challenges of today *and* tomorrow.

Through a strategic partnership with Motorola — the world leader in radio communications — Toro has applied the latest advances in radio communications to the best research and technology in irrigation.

Setting the standard for customer service in the irrigation industry, Toro has established the National

Support Network. An exclusive Toro offering, the National Support Network provides comprehensive customer support for central control systems.

The Toro Company has been an international leader in the Green Industry for more than seventy years. Toro markets golf, residential, commercial, and municipal irrigation, lawn care and snow removal products to more than thirty countries around the world.

We are proud to be a patron member and long-standing supporter of the Irrigation Association.

Helping you manage the world's landscapes — beautifully

"BRINGING THE BEST TOGETHER"

UNDERHILL INTERNATIONAL has supplied worldwide irrigation needs since 1980.
We specialize in efficiently providing materials and technical services
from the best manufacturers to the world markets.

AGRICULTURE
Drip • Sprinkler • Gun • Pivot Systems

LANDSCAPE & GOLF
Sprinklers • Valves • Controls

Pumps • Pipes • Accessories

UNDERHILL INTERNATIONAL CORPORATION
430 Forest Avenue, Laguna Beach, California 92651   U.S.A.
TEL.: (714) 494-7756 • FAX: (714) 494-7886

Weather-matic Salutes

M.E. "Max" Snoddy
Industry Pioneer

M.E. "Max" Snoddy 1912-1987
Weather-matic Founder

Max Snoddy's Industry Innovations:

* First milled, match-precipitation spray nozzling
* First electric diaphragm valve
* First commercial solenoid-valve electric controller
* First "Reverse Flow" long-life diaphragm valve
* First plastic body sprinkler
* First controller with moisture sensing capability
* First solid-state controller
* First rain override device
* First rotary dial microprocessor controller
* First full-time staffed design training school for landscape irrigation
* Commissioned and co-authored first landscape irrigation textbook (The Turf Irrigation Manual)

Weather✳matic

P.O. Box 180205 / Dallas TX 75218-0205 / (214) 278-6131

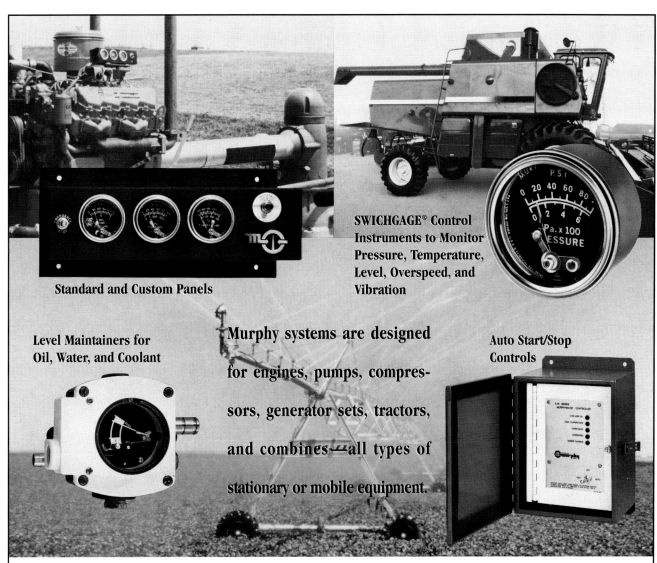

Standard and Custom Panels

SWICHGAGE® Control Instruments to Monitor Pressure, Temperature, Level, Overspeed, and Vibration

Level Maintainers for Oil, Water, and Coolant

Murphy systems are designed for engines, pumps, compressors, generator sets, tractors, and combines—all types of stationary or mobile equipment.

Auto Start/Stop Controls

Over 50 Years of Confidence
Equipment Protection and Automation

We're thankful for the confidence irrigators have put in our controls and shutdown systems since 1939.

From our simplest SWICHGAGE® to our most sophisticated micro-processor based controller, our best ideas have come from customers. This partnership has helped us develop controls to protect and automate nearly all equipment powered by engines or electric motors.

Customers told us that they wanted controls built to last. They wanted to save unnecessary replacement hassle and expense. We listened and built rugged alarm/shutdown systems. Over the years these systems have helped folks save money on equipment repair and replacement, and reduce their downtime.

Thanks for over 50 years of confidence in Murphy and we continue to work every day to keep your trust.

FRANK W. MURPHY MANUFACTURER P.O. Box 470248, Tulsa, Oklahoma, 74147
Tel. (918) 627-3550 • **Fax** (918) 664-6146 • **Tlx** 492332

 ®

■ **TEXAS**	■ **UNITED KINGDOM**	■ **AUSTRALIA**	■ **MEXICO**
TEL. (713) 342-0297	TEL. +44 722 410055	TEL. (61) 3 358 5555	TEL. (52) 48164081
FAX (713) 341-6006	FAX +44 722 410088	FAX (61) 3 358 5556	FAX (52) 48129071
■ **CALIFORNIA**	■ **REPUBLIC of SINGAPORE**	■ **FRANCE**	
TEL. (805) 272-4700	TEL. (65) 241-3166	TEL. +33 1 30 762626	
FAX (805) 947-7570	FAX (65) 241-8382	FAX +33 0 30 763989	AD 311A

A Winning Combination . . .
Cornell Pumps and You!

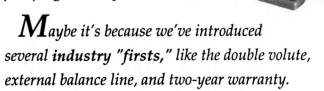

*Everybody loves a **winner**.*

*Maybe that's why Cornell has earned a reputation as a **leader** in the pumping industry.*

*Maybe it's because we've introduced several **industry "firsts,"** like the double volute, external balance line, and two-year warranty.*

*Maybe it's because we've had almost **50 years** to perfect our research and development and manufacturing procedures.*

*Maybe it's because we believe in value over time and high quality. **"Special" features** come standard on our pumps, like fully machined bronze impellers, replaceable bronze wear rings and shaft sleeves, heavy duty bearings for a minimum B-10 bearing life of 20,000 hours, and heavy duty modular bearing frames that are adaptable for direct coupled or SAE engine mount configurations.*

*Maybe it's because we have **rugged pumps** like the 3HM -- designed specifically for manure slurry applications.*

*Cornell was founded on the philosophy of value over time with engineering innovation to meet the challenges of building **quality pumps**.*

*Since 1947, we have prided ourselves on maintaining this philosophy, and that's why Cornell pumps are **the best on the market** in terms of ruggedness, dependability, and quality.*

*Cornell pumps . . . designed for **efficient, economical operation**, and built tough to offer value over time.*

*Cornell Pump Company . . . **we stand behind what we say and what we sell**.*

*Cornell pumps and you . . . put us to the test and become part of **a winning combination**.*

For more information, contact Cornell's Agricultural Market Division today!

Cornell Pump Company
2323 SE Harvester Drive ● Portland, Oregon 97222-7592
Phone (503) 653-0330 ● Fax (503) 653-0338

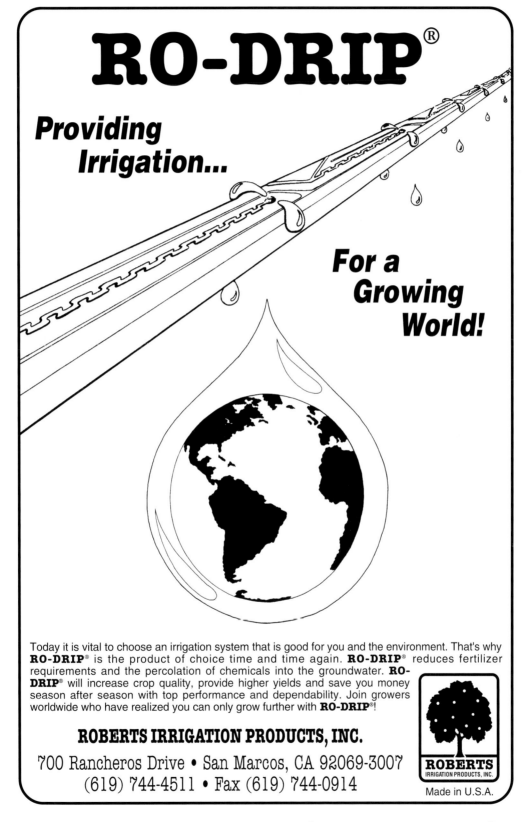

Over Half A Century of Successful Distribution

One of the "hot beds" of turf irrigation history is in Southeast Michigan. From Henry Ford's underground sprinkler system in 1916, to John Brook's sprinkler patents in the early 1920s, Southeast Michigan has played an important role in the development of the turf irrigation industry. This region also brought one of the nation's leading wholesale distributors of sprinkler irrigation supplies.

In 1970, Ernie Hodas, current owner and president of Century Rain Aid, acquired a single store operation of Century Lawn Sprinkler in the Detroit suburb of Berkley, MI. In early 1972, Century acquired a 30-year-old competitor in Southfield, MI named Rain-Aid. After a brief flirtation with the agricultural irrigation market, Century began to focus on geographic diversification and concentration on the turf irrigation market. Century began an aggresive growth plan that would lead them down the Dixie Highway, today's I-75, straight into the heart of the Southeast and into Florida.

Growing from both acquisition and new market development, Century's growth led to additional branches in Illinois, Wisconsin, Indiana, Kentucky, Georgia and Florida.

Currently with 24 locations, Century distributes sprinkler irrigation products to the residential, commercial, and golf markets, in addition to providing landscape lighting, floating aerator fountains and drainage materials. Aligned with key manufacturers in the irrigation industry, Century continues to expand by dedicating itself to exceptional customer service, and by building partnership relationships with customers, vendors, employees, and industry related trade associations.

Mission Statement

CRA People To provide an atmosphere and opportunities where competent and dedicated CRA people can grow in both their personal and professional lives. This will be accomplished by involvement, communication and mutual understanding of the basic tenets necessary to operate a successful business.

CRA Vendors To associate with vendors in a partnership relationship which will allow us to provide our customers with high quality and price competitive products.

CRA To open, when fiscally prudent, new establishments in markets needing the products and services in which we excel. To support our Industry and associations by participation, financial support and volunteer services. To support and encourage local and related educational institutions in teaching the importance of Business and Wholesale-Distribution. To acknowledge and contribute to civic, community and charitable institutions.

CRA Customers To be a "Customer Driven" Wholesale Distributor of Water and Landscape related products in geographic areas where we can meet customers' needs and wants and exceed their expectations.

CENTURY RAIN AID

1-800-347-4272

Bibliography

Chapter One: Controlled Surface and Sub-Surface Irrigation

Burt, Charles M., Ph.D., California State Polytechnic Univ., San Luis Obispo, Calif.

Conner, Charles S., "No Ups and Downs," 1987.

Davis, Arthur Powell, "Irrigation Engineering."

Dedrick, A.R.; Replogle, J.; Erie, L.J.; "On-Farm Level-Basin Irrigation," 1978.

Dedrick, A.R. and Erie, L.J., "Level Basin Irrigation," 1979.

Dedrick, A.R., "Control Requirement/Field Experience With Mechanized Level Basins," 1986.

Fireman, Milton, "Quality of Water for Irrigation."

German, Douglas, "The Milo V. German Story."

Heerman, Dale E., Research Agricultural Engineer, USDA ARS, AERC, Colorado State Univ.

Houk, Ivan E., "Irrigation Engineering," Vol. I.

Kruse, E.G. and Willis, W.O., "The Role of the Parshall Measuring Flume."

McCavitt, John H., 11th IA President, "The Irrigation Industry."

Rouse, Hunter, "Hydraulics, Fluid Mechanics and Hydrology at Colorado State University."

U.S. Bureau of Reclamation, Denver Regional Office.

U.S. Department of Agriculture, Bulletin 1243, "The Border Method of Irrigation."

U.S. Department of Agriculture, "Laser-Leveling: Flat Fields Made Easy," 1980.

U.S. Department of Agriculture, "Water Use and Management," 1979.

U.S. Department of the Interior, "Irrigation Water Use and Management."

Wilson, Hubert M., "Irrigation Engineering."

Chapter Two: Twentieth Century Manmade Rain

Barrett Supply Co., Augusta, Georgia.

Beardsley, James, San Joaquin County Agric. Museum, Stockton, Calif.

Bruce, Curt, Hunter Industries, San Marcos, Calif.

Dalton, Frank J., "History of Center Pivots in America."

Gray, Robert, Rain Bird Sprinkler Mfg. Co., Glendora, Calif.

Hagood, Mel, Washington State Univ., USDA, Corvallis, Oregon.

Kidder, Ernest H., Prof. Emeritus, Michigan State Univ., E. Lansing, Mich.

Kuhlman, Donald, Buckner, Fresno, Calif.

Mathis, Deb, Nibco, Inc., Elkhart, Ind.

McCavitt, John, 11th IA President, Peoria, Ill.

Sarratt, William, Edit. Dir., "Irrigation Engineering & Maintenance, " New Orleans, Louisiana.

Shank, Bruce F., Publisher, "Irrigation Journal, Landscape & Irrigation," Cathedral City, Calif.

Shearer, Marvin, Oregon State Univ., Agric. Engr. Dept., Corvallis.

Skinner, Robert E., CID, Athens, Georgia.

Smith, Mark, G.P.M. Irrigation, Houston, Tex.
Splinter, W.E., University of Nebraska, Agric. Engr. Dept., Lincoln.
Swanson, Gloria, Water Well Journal, Dublin, Ohio.
Talifero, Ben, Central Supply Corp., Madison Hts., Mich.
Williams, Milo B., "Spray Irrigation," USDA Bulletin 495.

Chapter Three: Low-Volume Irrigation: Drip and Micro-Spray

Canterbury, Mel, Canterbury & Assoc., New Port Richey, Fla.
Chapin, Richard D., Chapin Watermatics Inc., Watertown, New York
Gustafson, C. Don, AES Farm Advisor, San Diego County, Calif.
Hall, Benarr J., Cooperative Extension Service, University of California, San Diego, Calif., "History of Drip/ Trickle Irrigation," 1985.
Kimmell, Thomas H., Olson Irrigation Systems, Santee, Calif.
Loper, Farrest G., T-Systems International, San Diego, Calif.
Phene, Claude, USDA-ARS, Water Mgmt. Res. Lab, Fresno, Calif.
Phillips, Kenneth, Yardney Water Mgmt. Systems, Riverside, Calif.
Roberts, James and Betty, Roberts Irrigation Products, Inc., San Marcos, Calif.
Shoji, Kobe, "Drip Irrigation, Scientific American," Nov. 1977.
Thayer, Susan, Maxijet Inc., Dundee, Fla.
Tobey, Sam, Salco Products, Inc., Hawthorne, Calif.

Chapter Four: Great American Reclamation Projects

Bonneville Power Administration, "Columbia River Power for the People."
Bureau of Reclamation, "1902-1977, Water for the West."
Bureau of Reclamation, "Hoover Dam...Fifty Years."
Bureau of Reclamation, Western States individual reports.
Bureau of Reclamation, "The Story of the Columbia Basin Project."
California Office of Planning, "California Water Atlas."
Green, Donald, E., "Land of the Underground Rain, Irrigation on the Texas High Plains, 1910-1970," 1973.
Reisner, Marc, "Cadillac Desert, The American West and Its Disappearing Water," Penguin, 1991.

Chapter Five: Pumps, Pipe and Power

Bacvar, Sharka, National Tank and Pipe Co.
Diamas, John L., "Vertical Turbine, Mixed Flow, Propeller Pumps."
Lundy, Everett W., "A History of the Deep Well Turbine Pump Industry."
Pogue, William, "Aluminum Industry Notes," Irrometer Co., Riverside, Calif.
Steel Pipe Handbook, American Rolling Mills Co.
Swanson, Kenneth R., historian, National Water Well Assoc.
Zake, Mohamed, "The Journal," Johnston Pump/General Valve, Inc.

Chapter Six: Wastewater Reuse

Freshwater Foundation, Freshwater Society.
Irrigation Association, "Wastewater Resources Manual," by Norum, Edward M. and Bohley, Paul M., Wastewater Resources Committee, 1975.
National Assoc. of Conservation Districts.

Reynolds Metals Co.
Thomas, Richard E., environmental consultant, former EPA sewage engineer, Annondale, Virg.
U.S. Environmental Protection Agency, "The EPA Journal."

Chapter Eight: A Century of Irrigation Research and Development

Bean, R.C., Coop. Ext., Univ. of California, San Bernardino County.
Blair, A.W., chairman Agric. Engr. Prog., New Mexico State University,
Heerman, Dale F., USDA ARS, Agric. Engr., Colorado State University.
Keller, Jack, Agric. Engr. Dept., Utah State Univ.
Kidder, Ernest, Professor Emeritus, Michigan State Univ.
North Dakota State Water Commission, Bismark, North Dakota
Shearer, Marvin, Professor Emeritus, Oregon State Univ.
Stetson, LaVerne E., USDA ARS, Agric. Engr., Univ. of Nebraska
Stringham, Glen E., Professor Emeritus, Utah State Univ.
Willardson, Professor, Utah State Univ.
Woodward, Guy O., Salt Lake City, Utah

Government Irrigationists

Widtsoe, James, A., 1895. Author, "Principles of Irrigation Practice, 1914."
McLaughlin, W.W., 1896. Chief Irrigation Division, Soil Conservation Service.
King, F.H., 1896. USDA, early irrigation studies in humid climates.
Humphries, I.H., 1897. Utah State Engineer. Drafted groundwater law.
Harris, Franklin S., 1907. Irrigation scientist, Utah State University.
Windsor, Luther M., 1911. Researcher in flood control.
Gardner, Willard, Ph.D., 1912. University of California.
Isrealsen, Orson W., Ph.D., 1912. Prolific author, "Irrigation Principles and Practices," University of California.
Jennings, David W., 1912. Cornell University.
Larsen, E.O., 1918. Director, Bureau of Reclamation.
Clyde, George D., 1921. Utah State Governor, Head Utah State University Irrigation Department, Irrigation Division Chief, ARS and USDA.
Scobey, F.C., 1921. USDA, Irrigation development, "The Scobey Formula."
Christiansen, J.E., 1927. University of California, "Christiansen Coefficient of Uniformity." Dean of Engineering, Utah State University.
Mitchell, George A., and Staebner, F.E., 1927. USDA. Both did initial eastern U.S. studies on "Spray Irrigation."
Richard, L.A., 1928. USDA, Univeristy of California, author,"Diagnosis and Improvement of Saline and Alkali Soils."
Viehmeyer, F.J., 1929. California researcher, soil moisture studies.
Blaney, H.F. 1930. USDA researcher. Studies on consumptive use ofwater by various crops.
Hutchins, Wells A., 1930. California groundwater law.
Rippon, Charles S., 1931. US Bureau of Reclamation, Chief, Design Section.
Lawrence, George A., 1932. USDA Soil Conservation Service, Utah State engineer.
Jennings, Robert W., 1933. Regional director, Bureau of Reclamation.
Thorne, W.D., and Peterson, H.B. 1933. Coauthors of "Fertility and Management of Irrigated Soils."
Bishop, A. Alvin, 1934. Utah State University, head of Irrigation Department for 15 years.
Peterson, Dean F., 1934. Head, University of Colorado Civil Engineering Dept. and world irrigation consultant.
Wood, Ivan D., 1934. Chief, Division of Irrigation and Drainage Service, USDA. Renowned irrigation educator throughout the U.S.
Lewis. M.R., 1935. Chief, Division of Operations, U.S. Bureau of Reclamation.
Armstrong, Ellis, 1935. U.S. Bureau of Reclamation.
Criddle, Wayne D., 1937. USDA, coworker of Harry Blaney, "Blaney-Criddle Equation for Consumptive Use." World irrigation consultant.

Woodward, Guy O., 1948. University of Wyoming, irrigation specialist; Irrigation Association, educational director; USDA Agric. Extension Service, Div. of Irrigation and Drainage, chief; editor, "Sprinkler Irrigation," second edition; worldwide irrigation consultant.

McCulloch, Allan W., USDA, and Shrunk, John F., University of Nebraska, 1955. Coauthored "Sprinkler Irrigation," first edition, sponsored by the Sprinkler Irrigation Association.

Pair, Claude H., USDA extension specialist.

Hinz, Walter W., engineer, University of Arizona.

Reid, Crawford. Second president of the ASIEM, irrigation engineer and consultant.

Frost, Kenneth R., University of Arizona.

State and District Irrigationists

Alabama — Cooper, A.W.

Arizona — Dedrick, Allen R.; Fletcher, Joel; Halderman, Allen; Schwalen, H.C.; Middleton, J.E.

Arkansas — Battis, James

California — Booher, L.J.; Scott, Verne; Strong, Winston; Burt, Charles M.; Dobbs, Glenn; Mathews, Floyd; Hung, Joseph; You-Tsai.

Colorado — Code, W.E.; Brown, Floyd; Heerman, Dale F.; Kruse, O. Gordon; Parshall, Ralph; Rohwer, Carl.

Florida — Dowling, Elmo; Skinner, T.C.

Georgia — Carreker, John; Huston, Willis.

Hawaii — Hart, William; Norum, Ed.

Idaho — Corey, G.L.; Larsen, Dorrell; Humphreys, Allan S.; Myers, V.I.; Schockley, Del; Milligan, James.

Illinois — McKibben, G.E.

Indiana — Williams, G.G.

Iowa — Reeve, Ronald C.; Schwab, Glen.

Kansas — Herpich, Russell; Mangus, Harry; Sebly, Walter.

Kentucky — Welch, Earl G.

Louisiana — Lytle, W.F.; Edling, Robert J.

Michigan — Kidder, Ernest.

Minnesota —Allred, Evan.

Mississippi — Grisson, Perin; Hogg, Peter; McVey, John; Raney,W.A.

Missouri — Jamison, V.C.; Thornton, John.

Montana — Monson, O.W.

Nebraska — Fishbach, Paul; Francis, C.E.; Schleusner, P.E.; Schull, Hollis; Sheffield, Leslie F.; Somerhalder, B.R.; Steele, John; Stetson, LaVerne E.

Nevada — Houston, Clyde; Mahanna, Clair.

New Mexico — Bloodgood, Dean W.; Currey, A.S.; Hanson, Eldon; Schockley, Dale.

New York — Lavine, Gilbert; Markwardt, Everett.

North Carolina — Bennett, R.R.; Ellis, Howard; Hawks, S.N.; Nau, H.H.

Ohio — Overholt, Virgil.

Oklahoma — Garton, J.; Ree, W.D.

Oregon — Schoenfeld, William; Price, Earl; King, Arthur; Kirk, Dale; Shearer, Marvin; Wolfe, John W.

Pennsylvania — Peikert, Frank W.

South Carolina — Heddon, Frank.

South Dakota — Weirsma, John; Erie, Leonard.

Tennessee — Van Horn, A.G.

Texas — Thurmond, R.V.; Keese, C.W.

Utah — Anderson, Bruce; Bertis, Embry; Milligan, Cleve; Bagley, J.M.; Keller, Jack; Hansen, V.E.; Taylor, Sterling; Stringham, Glen; Willardson, Lyman; Hill, Robert.

Washington — Bassett, Day; Hagood, Mel; Jensen, Max; Molenaar, Aldert; Mech, Steve; Morrison, K.R.; King, Larry.

Washington, D.C. — Quackenbush, Tyler H.

Wyoming — Brosz, Donald.

Chapter Nine: Today's Agricultural, Turf and Landscape Irrigation

Bishop, A. Alvin, "Surge Flow, A Revolution in Surface Irrigation."

Busch, J.R., Agric. Engr., Univ. of Idaho, "Irrigation Energy Efficiency."

Carborundum Co., "Croplink, A Crop Monitoring System," and "Schedular, Plant Stress Monitor."

Chapin, Richard D., "Turbulent Flow Drip Irrigation Tubing."

Cloud, Robert, Associated Irrigation Consultants, "The Miracle of Landscape Irrigation."

IA Irrigation News, "Crisis or Conservation," 1990.

Keller, Jack, Agric. Engr. Dept., Utah State Univ.

Kincaid, D.C., Agric. Engr., USDA, "Irrigation Energy Efficiency."

Laney, Diana, Western Municipal Water Dept., "Landscape, Southern California Style."

Solomon, Kenneth H., director, Center for Irrigation Technology, Calif. State Univ., Fresno.

Strigham, Glen E., retired, Utah State Univ.

Zoldoske, David, Center for Irrigation Technology, "Laser-Optical Technology."

Chapter Ten: Water and the Game of Golf

Beard, James, Ph.D., Professor, Texas A&M Univ., "Turfgrass Bibliography."

Clayton, Debbie, Clayton Communications, Horsham, Penn.

Cloud, Robert, Associated Irrigation Consultants, Los Angeles, Calif.

Cookingham, Peter O., Turfgrass Information Center, Michigan State Univ., East Lansing.

Cornish, Geoffrey, and Whitten, Ron, "The Golf Course."

Davis, William H., "100 Greatest Golf Courses."

Golf Course Superintendents Assoc. of America, "Golf Course Management," Lawrence, Kan.

Hardwick, Nancy, Hardwick & Hardwick, Carlsbad, Calif.

Hunter, William, Hunter Industries, San Marcos, Calif.

McWirter, Rod, National Golf Foundation, Jupiter, Fla.

Price, Charles, "The World of Golf."

Thomas, George C., Jr., "The Story of American Golf."

Wind, H.W., "The Complete Golfer."

It was cold that late Kansas day when this Fall pre-irrigation
side-wheel roll sprinkler system stopped, awaiting de-icing.
Circa 1955.

Index

Printed by Marrs Printing, Inc., City of Industry, CA